Found Among the Fragments

A Story of Love and Courage

Sarah Huff Fisk

Pinhook Publishing Company
Post Office Box 1545
Huntsville, AL   35807

ISBN Number 0-9655917-2-7

First Edition

Photographs by Emily P. Saile
Cover design by Pamela Nelson
Camera-ready copy by Kerry A. Pinkerton

Printed in the United States of America

Published by:

Pinhook Publishing Company
Post Office Box 1545
Huntsville, AL 35807

Additional copies may be ordered from the publisher for $15.95 plus $3.00 shipping and handling.

Write the publisher for inquiries regarding quantity discounts.

Preface

The fragments that came to form the backbone of this book were discovered in many places over a long period of years. The Record Room of the Madison County Courthouse provided property deeds and probate information. Exhaustive--but fascinating!--reading of old Huntsville newspapers brought much to light. The Heritage Room of the Huntsville Madison County Public Library offers microfilmed Census Records and Service Records of Confederate Soldiers. There, too, I found Hartley & Drayton's 1861 Map of Huntsville.

Yet, it's doubtful that I would have searched for any of these items, had I not had a grandmother who kept a scrapbook, a mother who valued and saved family mementos, and an elderly cousin, who informally dubbed me "family historian" when I was only eleven, too young to know what it meant, but old enough to be impressed.

My grandmother, Mattie Elliott, whom you will meet as a little child in this book, was a very loving person. Her scrapbook, a back-less old statistical tome in which she enshrined with a mixture of flour and water (permanent beyond belief!): clippings (mostly undated), printed funeral notices, numerous poetry, and a few letters, not only grew to reflect its owner's warm nature, but also proved to be a valuable family record.

Grandmother passed her strong regard for family to her middle daughter, Nellie, my mother, who faithfully kept all important things, and considerably more! Exasperating as this was at times, all could be forgiven this loving, caring person, who was greatly missed when she passed on in 1983 at age ninety-five.

Afterward, when my sister, Martha Lee, and I began sorting Mother's bulky, haphazard collection, we were surprised--to say the least!--at the treasure we had inherited. Its contents opened doors long closed and quickly inspired us to write about our childhood. Before we could go further, however, my sister passed away. In essence, this present work is a tribute to her and to our happy collaboration in other creative fields.

There was another physical fragment that played an important part in this story: an unusual oil painting that is mentioned and described several times. This painting hung above the dining room mantel in the home where we grew up, and was pointed out to us by Grandmother Mattie with the words, "My father, William Elliott, painted that picture." And since I, too, exhibited some early artistic promise, she would sometimes add, "You may have inherited some of his talent, Sarah."

So are our paths directed in youth...mine toward history and art, both of which took a long time to bear fruit.

My delay in writing family history was partly due to the sheer mass of information we had. Our Cain ancestors came to Huntsville in 1815, a logical place to begin our story, were it not for early gaps that I could not fill.

I always wanted to write in story form. No talent was given me for making charts. Fortunately, several generous cousins have shared information, which Martha Lee's daughter, Emily Nell, has charted to show our descent from the ancestors portrayed in this story. This information precedes Chapter One.

My own interest has always focused on the character, life circumstances and experiences of our ancestors. It was just such information that Grandmother Mattie shared with us so willingly during our childhood. She could recall her own experiences and those of others, was a great reader, dedicated letter-writer, and a gifted raconteur. Stories told in her gentle voice were framed with the consideration and love for others that I came to know as a family trait, along with the wellspring of religious faith from which it came.

With many fragments found, only a beginning was needed, and it came, too, one night in March of 1995 in the form of a dream--one so unexpected and so vivid, that it will remain forever etched on my mind. This dream sequence is recounted in the first paragraphs of

Chapter One, which I began soon after. Without doubt, it was a "serendipity", the gift of the spark I needed.

As incredible as it seems, another such gift came within a few days when I read a reprint of an account written in 1914 by my grandmother's first cousin, Alonzo Elliott, who told of having witnessed on the public square in Huntsville on March 22, 1862 an event vital to this story--a lost fragment!

It is not easy--may even be presumptuous!--to write about family members and their friends of long ago; to give them character, flesh and blood, so to speak. But I did it with care, using every bit of information I could find, and always trying to consider their motivations resultant of the crisis in which they were forced to live. If I have misread either the character or motivations of any of those depicted herein, I am, of course, deeply sorry.

The servants in most families hereabouts were slaves. Many were probably taken advantage of, even mistreated; but not all! It is my firm belief that the servants (whether slaves or paid helpers) in the Albert Baker household, where this story centers, were treated with sincere consideration and affection, just as I have depicted.

All persons named in the book were real people, with exception of: the O'Casey family, the Lamperson Smith family, all Union soldiers (including Lt. Fraser), and poor Joshua, who could not remember his last name.

Homes and businesses mentioned are keyed to two hand-drawn maps based on two sections of the 1861 Hartley & Drayton Map of Huntsville.

Most of the main events were real, based largely on happenings reported in Mary Ione Cook Chadick's remarkable diary of the city during its occupation by Federal Troops in 1862. Less important, day-to-day occurrences were of my imagining and were inspired by family stories, or accounts of trials, shortages, and makeshifts recorded by writers knowledgeable about the period.

One of my primary aims was to portray, however I could, the continuing difficulties and awful uncertainties suffered by women and children, both white and black, during this crisis, and to recognize the courage and ingenuity with which they faced their problems.

As I wrote about my ancestors and others trying to survive the uncertain, almost hopeless, times in which they lived, my view of them blossomed to limitless admiration. I sincerely hope that my efforts may so enhance the view of any reader of this book.

Sarah Huff Fisk

Acknowledgments

I remember with gratitude so many who have guided and inspired me. You should all be named here, for it was your friendship that gave me courage to be creative in my own way.

Family members who generously shared information are: William R. Ormond, Lexington, Ky., Robert Emmett O'Neal, Columbus, Ga., and Carol Richter Purdy, Atlanta.

Catherine Hollan, Alexandria, Va., in researching "Virginia Silversmiths", found material for me on the Cain family.

Dewitt Uptagrafft kindly stopped in Lauderdale Springs, Miss., to chart and photograph the old Confederate Cemetery.

In the Heritage Room of the Huntsville Madison County Public Library, Archivist Renee Pruitt gave valuable assistance.

I must thank The Huntsville-Madison County Historical Society for publication in 1995 of "Maple Hill Cemetery: Phase One" by Robey, Johnson, Jones and Roberts, which not only lists tombstone inscriptions, but gives a record of stones signed as erected by the Baker Marble Yard and a photograph of the cemetery in 1863.

Artist Pamela Nelson has my gratitude for creating the meaningful cover design from photographs made by my niece, Emily P. Saile, of some of the old fragments that inspired this book.

Besides arranging the genealogical chart of the Cain, Elliott, Baker and Babcock families, Emily also spent hours proofreading.

My nephew, Kerry A. Pinkerton, having successfully introduced me to the computer, proved his true devotion by producing with skill and patience the camera-ready copy for the printer.

Venita Helton gave freely of knowledge gained as a published writer. I'm indebted to Barbara Longo for reading my original manuscript. Peggy Slate of Metro Printing gave expert guidance.

My research assistant, Barbara Lauster, not only read my early drafts, but made it possible for me to find time for writing.

And thanks to all who endured my chatter about this book!

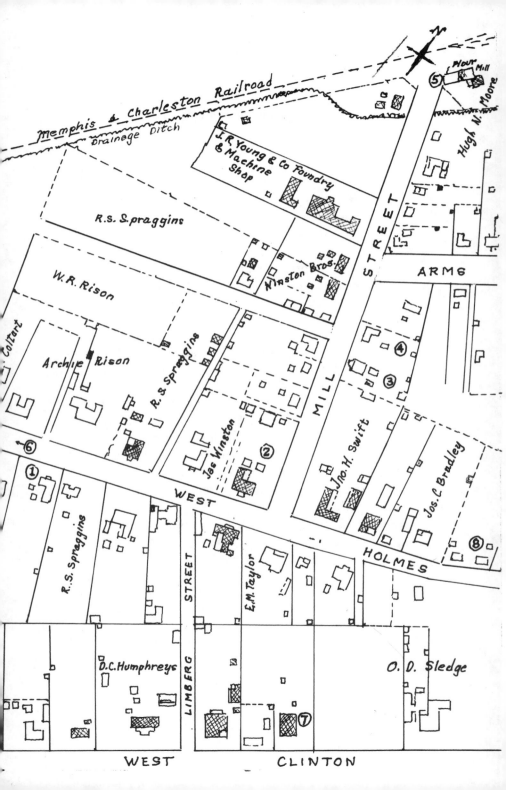

< At left: A Section of the Map of Huntsville, Alabama, 1861, Surveyed & Published by Hartley & Drayton, Louisville, Ky. (Redrawn by author)

Key

1 Residence of Elizabeth Cain Elliott and her daughter, Mary Ann Carlton Figg and husband, Littleton G. Figg, and their children: Caroline and Robert Emmett

2 Residence of Albert A. Baker and his wife, Elizabeth Babcock, and their children: Romeo, Edward, Archie, Bessie, and Alvah; also, Elizabeth's sister, Emily Babcock, her husband, William C. Elliott, and their children: Mattie and Enoch Carlton; also, Albert's nephew, Lucius Baker; also, several boarders: James Conway, Albert's partner in the Baker Marble Yard, and other stonemasons employed there

3 Residence of James W. Pollard and his wife, Caledonia Bibb, and their children: Susan, Mattie, Frank, and Clara

4 Residence of Andrew J. Bolton and his wife, Viora C. Stubbs, and their children: Addie V. and Charles

5 Moore's Flour Mill, Hugh N. Moore

6 To Pinhook Creek Bridge

7 West Clinton Street Church (also used as a hospital)

8 Residence of John Hardie and wife, Harriett Saxon, and their children: James, John, Ellen, Alice, Florence, and Jane

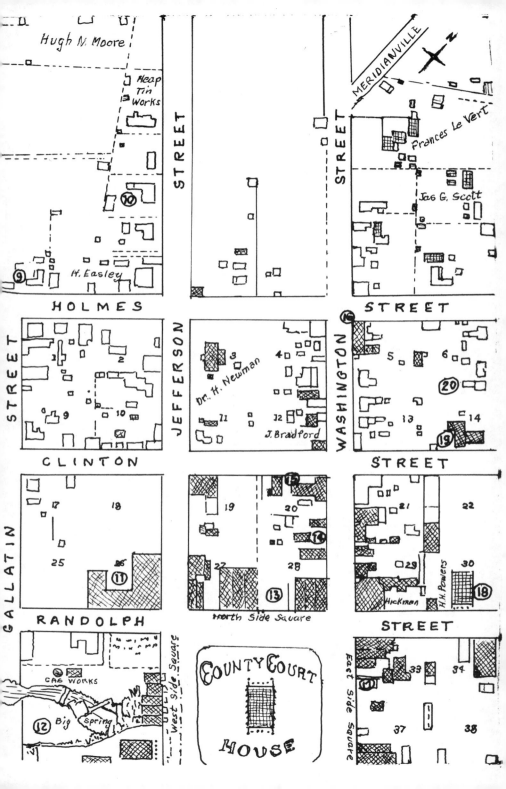

< At left: A Section of the Map of Huntsville, Alabama, 1861, Surveyed & Published by Hartley & Drayton, Louisville, Ky. (Redrawn by author)

Key

9 Conrad Beeman's Blacksmith Shop and family residence

10 Residence of Richard I. Elliott and his wife, Mary Elizabeth Stainback, and their children: Alonzo, Mary Josephine, Kate, Laura Ann, John Dugger: also, Mary Elizabeth's grandfather, Tinable Figg

11 Huntsville Hotel

12 The Big Spring

13 Site of Thomas Cain's Silversmith Shop, 1818-1850

14 Baker Marble Yard, Albert A. Baker & James Conway

15 City Market House, on corner, and Fire Station, facing Holmes

16 Windham's Grocery, Irvin Windham

17 Nevill & Figg Coffee House, James N. Nevill & Littleton Figg

18 Methodist Episcopal Church

19 Madison County Jail

20 Residence of David T. Knox and his wife, Susan Cain, and their daughters, Sue Harrison Knox, and Mary Ann Knox and her husband, John T. Patterson, and their child, Josephine

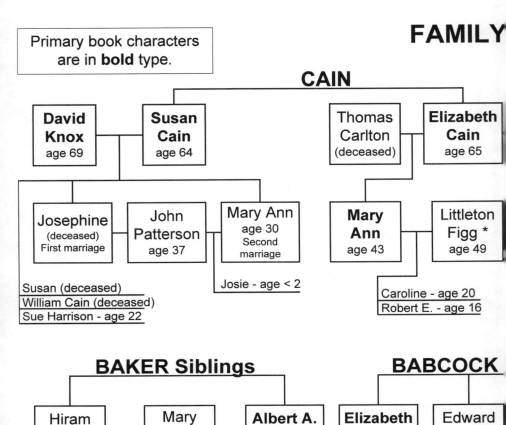

Primary book characters are in **bold** type.

FAMILY

CAIN

David Knox age 69 — **Susan Cain** age 64

Thomas Carlton (deceased) — **Elizabeth Cain** age 65

Josephine (deceased) First marriage — John Patterson age 37 — Mary Ann age 30 Second marriage

Mary Ann age 43 — Littleton Figg * age 49

Josie - age < 2

Susan (deceased)
William Cain (deceased)
Sue Harrison - age 22

Caroline - age 20
Robert E. - age 16

BAKER Siblings

Hiram Baker (deceased) — Mary Ann Searles — **Albert A. Baker** age 34

BABCOCK

Elizabeth Babcock age 31 — Edward Babcock age 34

Adaline - age 22
John Gideon - age 17
Charles Asa - age 16
Lucius - age 14
Ruth - age 11
Elizabeth - age 7

Romeo - age 12
Edward - age 10
Archie - age 6
Bessie - age 4
Alvah - age 1

RELATIONSHIPS as of 1862

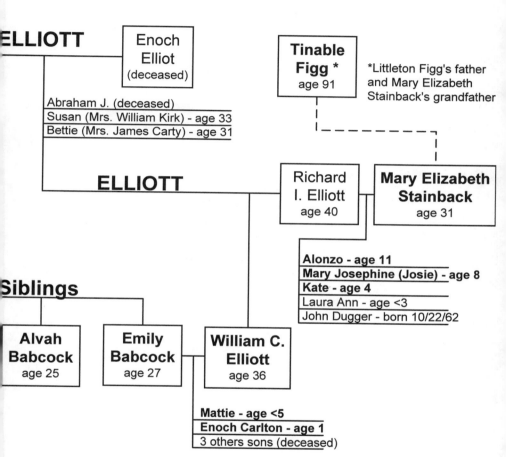

ELLIOTT

Enoch Elliot
(deceased)

Abraham J. (deceased)
Susan (Mrs. William Kirk) - age 33
Bettie (Mrs. James Carty) - age 31

Tinable Figg *
age 91

*Littleton Figg's father and Mary Elizabeth Stainback's grandfather

ELLIOTT

Richard I. Elliott
age 40

Mary Elizabeth Stainback
age 31

Alonzo - age 11
Mary Josephine (Josie) - age 8
Kate - age 4
Laura Ann - age <3
John Dugger - born 10/22/62

Siblings

Alvah Babcock
age 25

Emily Babcock
age 27

William C. Elliott
age 36

Mattie - age <5
Enoch Carlton - age 1
3 others sons (deceased)

NOTE: In later years, little Mattie Elliott married Albert Baker's nephew, John Gideon. They had four children: Archie, Emily, Nellie, and Edna. Nellie married O. C. Huff and had two daughters: Sarah and Martha Lee. Sarah Elliott Huff Fisk, the author of this novel, is the great-granddaughter of Emily and William Elliott. The Elliott's photographs are on the cover.

*WAR once stood on the corner there
and summoned men to his side.*

*But when he had mangled
their blood and their bones,
he tossed them all down,
and they died.*

*He tossed them down
on the sweet violet beds
while the women and children all cried.*

*And their tears flowed into
the sorrows of time,
where the deepest shadows hide.*

Sarah Huff Fisk
1996

Chapter One

March 21, 1862

"Hey there, girl! Your ma's a Yankee woman, ain't she?"

Mattie Elliott peered between the palings at the three boys on the dusty path beyond the fence. She had never been asked that in all of her nearly five years. Yankee woman! What did that mean?

"Well, ain't she?" The tallest, a thin, angry-faced boy, asked again. When Mattie did not reply, he added, "I'm knowing for sure she's from up north yonder!" and raised his right arm to point at the northern sky.

The sky! "But you are pointing up to heaven!" Mattie knew that much. "And Mama's not up there. She's right inside sewing on Mrs. Winston's green dress that's got to be finished today. You can go on in and ask her that question--but she hates to be shouted at."

Seeing that this invitation was not welcome, Mattie went ahead anyway to share some facts she knew about heaven. "I've got three little brothers up there with Jesus. They died before they said a single word to me. The least one was only about that long." Tears sprang to her eyes as she measured the approximate size.

The smallest of the trio, a little redhead, ran quickly to the fence and gazed raptly through at her. "Our pa is deaded, too. Is he up there with Jesus then?"

But before Mattie could reply, the angry-faced boy pointed his arm again, fist clenched, and warned, "Jason! How many times must I be telling you! No talking to Yankees!" With that, he wheeled, head erect, and stalked off along Mill Street, his feet shuffling up a cloud of dust.

As little Jason shrank back from the fence, the third boy took his

1

arm and, glancing at Mattie, said, "Don't be minding that too much, little lass. Our pa just got killed up north by Yanks...and my brother, Sean, he be mortal upset. Come on then, Jason."

As they turned away, Mattie stood still, not understanding.

"What all this yellin' an' racket out here?" Sophronia's ample form issued from the back door with a basket of wet clothes to be pegged to the line. "Who that you talkin' to, chile?"

"Some boys from that way." Mattie pointed towards Arms Street. "They called Mama a Yankee. What's that mean, Aunt Sophia?"

"Nothin' a-tall to you. Don't pay no heed to them." Looking up at the sky, she sighed. "I'm no sooner gonna get these things on the line than the rain'll come sloshin' down in buckets."

"I sure prays yer right, Sophia!" Uncle Pompous struggled to rise from his job of setting out onions. "The good Lawd know we be need'n rain. Here we is plantin' vegetables in the flower beds so's not to starve to death whilst they's all off a-fightin' each other. Fer as I can see, white folks is gone crazy!"

Looking again at the darkening sky, Sophronia hastily began to unpeg the few wet clothes she had attached to the line. "Mattie, chile, you head on fer the house now. And Pompous, you best pick up that hoe. Iffen it rusts, how Mr. Albert gonna find another?"

From the sitting room window, Emily Elliott saw the blackening sky and sighed. She would have to light a candle to see the tiny stitches in the bodice of the green taffeta dress she was making over for Mrs. Winston, who had chosen the new princess-line style shown in the March, 1861 issue of Godey's Lady's Book. By taking much of the fullness from the upper skirt, Emily had produced the graceful, new style, full-hooped only at the hemline.

A sudden onslaught of rain against the windowpanes brought her quickly to her feet. While taffeta slithered to the floor, lightning flashed, thunder exploded all about, and Enoch Carlton awoke screaming in his crib.

"Mattie!" Emily called, stooping to rescue the taffeta. "Where are you, child?"

"Right here, Mama. I heard the baby crying."

2

"I imagine so!" Emily had to laugh, for Enoch Carlton was such a funny sight, his mouth open wide enough to engulf his own head! "Watch the taffeta!" she warned, as Mattie moved toward the crib.

"He just needs changing. Can I do it this time?" Still struggling with the taffeta, Emily shook her head. "He's too heavy for you to lift, but you may watch."

Happily, Mattie jiggled up and down, sending her hoop swinging wildly against her long pantalets.

As thunder crashed again, Enoch Carlton tried shrieking. "Mercy on us! What's all the racket in here?" Sophronia's bulk filled the doorway.

"He just needs changing, Aunt Sophia," Emily laughed, "and our Mattie craves to watch the operation."

"Some folks has strange tastes!" Sophronia soon had the job done and bore the baby toward the door. "Jes so's you can finish that there fancy dress in peace."

Emily smiled to herself. The dress was bright, but in wartime it was necessary to remodel and make the best of what you had.

"Mama, can I ask you a question?" Carefully shifting her hoop, Mattie perched on a stool across the room. "Are you a Yankee? And what is that?"

Emily thought carefully before she replied, "That's really two questions with one answer: A person who was born in the North, as I was, is sometimes--by some people--called a Yankee."

"A boy out in the street just told me Yankees killed his pa! I was so sorry, Mama." Tears came unbidden.

"So am I." As Emily shook her head sadly, the black braids she wore coiled on her head glinted in a quick flash of lightning. Below them, her dark eyes were somber. "War is terrible! Not because Yankees are bad, or Southerners either. You know your papa is a Southerner, born in Tuscaloosa. What is bad is when they get to fighting each other and neither side will stop...that's war! A horrible thing! I just pray the good Lord will stop it somehow."

They both jumped as a crash of thunder seemed to punctuate her last statement.

Mattie sighed. "Then I'll tell my little brothers up in heaven to ask

3

Jesus to stop the fighting right away."

"You can just shut your eyes and ask Jesus yourself," said her mother. "He will hear you and do what is best. Now run along and find Bessie to play with, while I finish Mrs. Winston's dress."

"Yes, Mama." Obediently, Mattie got up to look for Bessie, her cousin and favorite playmate.

But Emily now found it hard to turn her mind from the war with its horrors. Her thoughts seemed suddenly to burst aloud into one impassioned prayer, "O God, please spare my William from service! You know he's not able to stand army life!" Yet even as her words rang in the quiet room, she sensed that similar pleas were rising from households all over the country.

She remembered the fear they had felt only a few weeks before, when the Federal Army had advanced as far south as Nashville. How certain it had seemed that North Alabama would be next! For both sides needed the repair shops belonging to the Memphis & Charleston Railroad which were in Huntsville.

But then a miracle had happened: suddenly the Union forces had turned west toward Memphis. Huntsville could breathe a brief sigh of relief! Yet, invasion was still possible, and, with the railroad tracks little more than a block behind the house, they had a special reason to feel vulnerable.

Now, Governor Shorter had called for ten additional regiments from the state. Madison County's share was to be one hundred new foot-soldiers. They would have to be older men with families, for most of the young men had already volunteered.

Exhausted from thinking of this problem over which she had no control, Emily forced back tears and, lighting a candle, returned to her sewing, a task she could understand and take pride in.

Rain continued to beat against the window, but no amount of it could wash away the anxiety that beset them all.

The kitchen of the Albert and Elizabeth Baker residence was in a wing of the house behind the dining room with its long table to accommodate the large family and several boarders. Lucius Baker, one of Albert's nephews, who had been sent down from New York two

4

years before to be educated and put to the stonemason trade, was now fourteen and considered one of the family.

Most of the boarders were expert stonemasons brought South by Albert from New York to help in his Marble Yard in cutting monuments, headstones, and mantels. They carved fancy pieces, built foundations, and executed all kinds of stonework, not only in the town of Huntsville, but for the whole North Alabama area.

The workers lived in quarters Albert had recently built for them facing Mill Street behind the big house.

The only boarders now living in the main house were Emily and her husband, William C. Elliott, with their children, Mattie and little Enoch Carlton.

Emily, who was the younger sister of Albert's wife, Elizabeth, had moved with them from Tioga County, New York, in 1851. She had met and married William in Huntsville when she was eighteen. They had at times in the past boarded with William's widowed mother, Elizabeth Elliott, on the south side of West Holmes; but in 1862 they were with the Bakers where they were always welcome.

William Elliott and his older brother, Richard, ran a painting business that offered house, sign, and ornamental painting...such as gilding and glazing...also paperhanging. William, a talented artist, liked to paint pictures, particularly landscapes.

Since their business catered to a large area, it was often necessary for one of them--usually William--to be away for extended periods. By boarding, Emily could avoid being left alone with the children. While in the Baker household where there were several slaves to help, she could find time to make extra money with her dressmaking.

Besides Sophronia and Pompous, there was Magdalena, the children's nurse. A Mulatto, like Sophia, she was an orphan now about fourteen years old. Blessed with a willing and sweet disposition, she was adored by the children.

When the weather was unsuitable for the younger children to be outside, as it was today, they were usually downstairs in a small room behind the sitting room. The night-nursery upstairs was too inconvenient for day use.

The two older Baker boys, Romeo and Edward, were day-students at the private school taught by Mrs. Sarah McCay and her husband, Prof. William McCay.

Today, Mattie found all the younger children in the playroom. Magdalena had Enoch Carlton on her lap, while she watched six-year-old Archie play with his tiny brother, Alvah.

Bessie, however, was seated on a low stool turned to face the corner of the room--a sure sign of punishment.

Magdalena greeted Mattie with a grin. "Miss Bessie not s'posed to talk jes now, but I reckon she can tell you what she done."

Mattie carefully moved past Archie and Alvah to Bessie's side. There she got a quick confession, "I was 'pertinent."

"Who were you 'pertinent to?" Mattie, only a few months older, understood the charge. "Who to?" she insisted.

The answer came in a whisper, "Mama."

"She can get up soon as she ready to tell her mama she sorry!" Magdalena stated the terms of punishment, "But she stubborn!"

Mattie sighed. She knew impertinence was an awful bad sin for children to commit. "Well, while you're deciding, I'll work on my letters." Taking the slate and slate pencil from the mantel, she swung her hoop aside and perched on a stool. Learning her letters was serious business. Though she liked being read to, she longed mightily to find out how reading was done.

"What that letter you makin'?" asked Magdalena.

"I'm still working on my big M."

"Well, show me how to make it then...That my letter, too."

"I know how," bragged Bessie from her corner. "You go up..."

"...quiet dere, miss! You ain't s'posed to ope' you mouth!"

Right then Bessie had had enough. Staring at the corner was no fun when Mattie was in the room. She yanked her hoop around until she faced Magdalena. "I'm ready to 'pologize!"

Mattie immediately jumped to her feet to lend support. They made for the door together, jamming hoop skirts in the opening. It was Bessie who spoke. "Drat these!..."

"What that word you jes say?" Magdalena eased Enoch Carlton to the floor and rose to her full five feet.

Bessie racked her brains, but Mattie came to the rescue, "That these hoop skirts..."

Magdalena gave up and directed her full attention to the three little boys playing at her feet.

Because the kitchen windows had to be kept lowered against the rain, the room was steamy-hot. Perspiration dampened Elizabeth's white forehead beneath her slightly-curling hair. "I'll declare," she moaned, "but I can't think of a thing to fix those hungry men for their dinner...except corn bread!"

Sophronia's pale brown face lit with a sympathetic smile. "But yer bread's jes like cake, Miss 'Lizbeth. Nobody gonna spurn it! 'Sides we got some cracklin' to put in. They's some of them brown beans, an' I could finish out with a little rice."

Elizabeth thought for a moment. "It'll have to do. We can't go out in this downpour...not that the store would have much anyway! I do believe the whole country's quit raising food, or trying to ship it." She sighed. "Who's going to carry dinner to the Marble Yard? Uncle Pompous can't--not with his rheumatism threatening!"

Sophronia kept her smile in place. "It'll work out! We jes has to keep on tryin'!"

All at once Elizabeth saw the little girls waiting at the door and felt ashamed. She always tried to appear optimistic before the children.

Mattie stayed in the doorway while Bessie stepped forward. "Mama, I came to say I'm sorry."

"For what are you sorry?" With a determined effort, Elizabeth kept her face stern.

"'Cause I was 'pertinent to you. I didn't mean to be."

Her mother brought out her forgiving smile. "Well then, you're forgiven. God forgives us, so must we all forgive each other."

"Yes, Mama." Bessie looked up, happy.

But Elizabeth noticed tears in Mattie's eyes. That child is so soft-hearted! she thought. How will she ever survive the bumps of this hard, old world?

An hour later the rain had slackened, but water gushed in twin rivers along each side of West Holmes Street. The center surface, macadamized some twenty years before because it was the main road to Athens, now gleamed darkly wet with raindrops hopping about it in a random pattern almost mesmerizing to the observer. And down in Pinhook Creek the water was rising steadily.

Emily--freed at last from the yards of green taffeta--listened in concern to the swelling roar before she called Elizabeth. They ventured together onto the small front stoop. The roar was louder there, and a cloud of mist hung above the low area to the west.

"I doubt that we're in danger," Elizabeth reasoned, "for we're more than a block away. But I do hope the bridge doesn't go!"

Emily was gazing toward town. "Isn't that Romeo and Edward coming? What are they doing out of school at this hour?"

The two boys, barefoot with breeches rolled above their knees, were picking a way along the center of the road. Romeo had their oilcloth booksatchels strapped across his shoulders, while from Edward's neck, four shoes dangled by their strings. Upon sight of their mother, they each let out a loud whoop and, abandoning all caution, came the rest of the way in long splashing leaps.

"Hold right there!" Elizabeth greeted them with upraised hand. "Don't even think of coming in the front. Go directly to the back porch, and I'll talk to you there."

Extremely wet and somewhat crestfallen, the two were met first by Sophronia, who took shoes and books. "Jes you stay put till yer ma can get a good look at you! My! If you ain't a sight!"

Their explanation, as gasped out in spurts by Edward, the more excitable of the two, began, "Lightning struck a tree back of the school and it just flew all to pieces--the tree, that is!..."

"And with the gas lights going off, I guess Mrs. McCay decided we wouldn't have to have school today," Romeo reasoned.

"So we thought you might need us at home!" added Edward. "Just in case the creek rises so high we have to swim for it..."

"...because you could count on us to get the babies out!" said Romeo, his face lit with zeal at the thought of their bravery.

Elizabeth, nearly overcome with a desire to burst out laughing at her sons' reasoning, so swiftly wavering from comic to heroic, finally managed to gasp, "Very exemplary! And since you're both wet already, go on to the woodshed. Chop enough to fill the stove box in the kitchen. Then you can take dinner up to your pa and the men at the Marble Yard. Uncle Pompous is poorly with his rheumatism. Hustle along now!"

Their father's Marble Yard was a few doors north of the public square on Washington Street. Edward loved to visit there, even if visiting was all he could do. At ten, he was too young to cut, or carve, or polish--certainly to help lift the heavy stones. Still, it was what he aimed to do when he reached sixteen, or maybe even younger, for he loved the great stone blocks placed all along the passage from the street back to the stoneworking area.

Today, pools of water stood on the gravel-covered entrance, as they had everywhere the boys had been. Still barefoot, they were not afraid of getting wet. "But if we get mud splattered in these baskets, it'll be remarked on!" Romeo warned.

"Plenty worse if we drop one!" Edward had just stubbed his toe on a rock and nearly experienced disaster.

"Ho! And just look at the lads a-bearing in our dinner pails!" James Conway's broad Irish accent greeted them.

Albert Baker came hastily out of the shop office. "What I'm wondering is why my boys are not in school learning something in return for the dollars I have to lay out to keep 'em there?"

"But, Pa," Edward hastened into their story, "lightning simply crushed a tree right outside the school window..."

"...a chinaberry...and not much account," Romeo interrupted hastily. "But I think the thunder clap made Mrs. McCay nervous!"

"She near fainted!" Edward clarified. "So we got dismissed for the day, Pa." Then reaching out to pat a nearby stone, he made a valiant effort to divert his father's mind. "What is this?"

"Why, it's marble, as well you know! You can put those baskets on the table inside. We all appreciate your bringing them through right-side-up." He turned away, then back. "Since you've got the afternoon free, I want you to aid your ma in whatever way you can, for

9

tomorrow we're all going to start making a big garden on the back of our lot and behind Winston's all the way to Spragin's Alley... fence it, at least! Probably be too wet to plow."

The boys' ears rang at the prospect of the work that was bound to entail, but they tried to bear up. It would never do for their pa to see them flinch from work! That would only call to his mind memories from his childhood days up in New York state, where boys had been expected to slave from dawn to dusk, never complaining!

So they bravely chorused, "Yes, Pa."

"Hurry home!...and don't go near Pinhook Creek!" With one final wave they trod the passageway, leaping puddles. Out on Washington Street, they paused to whiff the good smells of Scott's Bakery across the street. But they were penniless.

"All our spending money goes to schooling!" Edward lamented. They ran now, minds focused on dinner. But Beeman's Blacksmith Shop on the north side of West Holmes, east of Church, was a hard place to pass. Something was usually going on there.

They found Mr. Beeman shoeing a handsome chestnut horse, while its owner stood by talking. "I sure hate to part with Old Caesar! He's been a faithful horse to me! But I have to sell him to someone as can use him. For it'd be nothin' but a worry to my wife to feed an' water an' exercise him whilst I'm off to the war."

Mr. Beeman's hammer poised in midair. "You goin' then? Soon?"

"Looks that away," the man replied. "John Dickson's in town with a captain's commission for a new company...Be gatherin' what men he can persuade up on the courthouse square tomorrow."

"So I'm hearin'," said the blacksmith, as he brought his shoeing hammer smartly down on a nail.

"It's a hard decision to make." The horse owner stood shaking his head. "On the one hand a man suffers at leavin' his wife an' chillun to fend for theirselves. Then, on the other, you gotta do what you can to defend your country, or be branded a 'coward'!"

Sensing suffering on display, the boys turned away wordless. It was hunger that sent them racing for home, where the sound of the dinner bell caught them at the east gate.

"Best not say a word about what we just heard," Romeo advised, as they went to the well house to wash up. "May be just a rumor!"

Edward looked at him in disbelief. "Rumor or not, I plan to be up on the square tomorrow to see!"

"You'll be out in that garden, is where you'll be!"

But Edward's imagination stayed busy picturing the scene downtown next day. It occupied his mind while he ran errands, fed the chickens, and helped to chop more firewood, even while they cared for their horse, Owego--named after Albert's hometown up in Tioga County, New York, but usually called Wego.

Uncle Pompous, who stood by leaning on his stick, soon got out of patience. "Marse Edward, whar yer mind? Wego liable to aim he hoof right smack at yer front teeth, you don't watch out, boy!"

Even that awful warning failed to dim the vivid scene Edward's imagination had conjured up.

By suppertime, it was all ready to blossom into words.

The younger children ate supper in the kitchen under the firm direction of Magdalena, and were put to bed soon thereafter. Only Romeo and Edward were considered old enough to come to the dining table with the family and shop crew.

Tonight, appetites had been sharpened by a slight cooling that had followed the rain.

"More'n likely this is Dogwood Winter comin' in," William, the only true Southerner present, observed in his soft drawl.

"What may this Dogwood Winter be?" James Conway questioned, as he eyed with disappointment a nearby bowl of mashed turnips.

"It's what folks call a cool spell that comes when the dogwood trees bloom. I reckon you've seen them on the mountainsides. Ma likens their white four-petal flowers to the shape of the Cross."

"Mother Elliott has such a fund of knowledge about trees and flowers," commented Emily. "I'm trying hard to learn from her."

At that moment, the kitchen door flew open, and Sophronia came through, her face creased in a grin. In her hands she gripped the ironstone platter heaped high with luscious pink slices of ham.

A gasp of delight swept around the table.

"Ham! Ham?" Albert was unbelieving. "Where did we get that?"

"Mr. Stewart from out at Hayes Store," Elizabeth said, "and he wants you to apply it on his bill, Albert. He's short of cash."

Albert laughed. "We're all sailing in that boat! And, believe you me!, I'll take ham in place of money most any old time."

Emily held up a bowl of relish. "When we took Mother Elliott a few slices, she gave us some of her famous chow-chow!"

All this bounty claimed immediate attention, and even Edward's busy fancy shifted briefly to food--at least until one of the men said, "Seems we can expect a sunny day for tomorrow's exercise."

Heads nodded, while words suddenly flowed from Edward's mouth, "You mean because Captain Dickson will be up on the square in the morning to raise a volunteer company. That will be some sight!"

"I was speaking of your pa's garden work..."

"Edward!" The thunder of his father's voice swept away some of the sudden quiet that had gripped everyone present. "You were not addressed and had no reason to speak! Kindly remove yourself and your plate to the kitchen...I'll see you in the parlor later. And you, too, Romeo!"

While Edward crept shamefaced toward the kitchen, Romeo looked affronted. It hadn't been his fault!

Conversation immediately exploded among the men. Only Albert and William sat silent with heightened color.

Elizabeth and Emily looked at each other in alarm. A fearsome dread seemed to be wiping all but one thought from their minds.

Sophronia saved the awkward moment by bearing in two pies that looked like pumpkin. "But they's really made from one a' them big squashes seasoned up wid cinnamon an' spices...good as punkin'!"

Everyone agreed. Only Emily was ever after to associate squash pie with bad news and heartache.

Later on, Elizabeth watched in concern as William escorted his wife upstairs. Surely he wasn't going to!...

But at that very moment, he was struggling to explain, "I just have to tell you, Emily...Please listen now! I'm joinin' up! Do you hear? There's no way I can keep out of it." As logical words suddenly failed his tortured mind, he could only beg, "I want you to understand. You must! I can't bear it if you don't!"

For awhile, Emily could only stand at the window, gripping the curtain and staring into the pool of darkness below. Not a crack of light rose to help her! Even though she had feared such an announcement, to have it sprung so swiftly was almost too much even to grasp; yet she knew she must grasp it and accept it...at once!

Turning, she tried desperately to compose her face, her voice. "I'm trying to understand, William. It's just that you're thirty-six years old...and you know you tend to get the fever so easily! You're not used to rough living out-of-doors. And what is Richard going to do without you?"

The last was the only question he could readily answer. "He's joinin', too!"

"Oh, surely not! Why, he's even older! Does Mary Elizabeth know yet? And what will happen to your painting business?"

"I expect Mary knows by now." William appeared to be suffering confusion, even agony. "As for the business, you know there's not much now. Few people have the heart or the money for sprucin'-up their place. Emily, face it! You know that somethin' has got to be done to stop this war, or we're all gonna go under!"

It was true! Of course Emily knew that. "I feel so for Mary," she whispered. "Four children! Who is to care for her and them?"

"Mary will probably manage. She has the Figgs: her Grandfather Tinable an' her Uncle Littleton."

"And I've got Albert and Elizabeth," Emily remarked, giving in suddenly to a strange feeling of calmness. "Does Albert know?"

William nodded. "He wanted to talk against it, but he ain't a Southerner and don't entirely understand."

Emily nodded. "That's the very situation I'm in, William! Have you told Mother Elliott?"

"Not yet. I'm dreadin' that!"

"I suppose you'll be joining tomorrow then--up on the square?" William nodded. "We'll be there, of course." Then a fleeting look of embarrassment crossed his face. "But we actually enlisted yesterday. A. B. Moore swore us in up at the courthouse. Only the matter of a few minutes."

"Only a few minutes," whispered Emily. A few minutes to reduce a person to almost no worth! To erase all that had been struggled for with such hope and enthusiasm.

She looked sorrowfully at her husband, some six inches taller. His blue eyes were misted with sadness; his fair complexion paler than usual. Reaching up to straighten his light hair, she let him lock her close in his arms.

"It's all right," she murmured. "We must ask God to guide and to strengthen us, to protect you, and bring you safely home."

It was only then that she cried and felt William's tears mingle with her own.

Downstairs in the parlor Albert was trying to explain to Romeo and Edward what it meant to be a Yankee in the South at wartime.

"I'm not a Southerner," he said, "and probably won't be called to fight for the Southern cause. But I deeply sympathize with all that go, and your Uncle William and his brother, Richard, will be among them. Most of the shop men are in the same boat as I am. Those who wanted to fight for the Union went home months ago."

He drew a deep breath. "As for your mother and me, we're trying to stay neutral, to tread lightly, think before we speak, and be as neighborly and sympathetic as possible. We love the town of Huntsville and people of the South...and want to stay here, if we possibly can."

He turned to clap both boys on the shoulder. "In actual fact, you, Romeo, are a Northerner. We brought you South when you were about one year old. But Edward was born here, and he can consider himself to be Southern. Yet you are both underage, and if people think of your mother and me as 'Northerners', they will think the same of you. Understand?"

Both boys nodded, too overwhelmed with confusion to speak.

"So you best adopt the same policy we do. Be careful what you say. Be kind to your relatives and neighbors, for many are in real trouble now--and your Aunt Emily will be one of them!"

"Yes, Pa." They looked up at him earnestly.

14

"It won't be easy!" he warned, eyes on Edward, "but it will be worth the effort. It's how men must act; and this is a time when boys have to become men quickly."

Gravely, he shook hands with each of them. Then, bidding them, "Goodnight," he was suddenly moved to give each a hug.

And out in the night the whistle of the east-bound train pulling toward the Huntsville Depot seemed to split the world in two!

Chapter Two

March 22, 1862

After breakfast next morning, Albert stepped out back where he found the air brisk and dandelions sparkling in the grass. Trees seemed all to have burst into bloom at once. What a beautiful and promising place this Southland is! he thought. If only it can be freed from its present misery!

Casting aside that thought, he determined to concentrate today on making a garden--a job he disliked. He had grown to manhood in Tioga County, New York, and still owned his dairy farm there, but working with stone was what satisfied him most. He was very proud of the many building foundations and stone steps erected by Baker Marble Yard in Huntsville, as well as the intricately carved and lettered monuments they had made for town cemeteries, church burial grounds, and family graveyards in Madison and adjoining counties.

As for his New York farm, Albert knew he was fortunate to have John Gideon Baker, the oldest son of his late brother, Hiram, to help manage his place. John, though only seventeen, had good judgment, ability, and initiative that promised to lead him far. Already a talented carver of statues and designs in stone, he must eventually be offered an opportunity in the business, the same as was now being given his younger brother, Lucius.

Albert peered down Mill Street. The shop crew would be pulling in soon with a wagonload of posts and rails from the big woodyard kept by George Jones near the depot.

Usually, his men were at the shop on Saturdays, but today only James Conway had stayed, in case someone in the crowd expected in town wanted to order a headstone, or--more unlikely still!--pay a bill.

Collecting money was a problem certain to grow worse!

"Looks like it'll be a fair day for gardenin'!" William hailed him from the east porch. "Wish I could help!"

Albert smiled as his brother-in-law came down the steps. "You are bound to have more pressing things to do!"

William nodded. "Truth is, I'm so rushed an' confused I hardly know where to turn. We plan to leave in the next day or so...soon as the Cap'n can get things organized." He reached in his pocket and drew out some paper money. "Albert, I sold some of my paints an' brushes, so I want to pay this toward the cost of boarding Emily an' the children."

Albert shook his head.

"Thing is," insisted William, "fifty dollars is already due me from the Confederate Army--because I enlisted before conscription began. I hear Governor Shorter aims to issue that order sometime this next week."

Albert still did not reach for the money. Instead, he asked, "Do you think the new order will include men over thirty-five?"

"Well, I don't know. But we been over all that, Albert. I told you how I've just got to go help." He waved the bills gently. "Of course, I know this money won't go far, but maybe it'll..."

"You needn't pay me one red cent, William! It's nothing but a joy to have Emily and the children with us, and I assure you that I'll do all in my power to protect them from harm, should it ever threaten here." He motioned away the bills. "You're bound to need that money to out- fit your own self."

William shook his head. "Can't take much: a few extra clothes, my Bible, some writin' paper. Emily's gettin' my pack together."

"You better take a good blanket and a waterproof of some kind. Lots of rain falls this time of year. What about a gun?"

"The army's s'posed to furnish one...later on. We're startin' out to drill with sticks."

"Sticks! Sticks?" Albert was incredulous.

William nodded. "That's right. But what I want to say now is," he cleared his throat painfully, "you been a friend to me through the years, Albert! None better! If anything happens to me..."

17

"...pray it don't!" interrupted his brother-in-law sincerely.

"...I'm afraid there won't be much comin' to Emily. We had two hundred saved. She's got it stashed away; neither of us tends to rely much on banks these days. Aside from that, there's the rest of my painting apparatus. I never accumulated much of this world's goods."

Albert cleared his throat. "What you have instead is plenty of friends--and respect, too, from everybody who has ever had you to work on a job. Believe me, that's about all a man can ask!"

"Thank you...most kindly, Albert," William labored on. "What I want to say is when Ma passes on--no time soon, I hope!--the children'll come in for a share in her property."

Albert nodded. Speech had become about impossible for either.

Returning the bank notes to his pocket, William said, "Then, this money will go to Emily. I'm thankful she can make a little with her pretty sewin'."

"Hey there, Bill!" The call came from the front of the house.

"That'll be Richard. We're headed over to tell Ma." He offered his hand.

Albert shook it firmly, his thoughts in a turmoil. Although he believed William was taking an unnecessary risk, he had to admire his courage. What a big step for a man to take! Had the situation been reversed, could he have taken it? There was no ready answer, only doubt, and he had enough of that already. If the war were to come into North Alabama, what would happen to him and his family? Should they try to go back to New York state? And lose everything they had worked for here?

"What is you gonna need fer tools, Mr. Albert?" Uncle Pompous called from the tool shed door. "Pickaxes? We's got two hatchets, an' a frow. 'Course I knows it too wet fer usin' a hoe!"

Just then Romeo and Edward erupted from the back door, "We're ready, Pa!"

Down the road the squeal of an axle signaled the shop wagon's turn from Arms Street. The crew, walking alongside to steady the load, gave him a wave. Suddenly, Albert realized that making a garden wasn't such a big problem when compared with some others.

Emily gazed down at the things she had laid out on the bed for William's pack. They were so few...so meager! Nearly everything she had selected had drawn his kindly, but determined, "Ain't got room for that!" Surely another pair of socks? Hoping they would not be noticed, she tucked them in the pocket of his extra shirt.

The most closely-woven woolen blanket they owned was there; an extra pair of pants and underwear; toilet articles, towel; needle and thread for mending, buttons. What was missing?...soap!

Elizabeth and Sophronia had assembled the medicines that might be needed. Since quinine was not to be had anywhere, they had put in willow tree bark...said to make a tea effective against fever. Watermelon seeds made a tea for relief of kidney problems. There were blue mass pills, small bottles of castor oil and turpentine, and a pack of mustard seed for poultices.

Sophronia had added a flask of whiskey and bottle of liniment. "These is what they's most likely to use!" she had advised. "They don't take no mixin' or soakin'!"

Emily sighed. Sophia was probably right, but at least they had tried. The bottles were tightly corked; the bark and seeds packed in small cloth bags; and all placed inside a leather pouch closed by a drawstring that could be slung from a belt.

"Mama!" called Mattie from the door. Her brown hair straggled around her shoulders. "Are you going to braid me?"

"My goodness! How could I have forgotten that?"

Mattie smiled shyly. "You were busy with Papa's things to take to war. Mama, where is war? Is it near Athens?" When her mother did not reply immediately, she asked, "You remember that day Papa took us riding in a buggy all the way to Athens? When Wego waded right on through all those creeks?...splash!...splash!"

Emily stood stricken while her mind was flooded with dozens of priceless memories of that wonderful trip.

Mattie peered up at her anxiously. "Mama! Why don't you answer me? Have you forgotten? That was the day Papa got my pawasol!"

The smile that Emily managed was as shaky as her reply, "Never will I forget that day, Mattie! Never! We had such a good time!"

Mattie was pleased. "Well, if war's in Athens, I don't mind!"

Her mother debated whether to let it rest there. But she could not! It would be wrong. "Athens is a nice place," she assured her little daughter, "but war is a long ways from there! So Papa will have to take everything he may need."

Mattie turned to the bed and began to consider each item. "But where's Papa's hat with the buckle on it?"

"He'll be wearing that--and his coat."

"He won't be wearing his pillow? Where's it? You know Papa has to sleep on his pillow, Mama, or he'll get the headache!"

Emily knew it, and the thought increased the pain that was about to burst her heart open. But why upset Mattie? "Of course Papa will need his pillow, honey! We'll lay it here with all the other things." (And where will I hide it after he leaves?)

"There's Papa and Uncle Richard now!" Mattie pointed from the front window.

Catching a glimpse of the brothers headed briskly toward town, Emily said, "They've been to Grandmother Elliott's, and soon as I braid your hair, I must step across there, too."

Of course, Mattie wanted to go. But that was not to be. "Run along and find Bessie to play with. Grandmother may not feel well this morning. I will just have to see."

As she dressed, Emily tried to think how she might comfort her mother-in-law, for Mrs. Elliott would surely be devastated by the news that both her remaining sons were leaving for war. She had been so grief-stricken back in 1856 when she learned of the death of her youngest boy, Abraham J., only twenty-three. A printer by trade, he had died and been buried so far away--in Helena, Arkansas--where none of the family could even visit his grave.

The Elliott home was a two-story frame with several additional rooms in a one-story wing behind. The fenced lot was large enough for a cow shed and garden, both absolute necessities in wartime.

This morning, Emily noticed that violets were already blooming in profusion beside the brick walk from the front gate. Sight of them brought a powerful need to linger--even to lie down in their midst. Everything ahead seemed so impossibly hard to face!

Resolutely, she drew a deep breath, opened the front door, and hallooed in the fashion popular in the South.

"Come in, Emily!" The voice came from the bedroom at the left of the entry hall, where its owner stood before the open doors of her walnut wardrobe. "Is it warm today? I'm tryin' to pick out a dress to wear up to the doin's on the courthouse square."

Emily was not only too surprised to speak, she felt ashamed of having misjudged her mother-in-law's strength and resilience, for this pioneer woman whom she had come to love, had suffered much. She could only gasp weakly, "You're going up there yourself?"

Mrs. Elliott turned and let a questioning expression cross her face. It was a face that had been altered to grimness by the loss of some back teeth, but one that was miraculously transformed, as at this moment, by her warm smile. "Certainly I'm goin', Emily! With my own sons joinin' up to fight for the Southland, I want to be lookin' on...proud as can be!"

Emily smiled in admiration. "I wish I felt that way, too, but I can't help worrying over William's health."

"That's natural enough, child. I worry, too. But Richard will look out for him. At least they'll be together, just like they've always been from childhood an' all through most of their workin' years. Close as two peas in a pod!"

Emily could but smile. She knew how true that was; the thought now relieved her worries somewhat.

As the old lady turned back to her wardrobe, the motion set aquiver the white lace cap she wore pinned over the back of her thinning gray hair. "Do you reckon I could wear that lavender muslin you made me last summer?"

"It should be warm enough," Emily replied. "But take a shawl." Together, they examined the dress for rips or tears. When none were found, its owner expressed relief. "It's a good thing, for I expect it'll have to last me a long time to come."

Emily was silent. She certainly had not intended to go to the square herself; had not thought she could bear to watch the scene to be enacted there. Now she realized how impossible it would be to admit such weakness to this unselfish, proud old lady. Some unplanned words came swiftly to her rescue, "I think I'll include Mattie in this trip, Mother Elliott. It will thrill her, although she won't understand what it's all about."

Mrs. Elliott nodded. "An' in later years t'will be a treasure in her memory."

The door opened slightly and Mary Ann Figg, poked in her head. "My soul! I thought I'd hear sobbing, but all I see are smiles!"

Mrs. Elliott regarded her oldest daughter briefly. "You oughta know your own mother better'n that!"

Emily smiled at her sister-in-law. "And if you knew me better, Mary Ann, dear, you'd guess that I'm crying deep inside. Are you going down to the courthouse square with us?"

But Mary Ann shook her head. "I'm expectin' Littleton home for dinner, also Robert E. You know Richard an' William let him take over that paintin' job they were workin' on. I'm just so thankful Robert E. is only fourteen! I couldn't bear up like Ma here, if my son had to go!"

"Aunt 'Lizbeth!" Mattie danced up and down in excitement. "I'm going downtown with Mama--and I can take my pawasol!"

"Really!" Elizabeth sounded surprised.

Considering an explanation due, Emily added, "I've witnessed a good example of how a Southern lady acts when both sons go off to war. Mother Elliott's so proud of them! And she's bound to see it all!" She sighed at the thought. "I just can't let her go alone! After all, she's sixty-six years old!--or should I say 'young'?"

"Maybe you should!" Elizabeth smiled sympathetically. "But I'd say that all three of you need an escort. Could you use Romeo and Edward? They would like it, and perhaps be of some service."

"That will be perfect," Emily agreed. "We plan to leave around ten-thirty. The boys suggested that time to their mother." It was then she realized that William had not even asked her! Because of how coldly she had acted, he must have believed she would refuse. Tears of shame threatened as she dressed Mattie and herself. I'll be strong! she thought over and over...no one will ever guess how I'm suffering over this.

22

They had only walked a little way along the south side of West Holmes Street before Emily realized that her mother-in-law, too, was determined to make this trip as painless as possible. As they passed under the beautiful old trees that were beginning to weave a lacy canopy overhead, Mrs. Elliott began to reminisce, "We came to live here on West Holmes Street around twenty-five years ago, an' it just seems to grow more beautiful each year."

Emily did a quick calculation. "Then you moved from Tuscaloosa in about 1837?"

"That's right. Till then, Enoch had enjoyed good business with his wagonmaker's yard. Since Tuscaloosa's a river port, there's much haulin' eastward from there, an' then the coal mines nearby in Walker County draw men with wagons from all around."

"What happened?"

"Two things. The depression of 1837 was bad; business fell off sharp! Then, as Enoch got older--he was more'n twenty years ahead of me!--it seemed best to live nearer my family, the Cains, so we up an' made the move. An' in no ways am I sorry, for Huntsville's a fine town an' has offered our children plenty. That's a fact!"

Here, a narrow place in the path caused the ladies to swing aside their broad skirts and walk single file. A wagon loaded with people passed noisily, followed by several men on horseback.

"Mama, am I holding my pawasol right?" Mattie marched slightly ahead of them, her light-blue dress swaying with its hoop and the yellow parasol held straight as an arrow over her head.

Emily and Mrs. Elliott looked at each other in amusement. "You may want to hold it more to one side," Emily suggested. "Just try tilting it so it shades you from the sun."

"Another object is to frame your face an' bonnet so you make a pretty picture," advised the older lady.

"Like this, Grandmother?" Mattie began a series of trial poses that caused the grownups to retreat slightly.

"What are you doing there, Mattie?" Romeo had turned to see if the ladies he was escorting were in order. "Careful, or you might poke someone in the eye!"

Mattie protested, "I'm watching careful!"

Again, Emily had a sudden vision of the day William had bought the yellow sunshade. This time the flash of memory was so vivid, so painful that she almost stumbled and fell.

"Aunt Emily, are you all right?" Edward called from the rear.

She forced herself to reassure him.

"The boys are sweet," Mrs. Elliott commented, "but seems a bit like we're in a flock of sheep caught 'tween herdsmen!"

The remark was so apt that Emily could not keep from laughing, and that somewhat restored her calm and determination. "Cameron's Paint Shop looks to be closed tight," she remarked as they passed it on their right.

"He's probably joinin' up," mused Mrs. Elliott. "My land! Just look at the horses in Lloyd's Livery Stable! Hitched everywhere!"

"There are a lot more than you see on a Sunday when people are attending the Baptist Church," Emily observed. The odors from the horse barns seemed to rise like a barrier between this busy scene and the pleasant residential area they had just left.

The sight of so many horses and the great variety of carriages and wagons so affected their advance guard that he came to a stop to gaze in awe, causing Emily to hastily warn, "Mattie, watch out or you'll poke Romeo with your parasol!"

"Move on!" shouted Edward from the rear. "A carriage is trying to turn in!"

"Well, where is it goin' when it gets in?" Mrs. Elliott wanted to know, as with a sweep of skirts she hustled everyone along.

On the corner of Gallatin, John Swift's Brass and Iron Factory and Machine Shop was operating full-blast.

"Looks like John is getting some work," observed Emily. He was their neighbor on the northeast corner of Mill and Holmes, and also a New Yorker.

Mrs. Elliott glanced at the factory. "Might have an order from the Confederate Army. More power to him if he has! We're far back in manufactories. It's a shame! So many gallant soldiers! But few firearms to supply them...or so I've heard."

Emily hastily thrust aside a frightening vision of William off to

24

battle with only the stick furnished him for drill. And all at once the whole idea of her kindly, artistic, sensitive husband in any kind of a fight was away beyond her imagining.

As they turned the corner onto Jefferson Street, Romeo stopped to point up ahead. "Just look at the folks, Aunt Emily!"

"Don't block the way, please, Romeo! And, Mattie, let me lower your parasol now. You may accidentally poke someone!"

"I can't see!" Edward complained from his rear position.

"Mercy on us!" Elizabeth Elliott urged. "Let's do push on! I'm near as anxious to get there as the boys."

As they negotiated the sidewalk along Jefferson in its gradual rise toward the courthouse square, they could hear noisy shouting from the crowd. A short way along the block they met a lady whose face was streaked with tears beneath her faded sunbonnet. She was being escorted from the scene by a young woman and small boy, both of whom seemed hardly able to restrain their emotions.

It was exactly the sort of scene Emily had expected to witness and wanted to avoid. Yet here they were in the very midst of it!

"Poor soul," whispered Mrs. Elliott. "Probably left with a lot of children, too many instructions, an' dreadin' what's to come!"

"-----Spotswood!" A thunder of voices took up the cry.

They were standing too far back to get the full name, and from the outer fringe of the crowd could not see over the tops of tall bonnets and, here and there, a towering stovepipe hat.

This was not a situation to Edward's liking. He yearned to see all that was going on. Slowly, he began to move around in search of a way through. But hoop skirts were everywhere, and he was fairly sure he shouldn't shove one of them aside!

"Robert Newton Cameron!" Another shout rent the air.

"I thought so!" whispered Mrs. Elliott. "Can we get closer?"

Suddenly there was a billowing shift in the wave of skirts and a number of people exited--some in tears, and others in positions of support, still others holding their heads stoically high.

Edward grabbed his aunt's hand and was first into the opening. Mrs. Elliott squeezed through next, bidding Mattie, "Hang onto my skirt!" Romeo easily slipped in behind them.

Now they were at the outer edge of the sidewalk along the west side of the square in front of Bank Row. The rise was a bit steep up to the great banking edifice built by George Steele, which now housed the Northern Bank of Alabama.

A long line of men stood at the lower end of the block all the way to the lobby doors of the handsome, new Huntsville Hotel.

All eyes were upon one man, Capt. John S. Dickson, slender and neat in his citizen's clothes, as he moved along the block waving his simple black cane and calling, "Volunteers for the War!"

Emily watched this man, who more than a year before, had given up his hardware business on South Side Square to enlist. And here he was now, trying to raise a new company of volunteers! His cry was so heart-felt and beseeching that she was amazed to find herself hoping that someone--not William!--but another man, would be willing to step forward.

As the Captain drew even with the Robinson & Rison Drug Store, a man stepped from the crowd and, facing the officer, sketched an awkward salute. They shook hands. "John Brooks!" Dickson shouted cordially. As the crowd took up and repeated the cry, the Captain continued his walk, and Brooks joined the other volunteers.

Before the call could be repeated, another man stepped forward to be welcomed by Dickson, who cried, "Lafayette Day!" The name seemed to appeal to the crowd, and they cheered wildly.

The next volunteer held a short confab with the Captain before stepping back to salute. Dickson shouted, "W. Young Derrick, also volunteers his horse! We'll be needin' three more horses!"

A great shout went up and some laughter in recognition of the horse's supposed willingness to serve.

Dickson was now making his way slowly toward those men waiting in line. No volunteer came forward now until he was nearly to the drug store, when two men stepped through the open door. They were Richard and William!

Mrs. Elliott gasped, but steadied herself. As for Emily, she experienced such a sudden and unexpected feeling of emotion--even of pride!--that before she could stop herself she had snatched up Mattie, parasol and all. "Look, Mattie!" she cried, "There's your own papa!

26

Look honey! See him shaking hands with the Captain!"

"Here are the brothers, Richard and William Elliott, joining the company together!" shouted Captain Dickson.

As the crowd's approbation rang in her ears, Emily saw William and Richard moving toward the line of volunteers. "William!" she called. "Here we are!"

The others joined in at the top of their voices. "Papa! Papa!" screamed Mattie.

Miraculously, their cries were heard. Both brothers turned to wave. While Richard looked pleased to see them, William's face simply glowed with thankfulness and relief.

Other men stepped forward; other names were called. But Emily could only think of the moment when William had seen them! What a consoling memory for a lifetime!

They were suddenly tired, and Emily felt concerned for her mother-in-law's strength. Mattie asked over and over, "What was Papa doing in that line, Mama?" While Romeo and Edward endlessly reviewed everything as dispassionately as if they had witnessed a scene in some great drama.

At her own gate, Mrs. Elliott leaned forward, hugged Emily and whispered, "I'm so glad you went with me. I'd never have made it alone! Thank you, boys!" As she leaned down to kiss her little grand-daughter, she promised, "Your papa'll tell you all about it, Mattie! Never you fear!"

Once back across the street, the boys made for the garden to describe the scene in elaborate detail to the fence-builders.

Bessie was waiting patiently at the front door. "I missed you, Mattie," she whispered. "Did you raise your pawasol?"

Emily replied for her little daughter. "She handled it beautifully, just perfect in every way. And as soon as I get her dress changed, she can play for a while."

In her heart Emily breathed a prayer of thanksgiving. She knew she had been right to watch William volunteer...that she had been rewarded! Now, she prayed, if only I can find strength to face whatever comes next!

The atmosphere at the supper table that night was more relaxed than the previous evening. Everyone now knew the Elliott brothers had closed their business and stepped forward to help protect their homeland and families. They had been heartily congratulated in public for their courageous decision.

That Emily was accepting the situation made all the difference to William. He was eager to talk of the plans Dickson had for his new company. "Not quite enough men stepped out today, but Cap'n Dickson's goin' 'round the county...thinks he can raise more!"

"How many would that be?" Albert wanted to know.

"Close to a hundred," William explained eagerly. "We've got to have a first lieutenant an' two seconds, then five sergeants--and four corporals. The rest'll be privates to start off with."

"What was it this lad here was saying about a horse that had volunteered?" James Conway nodded his head toward Edward.

"Oh, that was Old Derrick's horse! But I think the Cap'n was glad to get the news. We need three more."

"Only four horses for a hundred men?" asked Elizabeth.

"We're not a cavalry troop," William reminded her. "Our horses most likely are for the officers."

"Here's the res' of the ham, ya'll!" Sophronia bore in the big platter. "'Sides that, we got a mess of dandelion greens! Me an' the boys traipsed out in the field an' picked 'em today!"

Smiles quickly blossomed around the table; everyone welcomed a bite of fresh greens even more than ham!

"A fair reward for a fenced garden patch!" Albert glanced at the men. "We'll soon have more greens, the good Lord willing!"

"...and if the rabbits don't come marauding!"

"...or chickens!"

"It won't pay no sich to creep in wid Uncle Pompous 'round watchin'!" Sophronia settled that.

It was after supper that William spoke the words Emily dreaded most, "I guess we'll be off in the mornin' 'round dawn, soon as the rail cars get here to take us to Lafayette, where we'll begin drillin' in good an' earnest!" He reflected for a moment, then added, "So guess I'd better have a little talk with Mattie."

Holding hands, they walked down toward Pinhook Creek. What was said between them Emily never knew, nor expected to. Mattie only said, "I promised Papa two things...to learn my letters before he comes back...and to take care of you and the baby, Mama."

What a burden to place on a four-year-old! "And what did Papa promise you?"

Mattie looked up in surprise, "Why, to sleep on his pillow!"

And that night--that last wonderful night!--William's pack was made up ready, and when he left before dawn, his pillow no longer waited in its place on the bed.

Next morning Albert and Elizabeth took Mattie with them to the Baptist Church. Emily could not go out. She could only get as far as the parlor. There she pulled a chair around to face the empty fireplace and, closing her eyes, prayed for William's safety. Only after she had begun to feel some peace, could she allow her gaze to shift upward-- to embrace the beautiful landscape that William had painted in oils and framed for her on the occasion of their first wedding anniversary.

In subdued colors it depicted a lake whose water reflected the pure light and faint glow of the rising sun. Trees darkened each side of the water. In the lower right-hand corner, a canoe waited in an inlet. Its Indian occupant sat poised with paddle ready to steal forth across the lake, over waters reflecting the sunrise.

Emily sighed. As beautiful as was the painting, she could not penetrate its mystery. The scene had come from William's imagination, and he was the only one who knew its meaning.

"Oh, William," she breathed aloud. "I long to understand your painting...and this Southern cause! But how can I ever do it?"

But no answer came! And presently, the painting seemed to grow darker...to become static, leaving the Indian posed forever lifeless in his frail canoe.

Chapter Three

March 25, 1862

Two mornings later, their neighbor, Mrs. John Swift, stepped across Mill Street with two voluminous dresses over her arm. "I've seen the gown you made over for Mrs. Winston, Emily, and think it so cleverly done. Can you help me?"

Smiling, Emily led the way to the sitting room. "Did you have something special in mind, Elizabeth?"

"Yes, I did!" the visitor replied eagerly. "I wondered if you could take some of the fullness from the top of these skirts? It might be we could use the material to make some shirts for our three older boys, even a dress for little Eva May. Being muslin, it should do for summer wear. What do you think?"

After spreading out the skirts, Emily exclaimed, "What a good idea! Let me make an estimate of what can be removed."

While Emily was working, Mrs. Swift began to reiterate all the problems that people in the South faced for lack of new cloth. "I just don't see what we are to do with no mills down here--and few shipments getting through from England. What little yardage the merchants have to offer is priced too dear! I refuse to pay it!"

"Everyone feels that way," agreed Emily. "It's so unfair!"

"Yes, it is. Women are taken advantage of! I'd much rather you had my money, Emily, for I know I'll get value in return." As she concluded these remarks, Elizabeth Swift placed her hand gently on Emily's shoulder and looked into her face in a kindly way. "I was sorry William had to go--and if we can do anything?"

Emily smiled her thanks. "It's hard, but we're all in the same boat. As for doing something, you already have! You've given me a new idea! I see lots of material here, Elizabeth. There will be enough for a dress for your baby. I can surely get two or three little shirts. Maybe something else. You'll find your dresses to be more comfortable, too, without all that bunchy fullness at the waist!" she smiled gratefully. "And thanks for the idea!"

As she closed the front door, Emily heard Enoch Carlton's loud screams from upstairs. Morning nap over, he was hungry!

"Where do you get such lung power?" she asked, as she sat down so he could nurse. "With your black hair and solemn eyes, you are a true Babcock in looks. You have the Elliott family names: Enoch after William's father--and Carlton after Thomas Carlton, who was Mother Elliott's first husband, but died a short time after Mary Ann was born." She gazed fondly down at him as she added, "But no one in either family will claim that screaming ability, big boy!"

"Is it anything unusual?" Elizabeth asked from the doorway.

Emily shook her head. "Apparently this baby's hunger pangs are almost past bearing. I'm glad you came in, for I want to tell you about a practical idea Mrs. Swift brought me just now."

Elizabeth came in the room glad to see Emily cheerful and more interested in something than she had been since William left. "Do go on and tell me this good idea!" she urged. And as Emily began to explain what the scheme entailed, she immediately saw value in it. "It is a practical idea--and, with your talent, you can soon figure out how to make the needed changes in a way that will save the most material. But one thing you'll need is thread! And that must be almost as scarce as new cloth!"

"I have quite a stock on hand. Though much is in queer colors that never seem to match anything!"

"That's the reason I think you should go right to town now and buy all the thread you can find, whether it's what you call queer colors, or not. Try to find white, for soon now we may be cutting up sheets to make shirts and underwear. And get black, too, if you can!" The word "black"--so carelessly mentioned!--brought to mind another: "widows!"...widows soon to be everywhere!

"I'll shop around for the best prices; not buy too much in any one store."

They glanced at each other in complete understanding. It would

31

not do for their family to appear greedy!

"Try Bruckner's Sewing Machine Depot on the square," Elizabeth suggested. "Then there's Norvel's place on Franklin, and Shanklin & Scott on North Side Square. Who knows, of course, what any merchant has now, or even if they're still doing business!"

Rising, Emily lifted Enoch Carlton to her shoulder. "It'll be a search, but I needn't do it all in one day. I'll probably take Mattie along...Bessie, too, if you don't object."

Downstairs in the children's room, Emily gave Enoch Carlton to Magdalena. "I'll swap this one for two little girls."

Magdalena grinned. "Long as he not hungry, Miss Em'ly! That do be one awful trial to bear. Girls, you been asked for."

Bessie was the first to jump up. "I'm ready, Aunt Emily! Where are we going? Can Mattie take her pawasol?"

"Why, to town, Bessie. And no parasols! We'll have packages."

"Look, Mama!" Mattie held up the slate covered with all shapes and sizes of M's. "Those big ones are Bessie's. These are mine."

Bessie pointed. "Those with the crooked legs are Mag'lena's."

"Never you mind 'bout crooked legs, miss!" protested the young nurse. "I aims to straight'n they legs out quick enuff!"

Mattie looked at Bessie reproachfully. "But this was the first time Mag'lena ever wrote on a slate! She can't make those letters big as you do yet." Sympathy glowed in her blue eyes.

"You made a really good start," complimented Emily. "And maybe tomorrow we'll all learn to write big A. What do you think M and A put together spell?"

Heads were shaken, and eyes questioned.

"It spells MA...and two of them, side by side, make MAMA!"

"Jes listen to that, chillun!" marveled Magdalena, as she set Enoch Carlton on the floor. "Soon, we gonna learn to write a real word! Never 'spected to do that." Her eyes sought Emily's. "I can barely 'member my own ma--jes how pretty she wuz, an' her hands."

More than one pair of eyes misted in sympathy.

Without the noisy, emotional crowd of the past Saturday, downtown seemed quiet, almost deserted. People walking about, entering one store after another, appeared confused. No wonder! thought Emily. There's a lack of everything! And the prices!

None of the sewing machine stores offered encouragement. They must have stocked thread, but not a spool was on display!

Samuel Shanklin, who often visited their neighbor, Archibald Rison, asked Emily point-blank, "Have you a sewing machine, Mrs. Elliott? Because I tell you frankly, we give our sewing-machine customers first chance at what little thread we can find. Seems only fair!" Then he suddenly said, "However, since your good husband's gone off to fight, and I know you're a seamstress, you can have six spools of white."

Emily smiled her thanks, though the price charged did not make her feel grateful. "As a dressmaker, Mr. Shanklin," she told him, "I have a real need and desire for a sewing machine. Those I have seen demonstrated surely are wonders, but the present shortage of material makes me think it might not be a wise purchase. When you next have a sale..."

At Johnson & Seat on North Side Square they fared much better. The old clerk there (few stores now had young salesmen) seemed to recognize Emily. "I've known Albert Baker ever since he came to Huntsville. Hadn't been for him, I couldn't have marked my Ella's grave when she died five years back. Is it thread you need?"

When Emily nodded, he glanced quickly around the store, before leaning down to dig beneath the counter. Finally, he came up with a good-sized covered box. "Now here's some odd colors we've had a long time, an' if you can use these colors," he said, tipping the lid enough for her to see within, "you can have the whole box for two dollars."

And now she did feel gratitude! As she loosened the strings of her cloth reticule, she was surprised to hear herself stammering, "I'm a dressmaker...and my husband has just this week gone off to war! Oh, sir! This thread will be such a help to me. Thank you!"

He nodded in understanding, as he tied the box top on with a bit of string. When he handed it over, he smiled and said, "Give my regards to Albert an' his missus."

"I will," promised Emily. Then as she added, "Good day to you, sir!" she was surprised to hear, "Good day, sir!" repeated by the girls, each of whom then curtsied politely. Wait until I can tell Elizabeth about this! she mused. How true it is that children instinctively follow your good example!

"I'm very proud of you," she complimented, once they were outside. "You are being so polite and such a help to me!"

Mattie looked up in surprise. "But, Mama, you know I promised Papa!"

"And I'm helping Mattie, Aunt Emily," added Bessie cheerfully.

As they turned the corner on Washington Street, an old Negro woman with a heavy basket on her arm stepped politely to one side with a low, "Mornin', mistress!"

"Good morning to you, auntie!" replied Emily with a smile. "It is such a pleasant day, isn't it?"

"Yes'um," replied the old soul. "An' I'se proud of it!"

The girls, not knowing how to handle this encounter, closed it with, "Good day to you, auntie."

"Mama, who was that?" whispered Mattie, when they had gone on.

"Why, I don't know her name," Emily replied, "but I often meet her right along this block. She is a polite and kind person, like we all want to be. Now, Bessie, we're nearly to the Marble Yard. Do you want to stop in?"

Jiggling happily, Bessie said, "Oh, yes, Aunt Emily!"

When they reached the open passageway that led from the street back to the shop area, they found Ebon, who lived on the back lot to care for the mules and wagon that were so essential to the business. He was busy smoothing the gravel passage with a rake.

"Where are the mules, Ebon?" inquired Bessie.

Ebon cackled with laughter. "Why, Old Joe he back there eatin' he head off. But Barnabas pullin' a wagon up the mountain for Mr. Albert an' Mr. Conway--an' that Mr. Broad as talks so funny."

"Don't guess I know Mr. Broad, Ebon," Emily said.

"No'um! He do be new to me, too."

"Well, we'll go on then," decided Emily. "I'd like to get some things at Mr. Windham's grocery. So, goodbye to you, Ebon."

"Goodbye, Ebon!" chorused the little girls.

At Windham's store on the southeast corner of Washington and Holmes, Bessie hung back in a very obvious manner.

Curious, Emily asked, "What's wrong, Bessie?"

Mattie put her arm protectively around her cousin. "Bessie doesn't like those naked chickens, Mama!"

Sure enough, several plucked fowls hung by their feet from the top of the store's window embrasure. Emily studied the naked carcasses. "They're ducks, I believe," she reported. "What I hate are all those flies crawling over everything. Just disgusting!"

Bessie quickly stepped back still further.

"Well, if you don't want to go in," Emily said, "you will just have to wait out here. Go and stand under that tree. There are no ducks there!" She handed Bessie the sack of white thread, and the box to Mattie. "Hold those for me and don't drop them. I wouldn't want to chase after spools rolling every-which-way!"

Bessie giggled.

"It wouldn't be one bit funny," Emily warned, as accompanied by flies, she made her way through the wide-open door.

Mr. Windham gave a hitch to the apron he wore around his waist and came forward with a cordial smile. "Well, I declare! I was just about to send word to Albert that I've found some of those codfish he sets such store by!"

Emily smiled. "All of us like it, Mr. Windham. You see we grew up eating cod in New York state. How did you get it?"

"I believe it was shipped to Savannah, then hauled. I bought a barrel an' would've got more, but few Southerners care for it!"

"Well, give me five pounds on Albert's bill. We'll have a real feast tonight! How about cheese? That's something we always loved in New York, but we made it ourselves. Do you ever get any?"

Mr. Windham put his finger to his lips to signal silence, even though they were alone in the store. He reached below the counter and handed over a small package, apologizing, "Tain't much!"

"We'll be glad to have even one bite apiece," she assured him. "Now if only I could get a vegetable. Have you anything at all?"

"These dried black-eyed peas aren't too bad," he said, showing her a handful. At her nod, he made up a small pack. "Then there's one of those winter squashes Albert bought once before."

Emily gave him the brightest smile she could muster. "I'll get that! Can you put it all in one package?" Just as she started out of the store, she suddenly spotted something on the front counter that caused her to pause and ask, "How much is this slate and the pencil to write with?"

"Why, twenty-five cents is all," the grocer assured her.

A thought came: extravagance! Ignoring it, she set her heavy package on the counter and dug a quarter from her reticule. Only one penny remained.

On the street, Emily found the girls talking to a little Negro boy who held fast to a broom taller than himself.

"...an' that dog was a-frothin' from he mouth--wobblin' an' staggerin' 'round!..." Here, the boy began a wild demonstration.

Seeing her mother, Mattie said in an awed voice, "It was a mad dog, Mama. A MAD dog!"

"A mad dog in the month of March?" Emily was incredulous.

"Yes'um." With his broom handle the boy began sketching in the dusty street his idea of the dog's erratic trail. "An' folks wuz runnin' ever which away!" His brown eyes glowed in excitement.

"What happened to the dog?" asked Emily, still in doubt.

"Why, he'um was shot. Yonder in front of Mr. Windham's store!"

At this news, the little girls both screamed and tried to hide behind Emily's skirts. "Please don't drop the thread!" she begged anxiously. "Who did the shooting?"

"Why, Mr. Franks! He do be the marshal as shoots dogs...an' people!"

Emily shuddered. She had had enough. Shifting the package, she rummaged in her bag for her remaining penny and presented it. "I thank you for telling us. Come along, girls. It's all over!"

At the Jefferson Street corner, Emily hesitated. She had hoped to stop to see Richard's wife, Mary Elizabeth; but burdened so with groceries and two tired little girls, she gave it up.

"Codfish!" Elizabeth was incredulous. "Albert will have a fit! You best put it right to soak, Aunt Sophia."

But Sophia was admiring the big squash. "I sees more'n one pie here. Them men'll be mighty proud!"

After Emily had shown the black-eyed peas and the tiny hunk of cheese, Elizabeth teased, "I don't know what method you used, for Mr. Windham never offers me things like this!"

"Just wait till you see the thread I found!" Carefully, she untied the box, setting aside the bit of string to add to the ball kept in the kitchen drawer. Once the cover was off, the thread could be seen in all its myriad colors.

Elizabeth threw up her hands in delight. "Mercy on us! Did it cost the earth? And where?..."

"Only two dollars!" Emily revealed. "All because an old clerk in Johnson & Seat remembered Albert making it possible for him to mark his wife's grave!"

"Oh, yes. I remember that nice old man, though I can no longer re-call his name...but I'll sure tell Albert."

As together they admired the thread colors--neither mentioning the absence of black!--Emily felt a tiny shiver of excitement.

While Mattie and Bessie ran into the playroom to give the boys and Magdalena a description and reinactment of the mad-dog-scare, Emily mounted the stairs. Once in her room, she got out the slate and printed a name across its wooden frame, indenting each letter with a penknife. Then she darkened each with a drop of William's paint. Sat-isfied, she took the slate and pencil downstairs.

Magdalena was busy changing Enoch Carlton's napkin. "He a good boy!" she reported. "Ain't cried once't."

"Won't be long!" Emily forecast. "Look at what I brought you, Magdalena. It's a little gift of appreciation for all you do for me and my children."

The young nurse accepted the slate and pencil with a smile for Emily. "What this 'long the top? A word?"

"That's your name spelled out," explained Emily. "Just to show everyone it's yours."

Bessie and Mattie ran over to see.

"Does that say 'Mag'lena'?" Bessie ran her finger over the engrav-ing. "I see a big M."

But Magdalena only stood with tears on her cheeks. "Oh, my! Is it for me to OWN, Miss Em'ly? ME! Oh, you do be one sweet lady!"

Of course Mattie immediately joined her tears, and both little girls hugged their nurse as hard as they could.

Emily backed from the room. If that was an extravagance, so be it! she thought happily.

The boys came from school full of the mad-dog story, with some embellishment: they had heard that two people had been bitten as they had tried to run away. But Bessie soon told her brothers the truth of the matter. Together, she and Mattie gave a highly exaggerated demonstration, obviously copied from their informer.

"That mad dog did not bite anybody!" Bessie stated firmly. "He was too wobbly!" Next came an imitation of a wobbly mad dog.

"That's quite enough, now!" insisted their mother. "Put it out of your minds, you boys. Go out and see what can be done to help Uncle Pompous. Ebon's coming in the morning to plow the garden. Then we'll all be busy planting, so you had better chop a good stock of wood for the kitchen stove."

Before they left the room, Romeo said solemnly, "Ma, we got some news today from the fighting at Corinth. It was Prof. McCay talking to another fellow. They said it was just awful, soldiers hurt, and a lot..."

"...even killed!" Edward grabbed the spotlight.

"I know it's awful," said Elizabeth. "Just be careful never to exaggerate! And don't breathe a word about the war in front of your Aunt Emily. She's suffering enough as it is."

That night as Emily entered her lonely bedroom, she gave only one brief glance at the wide, empty bed. I can just stand so much of this, she thought, and in an instant her decision was made.

As she unbraided and brushed Mattie's hair, she asked, "How would you like to sleep in the big bed with me for awhile?"

The child looked at her with wide eyes. "In the same soft spot where Papa sleeps?"

Emily nodded. "Right there!...but on your own pillow."

A smile illuminated the tiny face. "Oh, I'd like it, Mama, but first I have to 'splain to Bessie. She won't know where I am!"

"Then I'll go with you and tell Magdalena."

The nurse's quick comment was, "But, Miss Em'ly, how you gonna rest fer fear a' turnin' over on that chile?"

Emily laughed. "If I do, she'll yell, I expect. And tomorrow I plan to move Enoch Carlton's crib in there with us, too."

"Oh, you IS gonna have some yellin'!" Magdalena warned, as she hugged Mattie and reminded her, "Yer mama be hearin' yer prayers tonight." Then together they walked to the small bed where Bessie and Mattie usually slept together.

Bessie was already curled up, breathing softly. "Never mind, I be tellin' her iffen she wakes," promised Magdalena. "But we both gonna miss you!"

Since the big bed was too high for Mattie to kneel beside, she used a stool. "Now I lay me" and the rest came easily enough, but the little voice had a distinct tremble when it pleaded, "And God please bless Papa at the war."

"Amen," whispered Emily.

Mattie mounted the two-step stool needed for reaching the high bed and, sinking down in the soft feather mattress, spread her arms wide and whispered, "I'm a bird...flying and flying..." and flew off to dreamland!

Aware that loneliness had been driven into the shadows beyond the candlelight, Emily knelt to pray with a thankful heart.

"I'll take Bessie with us to Mary Elizabeth's today," proposed Emily. "She and Mattie can take their dolls and play with Kate. I think it's so nice they're about the same age. Would you mind if Archie went, too? You know Mary! She'll love to see them all."

Elizabeth nodded, thinking that Richard's wife was so motherly and sweet, and how awful it must be to be left....

"Bessie be ready soon's I get her shoes fasten," Magdalena said. "An' Archie do be waitin'."

"Have they eaten?"

"Oh, yes'um. They had they bread an' milk."

"Can we stop a minute at Mr. Beeman's?" Archie pleaded.

It was interesting, thought Emily, what fascination blacksmith shops held for little boys. She agreed to stop--though she hoped the smith wouldn't be striking his anvil so early.

But he was! Iron rang against iron and sparks flew to Archie's entranced delight. He seemed to know what was being forged and explained in detail as soon as they were beyond range. "He was making some firedogs, Aunt Emily, like those we've got in our parlor fireplace to lay the logs on. I wish he'd make me some!"

Emily sighed. Little boys did have the strangest notions! She wondered what Enoch Carlton would want when he reached six.

At Hugh Easley's Hotel corner they turned left on Jefferson Street, where Richard and Mary's house was the third on the left. It was a one-story frame, with a long wing extending back from its north side. Behind stood a small two-story building which held Richard and William's painting paraphernalia and supplies.

Old Mr. Tinable Figg, Mary's grandfather, glimpsing them, came hurrying down the steps. "Welcome to you all! Emily, my dear! An' Mattie an' Bessie!...Archie, too!" He shook hands with them all.

By this time, Mary was at the front door, smiling warmly, "I'm glad to see you! I declare I am!"

Emily kissed her sister-in-law and tried to explain her reason for not having come sooner. "Just seemed like I couldn't..."

But Mary held out her hand in sympathy. "I know. We're both of us sufferin' most beyond endurin'. Come in my sittin' room, where we can talk." She paused at the door and called, "Kate, dear! You have some mighty sweet company!"

Kate ran happily from the back of the house, little Laura Ann at her heels. Soon the girls were giggling together and playing with their dolls.

"Archie an' I are walkin' over to Heap's Tin Shop," called Mr. Figg from the front door.

"All right, Grandpa," replied Mary, turning to Emily. "How he does love to have a little boy to talk to! Alonzo is far too big for that! Now that he's near twelve, he thinks he's a man grown! Why, soon as he knew his pa was goin', he got a job next door at Mr. Heap's Tin

Shop; says he intends to be a 'tinner', of all things! But I'll change that idea in time, for I'm bound to see Alonzo get an education. So is Richard." Rising, she moved to the door and called, "Josie, dear, come an' greet your Aunt Emily!"

Mary Josephine came shyly into the room, dutifully kissed Emily and said in a somewhat grown-up fashion, "I hope you're well, Aunt Emily. Could you drink a cup of tea? I know Mama can."

When Josie left to get their refreshments, Mary looked proudly after her oldest daughter. "The child's only eight, but she helps me so willingly!" She leaned forward. "You know, I'm expectin' a little one about the last of October. We're so hopin' it will be a boy this time."

During the visit, Emily had a chance to mention her new sewing scheme, which Mary, also a fine seamstress, understood perfectly. "You're so smart, Emily! I wish you had a sewin' machine; it would almost pay for itself in time saved!"

They discussed machines, scarcities, and high prices for a few minutes before Emily felt they must leave.

"I hope we'll hear right soon from either Richard or William!" were Mary's parting words.

"In the meantime, I'll expect you to let me know when you need help in any way," Emily requested, "for not a day passes but what I think of you, Mary!"

On the way home, Archie held to two subjects: iron shaped on a forge and tin cut out in a shop. The little girls spoke mainly doll-talk, and Emily was free to consider her good luck in having such a sweet and congenial sister-in-law as Mary Elizabeth.

The smaller children were in bed. Romeo and Edward had gone to their room, supposedly to study their next day's lessons. In the sitting room, Albert, Elizabeth, and Emily--all replete with good portions of codfish and squash pie--were taking such ease as they could.

Elizabeth, knitting a sock, which she could do without looking at her work, broke the silence, "Emily dear, you are ruining your eyes trying to put in those tiny stitches just by the light from a candle!"

"Two candles," Emily corrected the count, "and they are making enough heat for eight! But I only have a bit more here." Holding up several good-sized pieces of muslin, she said proudly, "Saved this much just from one dress!"

"I knew that idea would work! Mrs. Swift should be pleased."

Albert laid aside The Democrat newspaper he had been trying to read in the poor light. "I'm still looking to find some coal oil! Seems little gets past the blockade. You know, I sometimes wonder what Southern leaders were thinking of to get involved fighting a war when they had almost no manufactories and little raw material for producing the supplies they'd need. It is past understanding! No cloth mills! No iron or steel! Few coal mines!" He hesitated a moment and then said, "Well, I'll have to take that back. There's coal--and not so far away! Right up on Monte Sano, in fact."

The women looked at him in surprise.

"It's true! I was going to tell you--just between us now! We found a right-promising vein when we were looking for a limestone outcropping. In fact, it appears so promising that Jim Conway and I plan to go into partnership on a little coal-mining venture."

Surprised, Emily asked, "You mean you're going to do the mining yourselves?"

"No. We've got a miner who's interested. He came from England where he had considerable experience."

"Well, what's his name?" Elizabeth wanted to know.

"Jonathan Broad. Nice fellow! Seems to know his business." He paused. "Now, I want you to understand that I wouldn't take James Conway in on this, if I could swing it myself. But I can't!"

Elizabeth smiled. "I do like James. It's been nice to have him as a boarder. And, though he's Irish, he's a New Yorker, too!"

"He seems well-liked around town, and has a real smart head on his shoulders. Besides that, he's got a bit of capital to invest, and-- goodness knows!--I need some from somewhere! Folks can't pay what they owe." He paused to look at them both. "So, what do you two think about this idea?"

Emily was the first to speak up, "Well, I think it is entirely up to you and Elizabeth."

"And I think you must make the decision, Albert. You know what is best," Elizabeth told him with a smile.

"I wish I could be that certain," said her husband hesitantly. "But I doubt if anyone knows what is best these days--unless it's the good Lord himself!"

A little later, Emily folded her work and, taking a candle for light on the stairs, bade them good night. At the door she turned to add, "Try not to worry, Albert!"

Upstairs, she found both children sleeping soundly, their soft breathing giving the once-lonely room a lovely warmth and a sweet hope.

Chapter Four

March 27, 1862

When planting began in the garden, it was soon evident to them all that Uncle Pompous knew best when and how to plant everything that grew. In the old man's view, the phases of the moon were the only dependable guide. "The Lawd done fix it all," he maintained, "an' iffen you don't do it right, nothin' gonna grow! All us Southern folks knows that, Mr. Albert. You jes trus' Pompous!"

Albert was willing. It was the first garden of any size he had attempted since he moved South, and this garden must do well for they would depend on it. "If you can get some food from this spot of ground, Uncle Pompous, you'll get our thanks. Believe me!"

"Yessir! But who gonna do the work?"

"Well, we know you can't do it all. Romeo and Edward will have to help. I hope you'll teach them your system, for every boy must know how to make a garden. When do you want 'em?"

"Today! We behind."

Albert smiled. "Today it is then! They'll be out here ready to work, right after school."

Pompous looked doubtful. "You gonna tell 'em, Mr. Albert?"

"I am, and I'll make clear they have to follow your orders!"

Romeo and Edward took the news about like they would that of a prison sentence. It dawned on them, too, that the often-mentioned New-York-state work methods had finally arrived in Alabama!

After several hours of: "Tha's the wrong way, boy! Iffen that potato eye not lookin' at the sky, whatcha think gonna happen?"

Edward did not know and hardly cared.

"It gonna grow down, 'stead of up, tha's what!" The old fellow

44

emphasized that awful eventuality by whacking at a weed with his hoe.

As they nursed sore muscles and injured feelings in their bedroom that night, Edward stated, "I was born in the South; so if I was old enough, I'd join up and fight for the Confederacy!"

"I'll admit gardening's awful," Romeo agreed, "but it can't be as bad as fighting. Anyway, we'll get things planted soon now."

Very late the next afternoon when their father came to inspect progress, he complimented them highly, and--besides that!--handed each of them two quarters.

Pompous looked at his in puzzlement. "What's this money fer, Mr. Albert? You want as I should buy somethin' fer you?"

"No, Uncle. It's your own for working so hard."

"Law, Mr. Albert! I been workin' hard all my born days an' not a soul--'ceptin' you--ever thought 'bout givin' me no money!"

Romeo looked from his own money to the bent old Negro, and his heart smote him. It smote him such an awful blow that, without stopping to think, he handed over his own two quarters. "You can have mine, too, Uncle Pompous. That's for teaching me how to make a garden."

The glance that Edward shot his brother would have been plenty hot enough to roast corn, had the garden produced any. But all he could do was hand over his own fifty cents.

"Let's go in and clean up for supper," said their father. Then at the back steps, he turned, "The measure of a man's worth," he said in his most serious voice, "can be found in the goodness of his heart. I'm proud that my sons are going to measure up!"

Later in the privacy of their bedroom, Edward--using a few words he wasn't supposed to know--assessed Romeo's worth as close to zero. "Wasn't for you, we'd have had some spending money! But, no! You gotta be an old show-off."

"I wonder if Papa is going to church today?"

Emily smiled down at Mattie, thinking how nicely the pink bonnet framed her face. "Oh, I'm sure they'll have preaching! Several Huntsville ministers have gone to war with the soldiers."

They were walking south on Limberg Street, for she had decided to take Mattie to the church around the corner on West Clinton.

Sometimes, they went with Mrs. Elliott to the Methodist Church downtown, but today her mother-in-law had said she was suffering from "spring fever" and did not feel like dressing.

"Well, then, why don't you go with us to the Baptist Church today?" Elizabeth wanted to know.

"I'd just like to try this small church, Sister. Be easier for me this time...and I may meet some new people. I already know one or two who go there." The truth of the matter was that she felt a sudden need to be independent, to make a few decisions on her own for a change. It was a strange experience, but one she liked.

They enjoyed the service and hymn-singing. Mattie should start learning songs, thought Emily, and all of the children would love singing! An idea suddenly blossomed. Here was something she could do--teach singing along with the alphabet. It would be one small way to repay Albert and Elizabeth for their love and care. At the idea, a spark of thankfulness came to warm her heart.

"Whoa! Whoa! Stop that horse!" Men were shouting and running toward the street.

With other women and children, Emily and Mattie hurriedly retreated into the churchyard. A billow of wide skirts formed a background for excited children jumping up and down while horse and conveyance flashed past.

"Runaway! Runaway!"

Frightened tears coursed down Mattie's cheeks. Thank goodness, the child doesn't scream and cry, thought Emily, as she sought to comfort. "It's just a horse that was scared by something. The men will catch it. If not, it'll stop by itself, like horses do."

Many of the congregation leaving the Baptist Church on the corner of Clinton and Gallatin also witnessed the runaway.

"Some men stopped that horse near to Washington Street," Romeo reported, after they had all reached home.

"A woman was driving," added Edward. "Probably she fainted and the little boy tried to take the reins."

"Why, Edward!" protested his mother. "You don't know the truth of that. I warned you about exaggerating things!"

"And not all women are liable to fainting spells merely at the sight of danger!" Emily hastily assured her nephew. "We are about as tough as men when we need to be."

By the following Wednesday, Emily had finished the sewing Mrs. Swift had brought and was able to hand over her two dresses neatly altered, along with three shirts for the little boys, two baby dresses, and a small set of underwear.

"I am surprised to get this many things from the extra yardage in only two dresses!" Mrs. Swift was all smiles. "And they're so neatly made! I shall try to find some more dresses that will bear altering!" She handed Emily ten dollars.

"Six is plenty," Emily protested, returning four. "After all, don't forget! It was you who gave me this valuable idea."

"Well, then, this once," Mrs. Swift agreed. "But I advise you not to let your prices get too cheap! Your work is excellent."

"That's what Elizabeth says, too," Emily commented. "She says I should let those who do shoddy work ask cheap prices."

"Mighty good advice! I'd take it, if I were you."

"Thank you," Emily laughed. "But please promise to let me know if ever my prices climb above your range, for I don't want that!"

Back in the playroom, Emily found Magdalena and the three children ready to work on their letters. Elizabeth had discovered two other slates, so now Bessie and Archie each had one.

They had already learned several letters, and could even print a few short words. Archie was chanting his: "MAMA, MOP, POP, MAP, PAPA..."

At that word, Enoch Carlton, who was crawling about, came to a stop, lifted his head, and said, "Papa!" His voice rang out clear and loud enough to surprise them all for a minute.

Mattie was the first to respond. She quickly knelt--her skirt spreading in all directions--and hugged her tiny brother. "Mama! you hear that? Buddy said PAPA so plain!"

Emily had heard! The word had brought joy, along with a deep wave of regret that William had not heard his son's PAPA for the first time. She could only answer Mattie with a nod.

But Magdalena came to her aid. "That boy gonna be a smart 'un, maybe a preacher! Somebody as talks loud."

"He might just grow up to be a singer," said Archie, who found singing lessons a great trial.

"Do-re-me," began Bessie, off key.

Magdalena rose. "It's time for me to do the milkin'. I'll work some more soon's I can, Miss Em'ly."

Magdalena came to the kitchen door, the empty milk pail in her hand. "I hates to tell Miss 'Lizbeth, but that Lulu Belle has run off agin!"

Sophronia threw up her hands and headed for the door. "Law, I never see sich a cow fer slippin' off! Well, we sure ain't gonna bother Miss 'Lizbeth. She done have to lay down 'count of that painin' in her head!"

Emily, who was helping in the kitchen, followed the others out the door. Seeing all three gardeners busy with their hoes away at the far end of the patch, she took off her apron and waved it.

With hands on hips, Sophronia stood regarding the open gate to Mill Street. "How do that gate jes open by itself ever' time that cow take on a wand'rin' notion?"

"Sophia, you don't s'pose Lulu Belle know how that latch work, do you?" asked Magdalena. "She a mighty smart lady! I talks when I'se milkin', an' she do seem to know what I'se sayin'."

Aunt Sophia looked at the young nurse in disbelief. "So maybe it's you has told her 'bout the latch!"

"What's wrong, Aunt Emily?" Romeo came running from the garden with Edward at his heels.

"Where are your hoes?" she asked, pointing toward the garden. For there came Uncle Pompous lugging all three hoes while he complained, "Ain't worth twenty quarters to keep up with them boys! They both short a' even one lick a' sense!"

In a few minutes Emily had the four searching in different directions. The cow surely had not gone far so close to milking!

48

"What's wrong?" Elizabeth stood at the back door.

"Jes that Lulu Belle out again!" Sophronia reported.

Emily started inside. "We tried not to disturb you. Did we?"

"No. I had a nap, and it seems to have cured my headache," her sister replied, as she mounted the back steps. "And speaking of cows, I think I'll ask Albert to try to find us another, for I do believe that would give us enough milk to make cheese once in a while. Besides, we'll need another cow when Lulu Belle goes dry."

"Or jes go off fer good!" Aunt Sophia put in.

Emily agreed. "Wouldn't it be grand to have cheese? That small bite Mr. Windham let us have just whetted my appetite for more!"

"Law, Miss 'Lizbeth," moaned Sophronia. "I don' know the first thing 'bout makin' up a ball a' cheese!"

Emily patted one of the woman's vast shoulders. "Then you will learn from two New-York-experts right here in this kitchen!"

"Mama!" Mattie came running in. "Mrs. Pollard and Susan are in the sitting room. She brought some dresses."

"Thank you," Emily said, as she hung her apron on its hook behind the dining room door.

"How are you, Emily?" Mrs. Pollard, their neighbor across Mill Street, rose politely.

Emily smiled. "I'm well. And you, Caledonia? And Susan? Please sit back down. We just had a little crisis here. Our cow got out again."

"We'll be glad to help look," they offered.

"Thank you, but we've got a pretty good search party out, so I expect they'll find her soon."

Mrs. Pollard laughed. "I remember once she turned up away over beyond the tracks."

Emily sighed. "Yes. I do wish she wouldn't choose such a dangerous route. But what do you have there?"

"Two of my old summer dresses. I was wonderin' if it would be possible to rip these up an' get some things for Susan to wear if we get a chance to send her to school again. Then Frank does need a shirt so bad! An' there's little Clara comin' on. Our Mattie's seven, but I doubt if we can send her to school anytime soon."

Emily spread out the two dresses. "There's lots of fabric here and luckily it's plain colors. Why don't I measure Susan and try to get her a dress from each? Then when we see what is left, I'll measure the others. How do you like your dresses made, Susan?"

Unsure, Susan could only turn to her mother.

Mrs. Pollard laughed. "I guess we hoped you had a pattern that would be nice for Susan. You need to allow plentiful seams, an' a tuck or two above the hem, for my girl's really sproutin' up!"

Emily took the young girl's hands and turned her around. "Are you about twelve now?"

"No, ma'am...just eleven."

"Well, you are going to be a lovely young lady, slender and tall enough to wear any style. I'll do my best for you, Susan!"

A little twinkle of gratitude shown in the girl's eyes as she said softly, "Thank you, Mrs. Elliott."

Next morning, to everyone's surprise, Emily was up well before the neighborhood roosters had quit their crowing contest. "I want to get started on Caledonia Pollard's things," she told Elizabeth eagerly. "Especially the dresses for Susan, for that child is so appealing she makes me want to design a whole wardrobe for her!"

Elizabeth nodded. "Seems to me Caledonia takes interest in all her children. I like that!"

With a feeling, part satisfaction, part excitement, Emily took her chair by the front window of the sitting room where there would be good light for ripping apart the rosy-beige dress that Caledonia had brought.

Before she started, she allowed herself a few moments just to think of her growing business and the likelihood that soon she would need a sewing machine. Resolutely, she made up her mind to try as hard as possible to make a go...

"Emily! Emily!" The call--faint, but urgent!--came from across the street. Mary Ann Figg was waving frantically from their front gate. "Emily! Mother's fainted!"

Letting the dress slide to the carpet, Emily ran into the hall and called, "Elizabeth, bring the smelling salts on over to Mrs. Elliott's! She's fainted!"

50

Running swiftly, she caught up with Mary Ann at the front door and asked, "Has she come to? What was she doing before?..."

When Mary Ann seemed unable to answer anything coherently, Emily pushed open her mother-in-law's bedroom door. There she lay stretched on the carpet, seemingly asleep. Emily knelt, listening to her breathing. Then she felt for a pulse and gingerly raised one eyelid. At least she was still alive!

Giving Mary Ann a hopeful smile, she glanced through the front window. Elizabeth was coming with the smelling salts. A short way behind, Sophronia waddled along with something in her hand.

"Mary Ann, please get some cool water and a washrag!" Emily requested, mostly in the hope of sending the distraught woman out of the room before the others arrived. It worked!

"Mercy on us!" Elizabeth knelt. "Here are the salts. Just let her breathe a tiny bit at once, so she won't choke!"

Emily nodded as she quickly uncapped the bottle and waved it a little way from Mrs. Elliott's nose.

"Here am a feather to burn, iffen you need it," offered Aunt Sophia, squeezing through the doorway.

"If this fails, we'll sure try it!" promised Emily. But Mother Elliott had stirred. "She's coming around. Let's step back some; not all be leaning over her when she comes to her senses."

Elizabeth went to stand by the wardrobe, and Aunt Sophia moved to help Mary Ann with the pan of water.

At that moment, Mrs. Elliott opened her eyes. At sight of them all, she seemed surprised.

"Don't worry, Mother Elliott!" Emily consoled her softly. "You had a little faint spell. You're better now, so let me bathe your face. That will help."

Mary Ann started to say something, but Emily placed her finger over her lips in caution as she carefully squeezed water from the washrag and tenderly bathed the old lady's face. "Hold the rag a minute," she requested, hoping her patient could do that.

Obediently, Mrs. Elliott reached up and grasped the rag. "I do feel right silly," she whispered.

"Don't think of it," begged Emily. "Just lie there till you're feeling better, and we'll help you get in bed. I'll take off your pretty cap so it won't get mashed."

As the old lady closed her eyes again, Emily rose and motioned the others into the hall. Caroline, Mary Ann's daughter, stood by the door. "How is she, Aunt Emily? I'm so worried!"

Emily tried to be as reassuring as possible, for she knew that Caroline herself was very frail. "It's not a stroke; probably only a dizzy spell. Was she doing anything unusual yesterday?"

Mary Ann's mouth flew open, "Of course! She worked most of the afternoon settin' out some rose-cuttin's Mrs. Jordan gave her."

"If she was doing much stooping, that was probably what caused her dizziness," suggested Elizabeth, looking at Emily.

Emily nodded. "It does seem old people are affected by leaning over, if they're not used to it."

"Why not see can we loosen her clothes, Miss Em'ly?" was Aunt Sophia's practical suggestion.

Heads nodded, and Mary Ann got the assignment, but needed Aunt Sophia's help to complete it. Mrs. Elliott, while she tried to assist, still complained of dizziness when she turned her head.

"You may be dizzy for awhile," Emily told her. "If it keeps on long, we'll call Dr. Burritt to come and examine you."

After they had carefully lifted the old lady to her bed, Elizabeth and Aunt Sophia left to see about things at home.

Emily caught them at the front door. "Call me when the baby wakes, or he'll disturb the whole neighborhood!"

Sophronia rolled her eyes heavenward.

"And, Elizabeth, if you'll send over my workbasket and that dress of Caledonia's that fell to the floor when I got up in such a hurry, I'll go on ripping, while I watch over Mother Elliott."

Mary Ann hastened down the hall. "And thank you both so much! Usually I'm pretty good with the sick, but when I found Mother on the floor..." Her voice broke.

Emily told her sister-in-law, "Why, it's perfectly natural for you to feel shocked, Mary Ann. Don't think of it! We're going to help you watch after her until she gets better."

It was several days before Mrs. Elliott was able to sit in her front-porch rocker. She no longer felt dizzy, only weak. "I feel like a wrung-out dishrag looks," she told Emily. "But I'm glad to be out in the air! An' thankful to you, my dear, for helpin' me! Though, what else could I expect? For you're more like a daughter than a daughter-in-law!"

Emily's eyes filled. "And you have been a mother to me!"

"I'd feel so much better if we only had a word from the boys!" Mrs. Elliott looked off toward the west. "Seems like they... "

"...maybe it's not their fault," Emily said quickly. "I expect the mail's probably tied up somewhere. You can't tell these days! Could you stand a short visit from the children? Mattie wants to come over to show you the letters she's made on her slate."

Mrs. Elliott expressed her pleasure at the idea, asking, "How is Magdalena gettin' along with her letters?"

"Well! And so proud! But I won't send her over for fear she'd be embarrassed."

At home, a short argument arose over the proposed visit. Emily wanted the children to sing their "do-re-me's," but Archie simply refused. He did agree to show his slate and read the words on it. Then he made an offer more to his own liking, "I'll tell her all about making firedogs. She'll like that!"

Emily had serious doubts, but she sent the children on anyway. Mrs. Elliott would enjoy the visit and surely know the way to handle little boys with one-track minds.

Thankful for some quiet time, she settled in the rocker by the front window, where she could sew and still keep watch across the street. Even with Mrs. Elliott's illness, and by working upstairs nights by candlelight so as not to upset Elizabeth, she had now finished everything for Caledonia except two tiny shirts.

The dresses she had created for Susan had come up to all their expectations. The slender young girl, who carried herself like a queen, would be right in style at any social gathering in either dress.

One of the dresses Emily had ripped apart had been light green with a bodice of tucks and lace insertions. From the bodice, she had fashioned a bonnet that framed Susan's face very prettily.

"Now, Caledonia," she had cautioned, "this green bonnet should have some pretty dark-green ribbons. Maybe you can find some. And it's not to be worn with the green dress, for that would be too much. It will look more stylish with the rosy-beige."

"Yes, Emily. They're both just beautiful!"

"Miss Em'ly!" Uncle Pompous was calling to her from outside. "Them crows has come fer the corn!"

Startled, Emily drew back the curtain to see the old Negro out in the yard. "What corn?" she asked, perplexed.

"Why, those kernels we's jes planted. Them ol' black birds is a-cawin' an' a-croakin' ever'where out there! Iffen I scares 'em off, soon's I leaves the field, there they be back! What we needs is a scare-crow man--an' I know as how you can make one easy."

Emily nodded. She would have to try! "Give me a while to round up some old clothes, Uncle Pompous. You can start making a stand to hang him on."

The old fellow shuffled off muttering, "We gonna fool you, you ol' smart-aleck birds!"

But where were any clothes past using? The only thing she knew of was an old shirt William had worn when painting. That it was splotched with many colors would be all the better! But pants?

"For a scarecrow?" Elizabeth hesitated. "Seems like I remember an old pair left here by one of the New York stonecutters Albert brought down who did not like the South. I'll go and look in the scrap-bag." She was gone only a moment. "Well, here they are! And with this big hole in the seat, only a scarecrow would wear them."

"The very thing!" said Emily. "Now to make him a head." An old tan rag served and looked very natural with black eyes and a red mouth painted on with some of William's colors.

With the figure fastened together, stuffed with straw, and elevated on its stand, it looked real enough--especially after Uncle Pompous had provided it with a frayed, old straw hat.

Once raised in the field, the scarecrow not only fooled crows, it even fooled Edward! "Who's that down in the garden?" he asked. "Has Pa got somebody else to work, besides me?"

"No sich luck!" moaned Pompous. "That do be a scarecrow as is runnin' off the crows. He not workin' like you gonna be!"

Edward groaned and followed Romeo in to change clothes.

In spite of the family's concerted efforts to keep news of the war from Emily, she saw newspapers and heard enough on the street to make her aware of how bad things were on the battlefields of North Mississippi. The knowledge that Company E of the 35th Alabama Volunteers, the unit that William and Richard had joined, was either there, or on the way, was frightening!

Though many things served to distract her mind, the terrible dread was always there, ready to surface.

It was Monday, the seventh of April, before a letter came from William. Albert, who called at the post office daily, sent it right over by Ebon, and Elizabeth brought it upstairs.

Emily, who was busy nursing Enoch Carlton, almost shouted, "At last!" as she reached for it eagerly.

"I do hope it's good news," Elizabeth said. "Let us know. I'm getting the men's dinner packed for Ebon to take back."

When the baby seemed satisfied, and she had nestled him on her shoulder for awhile, she eased him to the floor. There, he looked up at her and gurgled, "Papa!"

"Yes, that's who this letter is from. I'm trying to find the courage to open it, for I'm not sure..."

Dear Wife, I would've written sooner but for all the things we have to do every day. Seems like I've left the real world behind--but can't be helped. I hope you and the children are keeping well. I'm pretty fit and so is Richard. Just my feet are some sore, so the liniment is coming in handy. I sure do miss old Huntsville. Guess it's the best place in the whole world--least as far as I'm concerned. For everything I hold dear is there. We're going to move on any day now. I'll try to let you hear where we go. Give my regards to Albert and Elizabeth and all the children and the shop men. I wrote Ma.

My love and these kisses are for you three. Write me!

Your loving husband, W'm.

There was a big X with Emily's name, a smaller one for Mattie, and a still smaller one for Enoch Carlton.

Tears rolled unchecked down Emily's cheeks. Over and over, she kissed the X meant for her, then pressed the baby's X to his soft red mouth. "That's the kiss Papa sent you," she told him shakily.

Finally she was able to steady herself. Slipping the letter in her pocket, she bore Enoch Carlton downstairs. As she gave him to Magdalena, she saw that Mattie and Bessie were playing with their dolls. Time enough for Mattie to kiss her own X, she thought. There is just so much I can stand at once!

"Magdalena, please tell Miss Elizabeth that I'm taking a short walk before dinner," she whispered, slipping from the room.

As she strolled along toward the creek, slowly waving tree limbs greeted her. The sky had darkened; thunder rumbled. We need rain, she mused. But what do the soldiers do when it pours and pours? Get wet! her mind told her. Get dripping wet! She gritted her teeth in misery. Somehow, William's letter, sweet as it was, had made her suffer more.

"Good day, Mrs. Elliott."

Startled, she looked up. It was Mr. Shanklin, probably headed to Mrs. Rison's Boarding House for dinner.

"I'm glad I happened to meet you, ma'am. Last week you told me you might be interested in a sewing machine, if they went on sale anytime. Well, I'm glad to report they'll be marked down by half the day-after-tomorrow. Hope you'll come by and look at them!"

Seeking for strength and reason, Emily found her voice at last and replied, "Thank you, Mr. Shanklin. I will try to come."

"Better run for it now!" he advised. "A shower's coming." But Emily could not seem to hasten her pace, though rain drops sifted, then finally tumbled pell-mell through the leaves.

"I'm getting wet," she said aloud. "Sopping, sopping wet! Just like you, William, my dear! Just like you."

Chapter Five

April 8, 1862

"Fie-Fie? That's no cow's name!" Doubt shown on Elizabeth Baker's face. "Are you real sure, Ebon?" They were admiring the pretty animal he had led all the way from the Marble Yard.

"Yes'um! Mr. Albert he do say Fie-Fie. Ever'body 'long the way allowed as how they like to have her fer they own. But I jes say Fie-Fie be goin' to Miss 'Lizbeth."

Elizabeth had to laugh. Not only was she charmed by Ebon's introduction of the cow, she was delighted to have such a gentle and handsome milker.

"Can I pet her, Mama?" Archie asked, stepping up eagerly.

"Me, too," begged Mattie shyly.

All the children had come to make the new cow's acquaintance.

"After Magdalena," decided Elizabeth.

"Cows all love Mag'lena," was Bessie's contribution.

"An' that do be one gal as loves cows!" Sophronia said, taking little Alvah from the nurse's arms. "She talk to 'em all time she milkin' an' they listens. Go ahead, Maggie, tell Fie-Fie how that gate latch work!"

Ignoring that remark, Magdalena stepped over to pet the pretty creature. Suddenly, she cried, "Why, she overdue fer milking! Who milk her this mornin'?"

"Milk her? Law, woman! Us don' know how to milk!" gasped Ebon.

"Albert does!" Elizabeth was shocked at his neglect.

"Yes'um. But he go off up the mountain wid that Mr. Broad."

"Moo! MOOooooo!" Fie-Fie had run out of patience.

57

Enoch Carlton--not to be outdone and hearing MILK--started his own racket.

Emily raised her voice, "I'll take him right in. Fie-Fie is a beauty, Elizabeth...gorgeous animal!"

"Hold her, Ebon," requested Magdalena, "while I go wash up an' fetch the bucket. I be right back, Fie-Fie. Mag'lena be comin'!"

"You might as well wait anyway, Ebon, and take the dinner basket back," Elizabeth directed.

Everyone left but Archie, who began circling Fie-Fie with that intense regard formerly reserved for firedogs or items cut from tin. At last, coming to a stop near her head, he looked deep into her eyes and tried several greetings, "MOo-ooo! Moo-Oo! Moo-Moo!"

No response came from Fie-Fie, but Ebon cackled mightily.

"Law! But that do beat all! Talkin' cow lang'age! You best talk yer own talk, boy! Fie-Fie probably know what you say, then. "

After Emily had put Enoch Carlton down for his nap, she firmly set her mind to making some plans. Her previous day's plunge into near despair after reading William's letter had made her ashamed. She must be strong. Stay busy! Idly, she wondered if a sewing machine might help. Tomorrow was Sale Day at Shanklin & Scott.

Did she dare risk it? Surely a machine would help her keep up with the rush of orders Mrs. Swift's practical idea had brought. Probably, it would help her get more done in daylight, too.

Even as she considered these aspects, another request came.

Mrs. Bolton, their neighbor across Mill Street, brought two of her summer dresses to be cut down. "Our oldest, Addie V--I say V, though her name's really Viora after me. It's just that she's got a notion right now that she fancies the name Virginia. Anyhow, the child's outgrown every rag she has! She's gone past the age for startin' her schoolin', an' Andrew keeps promisin' he'll find the money for sendin' her now that he's been named Railway Agent. I sure hope he does, for Addie's plenty bright enough!"

"Children's schooling is so costly!" Emily said. "Besides, not all schools are open now." She wanted to add: and not so many men are interested in paying for their daughters to attend!

"Besides," continued Mrs. Bolton, "I've been feelin' poorly of late an' can't seem to tackle sewin'. That's why I was so pleased when Caledonia Pollard told me how you were cuttin' down skirts."

Emily examined the two dresses carefully. "I expect I can take enough from both skirts to make Addie V. two dresses. Two dollars each is what I usually get, Mrs. Bolton, but if you can't..."

"...never fear, Mrs. Elliott. That's a fair price an' I'll pay you on time. Another thing, I noticed you have a new cow, an' was wonderin' if you'll have milk to sell. I was buyin' from a woman over on Arms, but her Biddie's gone dry."

"Both the cows belong to my sister, Mrs. Bolton," Emily had to say, "but I'll be glad to ask."

Hardly had Mrs. Bolton left than the Beeman girls sent down to see if she could do some alterations for them. She could only say that she had work on hand, but would put them on the list.

Now someone else was calling! It was Mary Ann Figg at the front gate. As she jumped to her feet, Emily's first thought was that Mrs. Elliott was sick again!

"Mother's all right," Mary Ann hastily reassured her. "I came over with an invitation from Aunt Susan Knox. She hopes you will come there in the mornin'--an' to please bring the children! She says it's been a long time since she's had a glimpse of them." Pausing, she confided, "Also, Emily, she has somethin' for you!"

Guiltily, Emily wondered how long it had been since she had visited in the home of David Knox and his wife, Susan, who was Mrs. Elliott's sister! "Why, I'd love to go!" she assured Mary Ann. "As for taking the children, I doubt if I can carry the baby that far. He's getting so heavy!"

Mary Ann thought for a moment. "Then he's sure to be too heavy for me to lift. Could you borrow Elizabeth's baby carriage? For I wouldn't mind goin' along to help."

To Emily, that seemed the perfect solution, but she had to ask, "Who'll stay with Mother Elliott?" She knew that Caroline, Mary Ann's daughter, needed to rest often.

"Why, Videlia will be there, of course!"

"I wasn't sure! Where was she the day Mother Elliott fainted?"

Mary Ann snorted. "Oh, just back in her cabin...havin' one of her spells. I never know for sure whether she's sick on those occasions, or just surly! But she seems all right now."

"Will about ten in the morning suit you?" asked Emily. "I can feed and dress Enoch Carlton and Mattie by then. Of all things, I must avoid one of the baby's famous hunger-pang fits!"

When Elizabeth heard of the proposed visit, she tried to think of a special treat she might send the elderly couple. But most good things were in such short supply!

"Do we have any extra eggs?" asked Emily. "Even six would be a nice gift. I don't believe they keep hens."

"Perfect!" agreed her sister. "I'll ask Aunt Sophia to see how many we can spare. More than six, I hope!"

Emily wondered several times that afternoon, as she kept on at her sewing, what in the world William's Aunt Susan could have for her! She was a dear old lady who had had so much sadness in her life. They had lost their only son, William Cain Knox, and then their beloved daughter, Josephine, who had left a tiny baby. And, try as they might, they could not save that precious baby!

It had been so wonderful, Emily reflected, how Josephine's bereaved husband, John Patterson, whom they all loved, had stayed on in the Knox household. Then, five years later, he had married Mary Ann Knox, Josephine's older sister. Now they had tiny Josie, the family's great joy and hope; for Sue Harrison, the only other living child of David and Susan Knox, had never married.

Emily's hands lay idle in her lap as she thought of the many strange coincidences in families. In the Cain family, it was the number of silversmiths. She had often heard Mrs. Elliott speak of that, for she and Susan Knox had three uncles who had become known in the trade: Clairborne, Thomas, and James. Although they were all from Petersburg, Virginia, they had set up shops in various towns. It had been Thomas who had spent most of his years in Huntsville.

Then, stranger still, when Susan Cain married, she had chosen David Knox, a Delaware man, who had settled in Huntsville to ply his trade of silversmith. Over the years he had built up a wide reputation for his beautiful designs and creations. Now his work was mostly as a watchmaker.

Last of all, Mary Ann Carlton, Mrs. Elliott's daughter by her first marriage to Thomas Carlton, had married Littleton Figg, also a silversmith. And now Littleton, too, had had to try other means of making a living, for silversmithing was a dying art.

Emily sighed as she picked up her sewing. None of those idle reflections had solved the mystery of the gift Aunt Susan had for her. But she knew it wouldn't be silver!

At supper that night Albert had a good laugh when he heard the cow being called Fie-Fie. "Her name's Fire Fly," he corrected.

"Well, that's still a strange name for a cow!" insisted his wife, "but she's a beauty, and we're mighty proud of her! How did you happen to find?..."

"Man south of town, getting ready to move his family down into Walker County in hope of finding work at the coal mines, couldn't take his cow. We tried to get him to help in our mine, but he didn't feel this part of the state was safe any..." He broke off, suddenly realizing what he had said. "Some feel so, and others don't!" he finished lamely.

Next morning, as she and Mary Ann Figg started out with the children, Emily felt a little thrill of excitement. The day was fair and sweet. Mattie's yellow parasol glowed like a beacon up ahead. Mary Ann followed, trying hard to keep the baby carriage on an even keel. Emily had always thought it unwieldy, even dangerous, since it could only be pulled by its long tongue. But Enoch Carlton, strapped in and tilted back in the small seat, seemed to be enjoying the ride.

At the corner of Jefferson, Emily handed the basket of eggs to Mary Ann and took control of the carriage. When the way was clear, they crossed cater-cornered to Dr. Newman's. With the baby gurgling happily at every bump, they reached Washington Street, crossed it, and were at the side of Windham's Grocery.

"Now we only have to go to Greene and turn right," Emily said in relief. She would be glad when the trip was over.

The Knox house, second from the corner of Holmes, was just behind the jail. A tall two-story frame, its front steps led down to the sidewalk. The lot was narrow, but very deep.

Before Emily could manage to lower Mattie's parasol, the front door was flung open, and both Sue Knox and Mary Ann Patterson were there to help them up the steps.

"Mother is goin' to be so delighted!" cried Sue. "We've all been wantin' to see these precious children!"

Enoch Carlton chose that moment to begin his "Papa" singsong. From then on, greetings merged and happily overrode each other. Mattie was admired and introduced to little Josie. Enoch Carlton, on his great-aunt Susan's knee, said his word twice more and then suddenly looked her in the face and gurgled, "Mama!"

Everyone was charmed!

Emily could hardly keep back the tears. "That's the first time he's said it!" she acknowledged.

"The little tyke looked at me an' knew that I wanted somethin' extra from him," marveled Aunt Susan. "What a precious boy!--the image of his mother, too! Did you know that William came here before he left? I was so proud of that! He has always been a sweet an' carin' lad. I pray for him each night--that God will keep an' bless him in his bravery."

Emily, struggling mightily not to give way, finally managed to say, "Thank you, dear Aunt Susan."

The two Mary Ann's had gone into the next room, but Sue waited for a chance to take Enoch Carlton. When it came, she said, "What a heavy boy you are! Let's go in an' meet our little Josie. Why, you two can just talk up a storm!"

Now that they were left alone, Aunt Susan reached over to take Emily's hand. "Sister's told me how hard you work on your sewing, my dear, an' that you have an idea for reducin' the width of these monstrous garments we all wear."

"It was really Elizabeth Swift's idea." Emily hastened to give credit where due. "With no new cloth available to make things for her children, she realized how much was wasted in her garments."

"Still, you are puttin' the idea to work, an' I commend you! I may even help some, for seven years back when our sweet Josephine died, she left so many dresses, almost the whole wardrobe that we had helped her gather for her marriage. Most of the things had never been worn at all!" She drew a long quivering breath. "There are two trunks of her clothes still packed away. After she died, we were all so distraught tryin' to keep her baby alive, an' when that failed, no one could bear to think of the clothes. Now, we all agree that, in this time of shortage, Josephine wouldn't want her things kept unused. So you must take them, my dear...to wear, make over, rip up...whatever seems best!"

Emily was nearly speechless. "But surely you don't want all of them to go! Maybe I could make some over for your Mary Ann, or Sue, or even Baby Josie."

Aunt Susan shook her head. "No, it's to be just as I said. But you'll have to transfer the things from the trunks to boxes, or bags, or somethin' to take them home with you."

Emily opened her mouth and words tumbled out. "It is just too wonderful to believe! Why, I was going today to look at a sewing machine on sale...and all the time I was wondering if I could ever find any material to sew! Oh! Aunt Susan, I will just prize Josephine's things so much, and try to use them wisely, too!" And dropping to her knees, she hugged and kissed the old lady.

"Well, don't take on so!" Aunt Susan begged. "And if that sale is today, why don't you go right now? Don't risk missin' it! The girls an' I will watch after the children. Take Mary Ann Figg along in case you need her."

Surely it was a miracle!...MIRACLE! The word kept repeating in Emily's head as she and Mary Ann almost ran the four blocks to the north side of the square. And they were none too soon!

"I wondered if you were coming, Mrs. Elliott," Mr. Shanklin said, as he met them at the door. "There's only one machine left! But it's a good one: a Wheeler & Wilson with interlocking stitch. So come over and let me demonstrate it."

Almost gasping for breath, Emily and Mary Ann watched while he seated himself before the machine. Its table rested on graceful iron legs that also supported the foot treadle. With the use of a small piece

63

of cloth, he showed how to thread, stitch forward and backward, and then how to oil and maintain the mechanism.

As she watched, Emily quickly became convinced that the sewing machine would be of great help to her, but...as she told him, "It is just that, even at sale price, fifty dollars is a lot. I don't know if I can make it back...."

"You sit down and try it, yourself," he insisted kindly.

With only a little coaching, Emily went through the operation without a hitch.

"See how easy it is? And we stock thread that you can get when needed, and if you require any help with the mechanism, just call on us at any time!"

"What do you think, Mary Ann?"

"Why, I wouldn't hesitate a minute! It's just what you need!"

Slowly unloosening the strings of her cloth bag, Emily drew out some bills. As she offered the fifty dollars, her eyes filled with tears.

Seeing them, Mr. Shanklin hesitated, then suddenly returned ten dollars. "In view of the fact that this is our last sewing machine of that type, I'm going to let you have it for forty!"

"Oh, thank you, sir. And I'm sorry to be so unsure...but I was thinking how long it must have taken William to earn that much...and that maybe I'm wasting it," Emily almost whispered.

"You're not wasting it, Mrs. Elliott!" Mr. Shanklin said with assurance. "Our dray can deliver your machine this afternoon, if you like."

On the way back to the Knox home, Mary Ann, observing her sister-in-law from the corner of her eye, was moved to say, "Now Emily, it appears you used some clever wiles on that salesman!"

Glancing toward her, Emily smiled. "Well, if I had been a man, I could have bargained him down. I've seen men do it! But ladies can't do that sort of thing--so I did the best I could. For after all, Mr. Shanklin was doing everything he could to pressure me to buy!" She laughed. "But please don't divulge my methods. I might have to use them again!"

Laughing in turn, Mary Ann promised. "I'll want you along with me, if I ever have to deal for myself!"

"Well, just pray you don't," was Emily's sincere advice.

After they had appeased the curiosity of all the ladies in the Knox home as to how a sewing machine could sew securely and still save time for its user, Emily thanked them all again. "I'll come about ten in the morning--if that is agreeable to you--to pack up those wonderful things," she said, as she gave Aunt Susan a hug.

"And I'll be with her!" promised Mary Ann.

When the sewing machine was delivered soon after dinner, they all assembled in the front hall for the event.

"I'm going to have it put up in our bedroom," Emily declared.

"Oh, no you're not!" objected Elizabeth, with as much force as she could muster. "We're not going to let you hide away upstairs, sewing day-in and day-out and probably even in the night! The machine is going beside the front window in the sitting room, for that's where you like to work and can get the best light! Why, if you're away upstairs, how can I call on you for help when I need you quickly?"

The last question, though spoken in a teasing voice, concluded the matter for Emily. In her heart, she knew the sitting room was the best place. Customers coming in would see the handsome sewing machine and realize they were dealing with a skilled seamstress. It might even make possible a slight price increase.

And the machine did look nice in the room! The black-enameled sewing arm on its handsome wooden table, supported by graceful iron legs, presented a modern touch to its surroundings.

"I'll get a scrap of cloth and show you how it works," offered Emily, peering into her workbasket. "Here's a piece that'll do!"

They all waited. Sophronia held one baby; Magdalena, the other; and Archie stationed himself near his favorite part--the working mechanism.

"That sure am somethin'!" Aunt Sophia was the first to marvel. "How long would it take to sew that much by han', Miss Em'ly?"

"Oh, at least twice as long! I'll make a test sometime to see. There's also something about sitting here at the table that's much more comfortable for my back than leaning over to work on my lap!"

"That, in itself, will be a great blessing," Elizabeth said, "for I know your back often bothers you."

It was Archie who posed the most questions. In fact, the pedal mechanism so quickly joined his other interests that by the time Romeo and Edward came in from school, he was able to answer their questions and would have given a demonstration had not his mother instructed him never to touch the machine!

"Elizabeth, may I ask Uncle Pompous to hitch Wego to the cart? Then to drive it over to Aunt Susan's to pick up the things I'll have packed?" Emily wanted to know.

"Of course!" her sister replied. "Are you going to pack them in bags or boxes?"

"Whatever I can find. Mary Ann has one bag I can borrow."

Sophronia looked up from her task of washing breakfast dishes and said, "Miss Em'ly, there's the bags we uses for the chillun's dirty clothes. Two is clean."

"That will be the very thing!" cried Emily, relieved. "And why can't I just use a sheet to wrap folded garments?"

"Of course you can! And I'll have Pompous clean the cart extra well, so as not to soil any of the containers."

By the time Emily had fed the baby, dressed Mattie, and folded two clean sheets and the various bags, she had received three urgent requests to ride in the cart. These were refused in order: first Archie, and then Bessie and Mattie. "You can help me more by staying here ready to give a hand with the unloading."

And some unloading it was!

"Just look at this lovely rich satin dress!"

"Mama, there's a pretty blue dress!"

"Didn't they even want the hoops, Emily?"

Emily shook her head. "They really didn't!"

"It do seem mighty queer to me!" Aunt Sophia muttered. "They's all sich fine goods!"

"Yes, they are," agreed Emily, "but they have been packed away so long, I expect Aunt Susan thought looking at them would revive too many sad memories. Then, with cloth so scarce, they all hoped that someone in real need could benefit. I'll be remembering that whenever I use them. It's a kind-of trust, I guess!"

"Look, Aunt Emily!" Bessie, almost hidden under a blue bonnet, posed self-consciously. Only her pigtails stuck out below.

Mattie objected, "But that's blue, Bessie. An' you know I like blue so much! You can have all the others."

"No one can HAVE any of them!" corrected Emily. "You know they are not for playing!" That said, she regretted it, for she was aware of how much little girls liked to dress up. "But I'll see if I can find an old bonnet or two for you to play dress-up in."

Elizabeth was marveling over four or five other bonnets. "And will you just look at these beautiful petticoats, yards and yards of hand-made lace! My! So many things could be made from these!"

The question of airing and storing the clothes suddenly became a vital one.

"Dresses like this taffeta need to be hung to get the wrinkles out, and aired all day," Elizabeth insisted. "Why don't we hang them on the east porch where they'll be away from the sun?"

"As long as we can block the view from the street!" Emily stated firmly. "For you know we wouldn't want our neighbors to think we were airing our own vast wardrobes."

"Certainly not!" agreed Elizabeth, shocked. "But how else?"

It seemed insolvable, until Aunt Sophia thought of tablecloths and suggested. "That long cloth that need ironin'...maybe stretch a line 'tween the posts an' peg it on. Folks couldn't see much!"

Emily nodded. She was hardly able to speak, for a realization of her indebtedness to William's Aunt Susan had suddenly almost over-whelmed her. How could she ever repay?...

The absorbing task of airing, sorting, and storing the dresses went on until nearly noon. It was an almost dreamlike morning, an experi-ence that benefited them all...a brief time of pleasure.

But pleasure ended when Mary Ann went home and then came right back with the sad news that Archibald Rison, their neighbor for many years, had died that morning. Shocked, Emily hurried over to inquire what her mother-in-law wanted to do. They decided to call at four o'clock. Meanwhile, Mary Ann would gather as many roses as she could, and, of course, go with them.

Elizabeth was trying desperately to find something edible that could be offered. Finally, they decided to use their only squash, though it was too small to make more than one pie. There was such a shortage of suitable food now that little choice was possible.

Sophronia offered to put on her best apron and take the pie to the back door before supper. "An' I'se gonna stay 'an help any way I can! Them poor, grievin' folks!"

As Emily changed to her black dress, which was far too warm at this time of year, she couldn't help but remember the kindness of Mrs. Rison when she and William had decided to marry. A long-time friend of Mrs. Elliott, the kind lady had insisted that they hold the wedding in her parlor and had invited their families. After the ceremony, she had offered a delicious cold collation.

Just thinking of that, and of dear William standing beside her as they took their vows, was almost more than she could bear. But I must! she told herself sternly. I must think of Mrs. Rison, for this is one time that I can make a small return of her kindness.

The Rison home was crowded, for many relatives, neighbors, and friends had chosen that hour to call. Mrs. Rison greeted all her callers and received their condolences in a manner so grateful that Emily could not help but be impressed. If only I could do as well at a time of such overwhelming sadness, she mused, I would be truly thankful!

There was not much to be done. They were told that only men would be sitting in the parlor throughout the night, and Mary Ann said that Littleton expected to be there. So after the roses had been put in water and they had greeted a few friends, they left. Invitations to the funeral would be delivered later.

At home, she found Elizabeth already dressed to call on Mrs. Rison as soon as Albert got home and had time to change his suit.

"It is rather warm over there because of so many candles!" Emily warned. "I must get this dress off before I faint! Then I will go to the kitchen and relieve Aunt Sophia."

On the way, she was reminded of her promise to find some dress-up clothes for the little girls.

"I want a shiny pink dress!" insisted Bessie, "and a great big purple bonnet with a long ribbon."

"Hmmmm!" exclaimed Emily. "I never saw anything like that, and I'm afraid you'll have to get by with whatever I can find."

"All right, Mama," agreed Mattie. "...So it's blue!"

Before long they were strutting up and down the hall, almost swallowed up in and dragging very odd assortments. Each wore one high-top shoe, with her other foot shod as usual.

Oh, well! thought Emily. They are getting ready for all the burdensome clothes women are prone to adorn themselves in.

Calls made and supper over, they settled in the sitting room. The boys, all talking at the same time, tried to explain to their father what they knew about sewing machines.

"I've seen them demonstrated," he assured them patiently. "And your Aunt Emily's choice is a good one. We're all happy for her!" As he turned to pick up his paper, he added, "And I never want to hear that any of you have touched it! Understand?"

Three heads nodded.

For Emily it had been both an exciting and sad day. Her letter to William was finished and ready to mail tomorrow. It told about her sewing machine and all the orders she had, touched on amusing things that had happened, and mentioned Mr. Rison's death. Unsure over that, she had only to reflect on how sympathetic her husband was, to know it would be right to tell him of this sad event.

Then she wrote one last sentence:.."I stood in the room, where our lives were joined into one life that has been so unbelievably happy for me, and realized yet again how precious you are...So be careful, my dearest!..."

After thinking for awhile, she said, "I'll have a letter to go to the post office tomorrow, Albert, if I can remember what date this is!"

"The tenth of April," Albert replied. "You'd better give me the letter right now so I can put it in my pocket--or something might happen to make me forget it!"

Elizabeth and Emily looked at him in surprise. Albert had such a good memory! They couldn't imagine any event that might cause him to forget to mail a letter!

69

Chapter Six

April 11, 1862

Sophronia was busy at the hot stove, frying pans of breaded streak-of-lean pork, while Elizabeth sleepily stirred a pot of cornmeal mush. Saucers of butter and pitchers of molasses were already on the breakfast table.

"Law, Miss 'Lizbeth!" Magdalena came in yawning broadly. "I do hopes Lulu Belle an' Fire Fly be more wake than me--else we won't get a drap of milk." She paused at the back door. "I peeped at the chillun...Miss Em'ly, too. They all sleepin'."

"Thank you! Then maybe you can finish the milking and get your own breakfast eaten before they wake up," Elizabeth said, as she dragged the heavy pot of mush to a cooler spot on the stove, then glanced quickly in the dining room. The spoonholder was full, and the table laid with knives and forks. Each person's napkin seemed to be in his napkin ring from the previous meal. Only mush bowls were lacking. She lifted them from the dish cupboard....

At that moment, the back door flew open and Magdalena stood in the opening, gasping and speechless!

"What in the world is wrong?" cried Elizabeth, nearly dropping the bowls.

"What'sa matter wid you, gal?" barked Sophronia.

But it was Uncle Pompous, close behind Magdalena, who replied, "The WAR done come! It right over yonder at the railroad! O Lawd! Miss 'Lizbeth! What's we gonna do?"

Elizabeth set the bowls down carefully. "Did you see soldiers? What color coats did they have on?"

"Blue! An' they's shootin' cannons! Don' you hear that racket, right

70

back a' us?"

Listening, they could hear the distant sound of firing. Albert heard it, too, and came bounding down the stairs.

"It's Union soldiers back at the railroad!" Elizabeth told him as she dropped weakly into the nearest chair.

Sophronia moved hastily to comfort. "Now, don't you give down, Miss 'Lizbeth. May be some mistake!"

But there was no mistake! Albert ran hurriedly upstairs where he could catch a glimpse of the railroad from the north window in the boys' room. Though the air was smoky from breakfast fires, he could distinguish blue figures--by the score!--running hither and thither. He could even hear shouts, with an occasional rattle of gunfire. Hastily, he closed the window.

"Get up now, boys! We've got a big problem this morning, and I want to see you both downstairs in five minutes...and dressed!"

Bleary-eyed, they gazed up at him in surprise.

"Move!" he shouted the word, "and don't go near the windows!"

Downstairs, all eyes were turned to him for guidance.

"Milking must be done!" he said to Magdalena, who hesitated only a moment before she picked up the empty pails.

But Pompous remained leaning--almost shrinking from fear. "Mr. Albert!" he quavered, "I do be mortal 'fraid a' them Yankees!"

Albert regarded the old Negro kindly. "Uncle, I can't see why YOU, Aunt Sophia, or Magdalena need fear Union soldiers."

"UNION soldiers!" Edward squeaked from the doorway, while Romeo stood round-eyed behind him.

Their father turned. "Back on the railroad. That's all we know yet. Now, Romeo, I want you to go across to Mrs. Elliott's. Tell Mr. Figg the news and that I'm trying to find out more. Come back as quickly as you can." He spoke to Edward, "Let Romeo out of the front door, then lock it, watch him, and unlock it when he starts back. No doors are to be left unlocked! Understand! And don't try to see out the windows either!"

"I'se ready, Mr. Albert!" Magdalena stepped forward.

Albert smiled. "Pompous and I are going out with you. And soon as you get started milking, I'll slip through the back lot to let our men know what's going on." He turned to Aunt Sophia. "We will eat our breakfast same as usual. Then, we'll see!"

Drawing a deep breath, Elizabeth rose. "I'll run on up to wake Emily. Hopefully, the little ones will sleep on for awhile!"

When she was alone, Sophronia threw back her head, and closing her eyes, spoke from her heart, "O Lawd! Do seem the Debil heself have drap in on us today! You do be here with us, too--ain't you, Jesus?"

Union soldiers in Huntsville! The words seemed to echo around the room and trail out the door after Elizabeth. They left Emily suddenly wide awake. Union soldiers? How? When did they?...

Knowing the answers to all these questions could only be found downstairs, she struggled to lace her corset, pull on a couple of petticoats and an old morning gown. It seemed to take forever!

With a glance at Mattie and Enoch Carlton to be sure they were sleeping, she pinned up her hair braids and rushed into the hall.

Breakfast odors wafted up the stairs. All activity was in the kitchen, same as other mornings. Only today, there were no sounds of happy talking and laughter. Voices were low, conveying a fear and dread that was even more noticeable in the room than the odor of fried meat.

Elizabeth came to hug her. "We don't know much," she said. "It seems there are Blue Coats everywhere back on the railroad; there has been shooting, too!"

"Where's Albert?" asked Emily.

"Gone to tell his men. Magdalena's milking, and Uncle Pompous is with her."

Romeo and Edward, round-eyed and unnaturally quiet, were at the kitchen table, eating bowls of mush and milk.

"Miss 'Lizbeth," broke in Sophronia. "Why don' y'all jes go on an' sit down right here at the table an' eat you breakfast, too? I'll serve the men soon's they comes in."

Emily looked at the mush. "Only a dab for me, Aunt Sophia, and some coffee...or whatever we're using that passes for it!"

"I wouldn't say it passes," said her sister. "But it is hot!"

They ate quietly, no one wanting--or even being able--to speak of their fears of what the day might hold.

A light tap at the back door caused Edward, acting doorkeeper, to dash over and shout, "Who's there?"

"Your pa. Open up!"

Once inside, Albert closed and bolted the door. "I just talked to Bolton at the back fence. He hasn't gone over to his office at the railroad yet...doesn't know whether to, or not. He said there were an unusual number of locomotives and rail cars in the repair shops and on the rail sidings, and apparently they were captured; also an incoming train." He sighed. "I hope to find out more, but go on now and dish up breakfast, Aunt Sophia. The men are on the way. I'll let 'em in the side door," he told Edward.

Sophia moved to the stove, and Elizabeth rose to help.

"I hear Enoch crying!" said Emily, jumping up. "I just as well get the babies and little girls up and dressed."

"Ma, do you think there'll be school today?" asked Romeo.

Elizabeth shook her head. "You won't be leaving the house!"

Romeo and Edward grinned at each other. They both welcomed the excitement...and NO SCHOOL!

Emily dressed Alvah and carried him downstairs. Enoch Carlton was next, and after he had been freshened and fed, she put him in his crib until the girls were dressed. Normally, Magdalena would have been there to help, but this was not a normal day!

"Are these Yankee soldiers, Mama?" Mattie asked when she heard the news. "'Cause, if they are, you know them, don't you?"

Emily had to decline the honor. "I do know lots of Yankee men, though, and they are nice. Why, Bessie's own pa is one, and think how nice he is! So we'll just hope for the best. And never fear them, for we'll take care of you!"

As they reached the kitchen, Magdalena was just coming in with two buckets of milk. "I saw one a' them soljers goin' west on the tracks," she said. "Had on he blue coat!"

"Did he have a gun?" asked Archie, eyes popping.

"Why, I never pay no 'tention," replied Magdalena. "But iffen I see that blue coat agin, I know it!"

73

"I like blue," Mattie observed conversationally, "so I'm going to like these blue soldiers, too."

And no one could think of anything to contribute to that!

Hastily changing the subject, Emily asked after the boys.

"They've gone to the shed with Albert and Pompous to get a few stacks of wood chopped for the cook stove. And the men went on to the shop. James Conway will try to let us know what has happened. Albert's staying here until he learns how things really are."

"Listen, little misses!" Sophronia focused her attention on the girls. "Set youself right down here by Archie an' eat you own mush without any messin' 'round!" She put two bowls with spoons on the table and refilled the milk pitcher.

It grew quiet in the kitchen, except for the sound of milk being poured into crocks for storage in the well-house trough.

"Miss 'Lizbeth, Lulu Belle didn't give as much milk as usual," Magdalena announced. "I talk to her, but that all she have!"

Elizabeth looked up. "I hope she doesn't take a notion to go off! Wouldn't it be awful if she went over toward the tracks?"

Magdalena shook her head. "Mr. Albert done tie up that gate latch, fer he say both cows gotta be hid in the stable fer now!"

"But that will mean buying hay!" exclaimed Elizabeth in dismay.

"Yes'um. They's both good eaters."

The door from the dining room opened and Lucius, Albert's nephew, stepped in. "I am to stay at home today. What can I do to help, Aunt Elizabeth?"

Sophronia spoke up, "Law, Mr. Lucius, you can bring them dirty dishes offen the table an' stack 'em right here." She pointed to a little table where other dirty bowls had been placed. "Jes soon as the rest a' us eats, I'll get after 'em! An', Miss 'Lizbeth, I put them dry beans to soak las' night. Can you think of somethin' else us can have for dinner? I sorry to tell you, but cornmeal's way low in the bin!"

Elizabeth sighed. "Well, make bread from what there is. I will be so glad when the garden comes in...even a few spring onions!"

"The ones Pompous planted first, 'round the side a' the house, am up pretty high, but he'd have a floatin' fit iffen we pulled a few!" Aunt Sophia sighed. "Sure would be mighty tasty though!"

Just then Lucius entered from the dining room, a tilting stack of bowls in each hand. Emily rescued the dishes, then cleared the children's places and sent them into the playroom.

A few minutes later, Albert knocked and was admitted. "I found out a little more from Jim Pollard, who had gone downtown shortly after dawn. Since he's street superintendent, I guess he felt he was obliged to. Seems the Union forces have taken control of the telegraph office and the post office. They captured the depot and railroad repair shops first thing!"

"The post office?" cried Emily. "Does that mean we can't send or get letters?"

"Probably," Albert replied, patting his pocket. "I have yours, and surely we can get it off somehow! There are bound to be brave men willing to act as couriers."

"Did Mr. Pollard say what happened at the depot?" asked Lucius anxiously. "I don't see how the Federals could slip in like that, without anyone knowing they were close."

Albert nodded. "That is a mystery. But seems some in town were warned last night that a large body of soldiers were camped above Meridianville, but folks thought it just another false rumor!"

"False rumor!" gasped Elizabeth. "I didn't know we'd had such rumors, Albert!"

"No, I expect you didn't. Anyway, this time, the rumor was not false...but, you know, even if we had had warning, there is not a thing that could have been done. There are no Confederate forces here to protect us, for they are all at Corinth--or other places. Some Confederate soldiers are in town on sick leave, business, or whatever, Pollard says, and they are fleeing east to the mountain in hopes of making their way down to the river and across."

"Well, I pray they succeed!" whispered Elizabeth.

"You asked about the railroad, Lucius. If Jim's information is correct, the Federals captured fifteen locomotives and dozens of rail cars, besides a train of injured Confederate soldiers that pulled in just at the wrong time."

"Oh, my!" moaned Emily. "I wonder what will happen to them!"

"Hopefully, local people can care for them. We'll just have to see.

Well, that's all I know now." He paused and then said, "Oh, and Jim thinks the Union soldiers will go house-to-house looking for Confederate soldiers who are sick or hiding. So I guess we might as well expect such a visit." At the shocked looks on the women's faces, he added, "I'll be right here!"

"Well, iffen they comes messin' 'round my garden," cried Uncle Pompous, suddenly very brave, "I be out there by that scarecrow wid ma big stick!"

"Both Edward and Romeo chimed in, "We'll be out there, too!"

"Nobody's going to be OUT anywhere today!" Albert stated, with a stern look at each one. "We'll all be inside. Another thing, if any soldiers come here wanting a meal or food, we'll have to give it to them...and as politely as possible."

"Law, Mr. Albert! How we gonna do it? Cornmeal 'bout down in the bin! All us got's dry beans an' a dab of streak-a-lean meat."

Emily spoke up, "They can have my share of that awful coffee!"

"As soon as I can, I'll see about getting us something more to eat," promised Albert. "But right now I'm going to watch from the front for a while. You boys keep the back and side doors locked, and call me if anyone knocks."

Albert had hardly left the kitchen before a tiny tap was heard at the back door. Edward dashed over, calling, "Who is it?" A child's voice replied, "It's just Addie Virginia."

"That's Mrs. Bolton's child!" Emily said. "Surely not alone!"

But she was, and when she stepped inside, it was obvious from the cheerful, matter-of-fact expression on her face that she knew no cause for fear. Her only problem was trying to move inside the tight-fitting, faded-brown dress she wore.

Emily spoke up, "Hello, Addie Virginia! Is anything wrong?"

"Nothin' wrong with me, but little Charlie's havin' one of his screamin' fits 'cause we got no milk for breakfast. So Ma's just wonderin' could you let us have some? I brought our bucket."

"Of course, we can let you have milk!" Elizabeth assured her.

"How is your mother this morning?" asked Emily.

A slight flicker of worry crossed the thin face. "She's not so pert, but then she's worried 'bout Pa 'cause he had to go over to the railroad where those soljers are." She raised the bucket for Aunt Sophia to take. "Soon as I get back, I'm goin' to watch out for him."

"Here the milk, chile," Sophronia handed the covered bucket to Addie, just as Albert came in the kitchen. "I'll carry that heavy bucket," he offered, "and walk back with you. You're a brave girl to venture out alone!"

She looked at him in surprise. "But I'm the oldest, Mr. Baker, so I have to be brave. Anyway, it ain't hard!"

"Goodbye, Addie! Come back!" called several voices.

She flung them a grin and said, "I will, and much obliged!"

As the morning passed, Albert became increasingly concerned about what was going on at the Marble Yard. "It does seem one of the men could have come before now to tell me!" he complained.

Elizabeth tried to comfort him. But it was nearly eleven when, from behind the curtain in the parlor, he asked, "Is that Conway coming out of Mrs. Elliott's front gate?"

Elizabeth took a peek and shook her head. "Never saw him wear a cap before! And what's he got over his shoulder?"

"It's Conway all right!" cried Albert, and had the door open the next minute. "Man, come in here! Are you being chased?"

"By the Saints! it could be," Conway admitted. Then seeing the ladies, he apologized for his appearance. "You may be sure I have something in this bag that would delight the heart of any of them Blue Coats! The thieving rascals are all about town looking for whatever they can filch!"

"What's in the bag?" asked Emily, unable to wait any longer to find out. "Not real coffee, is it?"

"None a-that! But it's a real ham and 'bout ten pounds of nice dried peaches!"

Elizabeth threw up her hands in delight. "Bring it on out to the kitchen!"

"Ma'am, my own belief is you'll be needing to hide it--or when those Yanks get to this street, they'll take it sure!"

"This street?" quavered Emily.

"Right here!" Conway declared. "Those Blue Coats are searching the town for Confederates first, and food second...or maybe it's the other way 'round!"

Albert had been thinking and now said, "Put the ham in the box by the kitchen stove and have the boys stack the wood on top!"

Emily had also been thinking. "Let's make a long, flat package of the dried peaches and hide it under the mattress in the baby's crib. If he's in it--and crying--they won't come near!"

"You can't beat that!" said Conway, and drew from his pocket a further surprise: a small sack of rice and a few cinnamon sticks. "From Windham," he announced. "That poor lad's been hard hit, by my way a-thinking! Near wiped out! But, Albert, he wanted you to know the invaders spurned that delicacy: salted codfish!"

"Well, I wish we had it then!" Albert declared.

While they were hiding the precious provisions, Conway slipped over to his room to freshen up. "You can count on me relating all my adventures when you see me next!" he promised with a grin.

None of the small children were told of the hidden food. "It'd be just like one of those sly fellows to question a little child!" Albert commented, disgusted at all he had heard about them.

Emily carried Enoch Carlton upstairs and settled him cosily on his mattress, which covered the precious dried peaches. Returning to the sitting room, she looked at her sewing machine. Yesterday its purchase had seemed so important!...but today?

Elizabeth sat in her rocker, while Albert stayed by the window keeping watch. Emily idly picked up her sewing. In a few minutes, the older boys slipped in, excitement mirrored on their faces. No one wanted to miss the story to come.

And none were disappointed, for Conway possessed that charming gift granted the Irish; he was a grand storyteller! Taking up his position in front of the mantel, he began his tale.

"When we got into the town this morning, our plan was to spare them Yanks a single glimpse of us. So in we slipped from the back street--Jefferson, that is--and no announcement made. You may all be sure our greatest fear was for our dear mules and Ebon! Though that foxy lad wasn't needing concern from the likes of us, for he had coaxed those precious craychers into that empty back shed and forked in some hay, and shut the door! So, you can picture their regular stable a-standing there empty in all its mystery!"

I'll have to say that was smart of Ebon!" Albert said.

"It was indeed! And when we got there, not a single one of the fa-mous Blue Coats had come snooping! Though they appeared to be sprouting like weeds most everywhere downtown!" He paused.

"So, what happened next?" urged Albert.

Conway chuckled deep in his throat. "The boys and me shifted a few big stones across to block the shed door. And, knowing they'd come visiting any minute, we set up a show, a-beating the stones, and--by the powers!--if we didn't make a big racket, and raise up enough dust to discourage a dozen snoopers!"

"How many came?" inquired Lucius, trying to get to the meat of the tale.

Conway looked at him, not liking to be hurried. Too, his reply was a bit deflating, "Only two came a-trailing in from Washington Street. Mean, they looked!" He paused for full effect.

"Did they talk, Mr. Conway?" asked Edward humbly.

"After their own fashion! Asked how many Confederate soldiers was hiding back there. "Not a one!" I told 'em, while the boys built up the racket. When they seemed doubting, I invited the two to step in-side the shop and look 'round for theirselves. Poor lads! They were easy fooled!" He grinned. "The lazy one stepped in the shop area. The other climbed the stairs, and what with the dust he found up there and that being raised by our men below, the poor lad was seized with a powerful fit of sneezing that put a stop to his activities." He paused again. "But its sorry I am to tell you, Albert, that the snoop who in-spected downstairs made off with those few precious cigars you had!"

"Well, can't be helped," said Albert. "I needn't be smoking in times like these anyhow. Did the marauders ask any questions?"

Conway laughed. "The lad that wasn't busy sneezing wanted some food. Seems they all missed breakfast in order to come a-sneaking in on us! We just shook our heads and went on making a racket!"

Albert laughed. "I'm so relieved that the mules were saved!"

"For now only! For we're not meant to know what tomorrow may bring! But, continuing my story, I told the shop lads to keep up a show whilst I ambled up the mountain to tell Jonathan Broad what deviltry was afoot down here in the valley."

"Good thinking!" agreed Albert. "Had he heard?"

"Not so much as a word!--when I found him at long last. That's some trek up through those woods!"

"Didn't you keep to the road?"

"No! For I wasn't anxious to meet a party of Blue Coats on the way. That lad Broad is agreeable to hiding until we give him the word. He has a cabin of sorts up there; not easy to come on!"

"What will he do for food?" asked Elizabeth.

"That was my wonder, too," said Conway, "but I learned there's small game to be trapped, if a man's desperate. Though I doubt a friendly lad like Broad will have much problem. He already knows the mountain folk thereabouts." Suddenly, he turned to Elizabeth, "Anyway, ma'am, I'm hoping that's by way of explanation as to the poor shape of me clothes...and this borrowed cap!"

"Bring the things over, James, and we'll clean and mend them," invited Elizabeth.

"But where'd the ham come from?" Lucius wanted to know.

Conway grinned. "Luck! Old Lady Luck! No sooner had I got back to the shop, than a lad came stealing from behind The Democrat newspaper office into our lot. Burdened he was with two heavy sacks, and him wanting to get to the hills! I set about to draw the poor lad a plan of the way--and the upshot of it was, he gave up trying to take both bags. Then you know, he up and swapped me the ham and peaches for twenty Confederate dollars!"

Albert reached in his pocket for his purse, but Conway raised his hand in a negative gesture. "It's I who'll be giving this one treat! The sweet thought of dear Aunt Sophia's dried-peach pie is payment enough for me!"

"How'd you get the rice from Windham's?" asked Emily. "Surely you didn't walk through the street to his store!"

"No, ma'am, that good gentleman stopped by, for he was closing up and going to hide out for a while. Who can blame the lad? As I came through Mistress Elliott's lot I called at the back door and left some of the dried peaches."

"Was Figg still there?" asked Albert.

80

"A-walking the floor," replied Conway. "Seemed doubtful about leaving the women with only his young Robert to stand guard. Yet, he was fearful that his partner, Jim Nevill, had failed in getting to their Coffee House--is it?--in time to hide what liquor was on the premises. By the powers! There'll be trouble if those Yankee lads get a-hold of that before they have their breakfast!"

Elizabeth said, "But surely their officers have control..."

Conway shook his head. "From what I'm hearing, there's nothing sure about this bunch--except a pack a-trouble! Rumor downtown is they raided farms along Meridian Pike, a-stealing animals, even killing all one poor woman's flock of turkey fowls!..."

Hoping to spare the ladies any further revelations and anxious about his own animals, Albert said. "I'm hoping I've got old Wego and the cows hidden well enough."

"Are the stable doors into the alley padlocked?" asked Conway.

"Securely, and Pompous has wired shut the alley gate into Mill Street, but there's the stable door that opens into the backyard. I don't have a lock for it."

"Well, why not have the boys move a stack of wood out front to block the door?..."

"...and let 'em chop on it right there," added Albert eagerly.

This plan cleared the room of men and boys in a hurry!

"I'll see if Aunt Sophia has dinner ready." Hastily, Elizabeth got to her feet. "I'm wondering how we're going to get it up to those poor men at the Marble Yard?"

Emily rose. "Oh, Albert will think of a way!"

It was James Conway who provided the means--for he intended to be the one returning to town. "I'm after thinking that your place is here, Albert, at least until the soldiers pay their visit." He turned to Elizabeth. "Ma'am, if you can pack the beans in a pail and wrap the bread, and give us a few grains of that so-called coffee, I can hide it all in my backpack--and none the wiser! We can build us a mite of fire for the heating of it!"

"Be careful," urged Albert. "I wish we could think of some way to help protect Ebon and the mules during the night to come."

But Conway held up his hand in his ever-confident manner. "You may be sure and we'll figure it out," he assured Albert.

It was nearly two o'clock before they glimpsed a Union soldier on that end of West Holmes. Of a sudden, there were three--almost in front of the Elliott home!

"I hope they don't upset Mrs. Elliott," Albert murmured.

But they passed on to Mrs. Jordan's, next door.

"So that's how it is!" exclaimed Albert. "Someone's pointing out the homes of Confederate soldiers and sympathizers!"

"What miserable coward would do that?" Emily asked, amazed.

"Several here," admitted Albert. "This area of Alabama was not for secession to begin with--and there's some who still favor the Union!"

Emily sighed. "I suppose they'll be here next, then. Well, at least Enoch Carlton is sleeping and the peaches well-hidden!" Albert nodded as he left the room to alert the boys.

"If they want food," mused Elizabeth, "there's some beans and a few pieces of corn bread left."

"Give them coffee!" urged Emily. "What have we for supper?"

"Sophia will kill a chicken and make dumplings--if she can get enough flour from the bin. I wonder when we'll dare to cook that ham? It's good odor will alert the whole neighborhood!"

"There! The soldiers have left Jesse Jordan's, and are heading west!" Emily reported from behind the front curtain.

"Then they'll double back on this side, and it will be a while before they get here." Elizabeth rose. "I'll tell Aunt Sophia to wait to kill the chicken. In fact, she should stay in her room!"

"If they see her, they'll want a meal cooked!" Emily agreed.

When Albert came in to report that the wood-chopping operation was in full swing, he told Emily that Elizabeth planned to remain in the kitchen and Aunt Sophia in her room. Of course, Magdalena was with the children.

Nearly an hour later, their gate was opened by a soldier. "An officer," whispered Albert as he went to admit the search party.

From the sitting room, Emily could hear the officer's greeting and statement. "We have been ordered to search your premises for

Confederate soldiers."

"Are you searching every house?" asked Albert. "For you missed some of those across the street!"

The officer replied as he stepped into the hall, "We'll get to all of them eventually. Are there any Confederate soldiers here?"

"No," Albert replied calmly. "My brother-in-law mustered into the Confederate Army just over two weeks ago. His wife and their two small children are living with us."

"You don't talk like a Southerner," observed the officer.

"We're all from New York state, but we've been living here all of ten years now. Like it very much. I'm a stonemason. My Marble Yard is downtown. I've got some New York masons who work for me and live in the house behind. We've nothing to do with the war!"

"Maybe not," said the officer, "but I must search anyway!"

"Go ahead," agreed Albert, ushering them into the parlor.

Suddenly, Emily heard the sound of Enoch Carlton's hunger-pang screams. What an inconvenient time for that! she thought, walking hurriedly to the stairs. Once upstairs with the baby in her arms, she realized that the soldiers might spot his empty crib and want to search it. An idea formed swiftly. There was no time to think, for the searchers were already on the stairs.

Now the officer was in the open door, with one of his men leering through. It was hard to make herself heard above Enoch's screams, but Emily tried, "Come in, if you like. I'm so sorry the baby is making such a fuss! We're afraid he's taking measles!"

The leering private stepped back in a hurry; the officer more sedately. He said, "We won't disturb you then, ma'am. Is it your husband who's in the Confederate Army?"

"Yes, my husband is a Southerner." With that said, she looked him full in the face, while her own mirrored the awful dread and fear she felt.

Slowly nodding, he gave her a sympathetic look, and turning, said to his men, "Check the other rooms up here quickly. Then we can finish downstairs. Good day to you, ma'am!"

With relief, Emily closed the door so she could feed the baby. Only later did she learn the rest of the story.

"When that officer and his men stopped at the playroom door and looked in," Elizabeth said, with considerable amusement, "our daughters rose and each dropped them a low curtsy. And yours, Emily, YOURS! said, 'Those blue coats are pretty, sir!' And that so delighted the officer that he hardly allowed his men to search any further."

"My daughter, 'The Diplomat'!" laughed Emily. "That was after I had frightened them by expressing my fear that Enoch Carlton might be coming down with measles!"

"You didn't!" gasped Elizabeth.

"Yes, I did! And it was true. I do fear his getting measles!"

Albert laughed. "You ladies saved the day! But I also think we were lucky to get a sympathetic officer. They hardly glanced out back where the wood-chopping was in full swing." He moved towards the door. "I'd better tell the choppers that the coast is clear!"

"And let me tell Aunt Sophia it's safe to wring that chicken's neck," Elizabeth said. "She'll be wondering what is happening."

"Law, Miss 'Lizbeth, I'se glad that over!" Sophronia rejoiced. "Did they find the ham or peaches?"

Elizabeth laughed. "Everything's safe, Aunt Sophia. Emily and the little girls placed a charm on those poor men, and they could only see what we wanted them to!"

"At least they didn't find the cows!" Emily added.

"Well, hallelujah! Even if we is out of cornmeal an' flour, I thanks the good Lawd that we got ham an' peaches, an' milk, too, fer another day!"

Chapter Seven

April 12, 1862

The most pressing question was FOOD. They longed mightily for a taste of something from the garden! But it was far too early!

"Last night's chicken and dumplings was so good, Aunt Sophia! I just wish we had more!" said Elizabeth. "But we can't afford to sacrifice our laying hens."

"That do be true! Miss 'Lizbeth, but I saved enuff from supper fer the chillun to have some today. What 'bout iffen I slices jes a bit offen the ham? I could boil out the salt, then cut it fine and mix it in some of that rice. Give a bit a' flavor! An' iffen Miss Em'ly hand me a few those dried peaches, I could stew 'em up wid a dab a' honey. I use the las' flour in the dumplin's'"

Elizabeth sighed, but couldn't think of an alternative. "Go on and cut off the ham. I'll send Edward to lift off the wood sticks and then hide it again. Such a nuisance! Emily can bring down the peaches as soon as Enoch Carlton wakes up."

As Elizabeth started to leave the room, Sophronia brought up a concern of her own, "Who guardin' us from them Blue Bellies, Miss 'Lizbeth, now that Mr. Albert have gone back to work?"

"Blue Coats!" Elizabeth corrected.

"I likes Blue Bellies better...more fitten!"

"Lucius is at the front door, and I'm sending Romeo back here. He can guard the door and also do the churning. Keep Edward, too, if you need him."

But Aunt Sophia replied emphatically, "One's enuff at a time!"

After Emily had held a short class with the children, she felt herself drawn irresistibly to her sewing tasks. The memory of the child, Addie Virginia, in her outgrown rag-of-a-dress was vividly imprinted on her mind. She was getting out the gowns brought over by Mrs. Bolton when Elizabeth came to the door.

"I'm available, if needed," Emily said to her, "but I just had to start on some of this sewing!"

"Do make something for Addie first!" begged Elizabeth. "I just can't bear to see her in that tight!..."

"Neither can I!" Emily replied, "but I'm thinking, too, of the wounded Confederates captured in the rail car. I'd help nurse, if I could. For if William gets wounded, I hope someone will..."

"We'll ask Albert tonight. But, right now, our most pressing--and it is pressing!--need is for flour or meal!"

"Aunt Elizabeth!" Lucius called and motioned toward the corner of Limberg Street where a group of Negroes had congregated.

"There's Videlia!" he whispered.

Sure enough, Mary Ann Figg's slave stood talking and gesturing to another woman in the group. One Negro man, stationed right on the corner, seemed to be acting as lookout.

"Poor souls!" whispered Elizabeth. "They don't know what is to happen. Many probably want freedom...who can blame them! But what will they do then?"

Coming into the hall, Emily whispered, "What about yours?"

"They love us, for we've always been good to them," Elizabeth murmured. "Besides, they're afraid of these 'Blue Bellies', as Aunt Sophia calls them. And rightly so!"

Suddenly, Lucius pointed across the street. The lookout had an arm raised and the group was melting away in all directions. By the time a squad of soldiers came in sight, the corner was empty.

Now Edward was calling from the back, "Mama, Addie Virginia's here!"

As Elizabeth turned, Emily said, "I'll bring my tape measure!"

Addie held to a covered bucket, her eyes taking in Romeo's motions as he churned. "I could do that!" she offered.

Certainly not in that tight dress you have on! Emily wanted to say, but instead, she smiled and said, "You can try it sometime!"

"Hello, Addie Virginia," Elizabeth greeted. "Does your mother need more milk?"

But the child shook her head. "No, ma'am. It's flour we need!"

"Law! But so does we!" spoke up Sophronia.

"My pa knows where we can get some," Addie told them.

"Oh, is your pa at home?" asked Emily.

"No, ma'am. But he was, just to tell us about the flour an' that he's goin' to try to find some more work 'cause the soljers in those blue coats won't let him stay at the railroad!"

Emily stepped forward with her tape measure. "Just keep right on talking!" she said, kneeling beside Addie. "I'm measuring you for a new dress."

"Whar's the flour at, miss?" put in Sophronia, unable to wait longer for the answer to that vital question.

"Why, Pa said that Mr. Moore at the Flour Mill down to the end of the street said if we'd come to the side door, he'd be glad to sell us flour. He don't want those men in blue coats to take it!"

Elizabeth threw up her hands. "Well, good for him! Are you going there now, Addie Virginia?"

The child had set her bucket on the floor and was holding out her arms to be measured. "Yes, ma'am. An' Ma wondered if you'd like to get some, too?"

"That was so thoughtful of your ma!" Elizabeth said. Romeo was busy churning, and Lucius standing guard. "Edward can go!"

Edward stepped forward, almost breathless with excitement.

Addie Virginia regarded him thoughtfully. "No need to feel one bit scared of those soljers, Edward, 'cause I know a way to slip 'round where they won't see us," she told him earnestly.

He opened his mouth wide to protest, "I'm not scared!"

"Maybe not," his mother put in, "but don't do anything risky! Promise me--before I go for the money. In fact, come with me!"

Looking embarrassed, Edward followed her into the hall.

"Miss 'Lizbeth!" called Sophronia. "You want him to tote more? Us got two clean, dry buckets with lids."

Two buckets were agreed on.

"Mrs. Elliott," asked Addie, "can you make my new dress bigger than this one? I've just growed clean out of it!"

Emily smiled reassuringly. "Don't worry, I will make it plenty large, even put in some tucks to be let out as you grow--and I'll get more than one dress--even some pantalets!"

With a satisfied smile, the child picked up her bucket.

As Elizabeth returned, she was cautioning Edward, "...try to remember all I've told you!"

"I will," he promised, picking up the two covered buckets.

As he passed the churn, Romeo warned in a low voice, "You take care of that little girl, Edward! And no showing-off!"

As soon as the children had gone, Elizabeth began to worry, "I hope I did the right thing to let Edward go."

"Don't you fear none, Miss 'Lizbeth," advised Sophronia. "That little chile gonna take care a' him!"

"Still, I'm going up to watch them from the northeast window!"

Emily couldn't resist joining her. Besides, she expected Enoch Carlton to start his hunger screams at any minute.

But the two children were not visible from upstairs. "They are probably following the route Addie spoke of," Emily said. "My! If that child isn't a refreshing delight!"

Elizabeth had to agree, "Yes, but I'd like to get a glimpse of them. Look! Can you see two small figures behind Andy Hays' back fence on the corner of Arms Street?"

Emily peered. "I can't see anything. But if it's them, Addie has chosen some back ways and is staying off the street."

Although they watched for some time, nothing moved. Elizabeth raised the window so they could hear from below, but dogs barking were the only sounds that broke the silence.

"I declare!" she murmured, "I'm tired of all this quiet...It's right eerie!"

"People are staying in--like us," Emily said thoughtfully. "I do resent being made to feel like a prisoner, and later today I'm going across to Mother Elliott's to see if they're all right! And I worry about Mary Elizabeth...and Aunt Susan!"

Elizabeth turned quickly. "Albert promised he'd find out about them all today!"

Suddenly, Enoch Carlton's screams rent the air, followed by Mattie's call, "Mama, the baby's crying!"

Poor darling, she thought as she freshened and fed him, no one wants to hear you screaming. Not even your own mama!

In the playroom, Magdalena greeted them cheerfully, "What that you screamin' fer, big boy? You ready to sing wid us?"

Looking up at her, he gurgled, "Mag!"

The young nurse was so delighted she held him up in the air to admire. "Did you hear that, Miss Em'ly? He speak to me! ME!"

Mattie came running. "Oh, Mama, I wish he'd say my name!" She took his hand. "Buddy, please say Mattie! Or just MAT!"

But the baby had created his sensation for the day.

While upstairs, Elizabeth still had not glimpsed the children.

"Well, don't fret," advised Emily. "There was probably a long, long line, if word had got around...."

They both stepped back! For a blue-coated soldier had come in sight on Arms, moving toward the corner of Mill Street.

"Mercy on us!" cried Elizabeth, letting the curtain drop.

As the man walked south on Mill, Emily could see a musket over his shoulder. He's a sentry! she thought furiously. They have had the nerve to place a guard on our quiet street!

The sentry was nearly to the Pollard's house when the branches stirred in a bush near him--and out stepped two children!

"It's Edward and Addie!" gasped Elizabeth, grabbing at Emily's arm. "Oh, mercy!"

"Shhh!" Emily wanted to hear what was said below.

Addie Virginia's treble piped clearly up to them. "Oh, Mr. Blue, you seen my dog anywhere?"

The soldier glared. "I've seen a hundred dogs, and one gets in my way, I aim to shoot it straight between the eyes!"

Emily could feel her sister begin to tremble.

"But, my dog wouldn't hurt you, mister," trilled Addie. "He's just a little black dog." She stooped to indicate height.

Suddenly, Edward tried his own voice. It pleaded, "Sir, please glance around for him. Poor child, she's so upset!"

And Addie, so naturally brave!, managed to look like she would burst into tears any minute. She even sniffed a few times.

Grunting, the soldier turned and stalked back toward Arms.

"His name's Blackberry!" called Addie, quickly covering up her mouth to stop the giggles.

The moment the soldier disappeared from view, Edward dashed behind the bushes to retrieve the two covered buckets. Then, with Addie Virginia on watch, he crossed to his own back gate.

When Elizabeth and Emily reached the kitchen, Romeo was helping his brother inside and saying, "I warned you about doing something foolish!"

Edward gave him a look. "Close the door quick," he gasped, "or that soldier may see where I went!"

The others might not have been impressed, but Aunt Sophia was! "You an' that little chile is big heroes!" She grinned broadly. "I gonna make you a special peach pie...all yer own!"

"And I'm going to make Addie at least two more dresses!" vowed Emily, who knew the correct one to credit for their success.

But Elizabeth could not forget all the misery she had been put to. She glared at Edward. "Now, don't you go in there and tell the children about this! I don't want them frightened!"

Romeo, though, took pity on his brother and promised, "You can tell it all at supper! For I'll ask Papa to let you. The men will like that story, I know!"

Right then, Sophronia brought the gathering to a close. "They too many feets in here! How'm I gonna make up pie crusts, when I can't hear myself thinkin'?"

Mary Ann Figg opened their front door only enough for Emily to slip in. Afterward, she firmly closed and bolted it. "Robert's guardin' the back. Littleton told him not to budge!" She leaned closer to whisper, "The Negroes were congregatin' this mornin'!"

Emily nodded. She almost expressed her sympathy for them, but managed to catch herself in time, for Mary Ann--a Southerner, and the owner of Videlia--probably felt differently. So, instead, she asked, "How is Mother Elliott taking this?"

Her sister-in-law laughed. "Sometimes I think she's furious at the

Blue Coats--an' then, I wonder if she's not secretly enjoyin' the excitement. Caroline's not so well. Right now, she's in bed."

Emily expressed her sympathy. "I feel I'm not doing a thing to help you, but the truth is that Albert stayed home yesterday--and wouldn't let us leave the house. Then today there have been a few happenings I thought both of you might like to hear about."

And they did! Laughing together lightened their load of fear and uncertainty. As Emily told about the flour, Mary Ann started to plan how she might get some. "I can't send Robert; he's not to stir from that door!"

"We can let you have some of ours," Emily heard herself say. A moment later, the relief mirrored on their faces was her reward!

"What do we have to exchange, Mary Ann?" asked Mrs. Elliott.

"Well, only hominy. We've had it so much we're sick of it."

"Hominy!" cried Emily. "Why, we haven't tasted a bite of that in ages! Is it some you made, Mother Elliott?" When the reply was affirmative, she suggested a swap of half-a-bucket of each.

"Doesn't seem fair to you!" protested Mary Ann. "But--I'll get it ready right away, for we sure need the flour!"

Emily turned to her mother-in-law, "How are you faring through all of this? I worry about you, for I know you feel as I do about not being able to get any mail through from the boys."

Mrs. Elliott nodded. "That's one bad thing about wars, bein' in ignorance of what's goin' on! I never experienced it before. Of course, I was only a girl back in 1812, when we fought Great Britain. It didn't affect us much in Petersburg, Virginia, though we heard a lot about the part Andy Jackson played."

"That was before you moved to Knoxville?" asked Emily.

Her mother-in-law nodded. "We went there in 1816. I can barely recall it now. But this has been home for a long time, an' to see strangers takin' over makes me really angry! Also, I don't like bein' kept in. I feel like an old hen penned up in a coop!"

"I know," said Emily, "and I worry about Mary Elizabeth and the children and about Aunt Susan...."

"Littleton saw Alonzo yesterday. The boy said that on Friday, while he was workin' at Mr. Heap's Tin Shop, the soldiers came to search their house, but nothin' was stolen. He said they were now afraid to pasture their cow across the street on that vacant spot on Jefferson where they usually take her. So they're keepin' the poor animal in her shed...just as we're havin' to do."

"So are we, and with two cows!" Emily said. "But tell me about Littleton. Are the soldiers causing trouble at the Coffee Shop?"

"Some, I think. Though I'm sure I don't get to hear the worst of it. They keep their liquor hidden an' serve only old customers when there are no Blue Coats in the shop. Of course, I'm sure the Southerners get up an' leave the minute the soldiers come in." She laughed suddenly. "This morning, Littleton told me one thing that happened last night. Seems a few of the Yankee officers came in an' ordered coffee--there bein' no liquor available--but, when they tasted the awful brew we're forced to use, some of them spat it out right on the floor an' stalked out of the shop."

"What rudeness!" cried Emily.

But one officer remained behind," Mrs. Elliott continued, "an' apologized. Later on, that same officer brought in a big package of real coffee."

"Real coffee!" Emily nearly shouted.

Mrs. Elliott nodded. "Littleton fetched some of it home an' we had a little for breakfast. I have to say it's mighty good!--even if it is 'Yankee brew'!"

To save herself, Emily could not keep tears from her eyes. She was so embarrassed. Crying over coffee!

"Mary Ann has a little pack fixed for you," Mrs. Elliott told her gently.

Ashamed, Emily wiped away her tears. "It's just everything together," she whispered.

And the kind old lady in the lace cap, who loved her, said, "I know!...I do know."

The hominy and ham, real coffee!, and fried peach pies, helped to soften the bad news Albert brought home. It was after dark before he and the men pulled in. Elizabeth, tired from worrying and waiting, wanted an explanation, but was put off until the starved men could eat.

After Edward had told of his adventures, and Emily had related Littleton's acquisition of the coffee, Albert finally sat back to tell his story, beginning with, "Last night, some scoundrel stole one of our mules!..."

"...surely not!" gasped Elizabeth.

Lucius leaned forward in concern. "Which one, Uncle Albert? It wasn't Barnabas, was it?"

Albert nodded. "The strongest, and leader, of our team!"

"But how!" asked Emily. "I thought they were hidden."

"So...did we!" put in James Conway, "but thieving cowards have got their ways, and evil they are!"

"But Uncle Ebon?" came from several throats.

"Poor fellow blames himself!" Albert said. "Here's what we're thinking happened. One or more of those Negroes used by the city corporation to repair the streets, and who sleep in that building behind the market house, just a few steps away on Clinton Street, must have seen Ebon either moving the mules or going in to see about them, and in the darkness of the night stole in and quietly led away Barnabas-- good-natured beast that he is! Anyhow, when Ebon came from his cabin this morning, the shed door was open and only Old Joe was inside."

"Clear hoofprints a-leading back to the market house," Conway added, "and a man's big barefoot prints were evidence enough!"

"We even went over and looked among the corporation's mules in case Barnabas was there," mourned one of the men. "But no luck!"

"That's because the Blue Coats have got him by now!" put in another in disgust. "Bound to have!"

Suddenly, Emily remembered the officer who had called at their house the day before. "Albert, do you think that officer who came yesterday could help to find Barnabas?"

"Might be," he agreed. "But I've got to inquire as to the proper way to make a complaint. General Mitchel, commander here, has set himself up an office at the depot, but he's been besieged with requests from the ladies of Huntsville who want to help care for the wounded Confederate soldiers the Federals captured in the freight cars...."

93

"Where are those men?" asked Emily. "I want to help, too!"

"In the Huntsville Female College on Randolph Street, or so we heard, under care of the women of the Cumberland Presbyterian, so you won't need to help, Emily."

"But, Albert, how can you care for the other mule--and what of Ebon? You can't leave him up there!" begged Elizabeth.

Her husband smiled as he explained, "We've already figured all that out! Tonight we hitched Old Joe to the wagon, put in it what hay was in the shop shed--quite a lot!--and had Ebon pack his own belongings and load them in the wagon. Then we pulled out across the back lots to Jefferson Street and on home. All of us walked alongside the wagon, just in case. There were soldiers about; but not a one questioned us!"

"I was watching out front, but didn't see you!" said Lucius, thoroughly puzzled.

Albert shrugged. "It was dark, and you weren't looking for all of us walking by the wagon. We went by and turned into Spragin's Alley, and back east into that passageway we left open north of the garden, and pulled up to the stable door. So now Old Joe's in with the other animals, the hay is all stored, and everything is locked--even the wagon's chained and padlocked to the fence!"

Emily regarded her brother-in-law with admiration. "It's lucky you had the foresight to enlarge that barn last year," she mused, "or it would never have accommodated so many animals."

He nodded, "And there's still one empty stall!"

"But where is Ebon?" asked Elizabeth. "Has he had his supper?"

James Conway laughed. "You can bet he has! For he's out there in Old Pompous' cabin. By jingo! If they ain't two happy souls!"

"On Monday morning," continued Albert, "we'll hitch Old Joe to the wagon...and Ebon and all of us will ride to work!"

Romeo and Edward, both of whom had been hanging on every word, now leaned back and looked at each other in silent recognition of their father's good sense and determination to care for his own.

As Albert rose from the table, he said, "It seems best not to attend Divine Services on the morrow, but we will worship God with readings from the Bible and prayer right here in our parlor at eleven in the morning...anyone who cares to take part."

There was a murmur of appreciation around the room.

"Thank you, Albert," said Elizabeth, smiling at him. "I'll let Sophronia know so she can invite the others to join with us."

Next morning, Emily mentioned inviting Mrs. Elliott to attend, and received a cordial response. "Why, of course!" Elizabeth replied. "And invite her to eat dinner with us afterward."

"Oh, she'll like that!" Emily said. "She confessed to me that she feels like a prisoner--'an old hen penned in a coop' were the exact words she used."

They laughed, though Emily, feeling that her sister would also interpret that phrase as 'on the way to the stew pot', hurried to add, "I think I'll send Mattie across with the invitation."

"You're not afraid for her to...."

Emily shook her head. "It does seem I've overcome my first big fear, but I'm still trying to be cautious. So could Romeo go over with her? I'll send a note."

"On the contrary, why don't I write the note while you dress Mattie? I'll tell Mrs. Elliott that Albert will come for her at ten-thirty."

Emily watched the children cross the street and saw them admitted. After a while, the Elliott's gate reopened and Romeo peered carefully to right and left before he escorted Mattie out.

"Just look what Aunt Mary Ann sent us, Mama!" Mattie held up a bunch of spring onions, cleaned and ready for the table, and tied together with a bit of red ribbon.

Emily clapped her hands in delight. "Did you thank her?"

It was Romeo who replied, "She did--even made a curtsy! Here's something else, too," He handed over a parcel in brown paper that had a faint odor. Tea! Real tea! "Mrs. Elliott said to tell Papa that she would be ready at ten-thirty," Romeo concluded.

When the children took the gifts to the kitchen, they were received with delight.

"Law!" cried Sophronia. "A bite a' onions! How many is it?"

Elizabeth counted. "Over twenty! Everyone can have one! Please brew some of the tea for dinner, too, Aunt Sophia!"

Albert had the boys moving chairs from all over the house into the parlor. On a table in front of the mantel he placed the Bible open at one of the passages he had selected. The hymns he left to Elizabeth and Emily, both of whom loved to sing.

Standing in the hall, Albert greeted everyone who came. It was evident that all had dressed in their best: a few Methodists, and several Baptists, and at least one good Irish Catholic--assembled to seek God's blessings.

Everyone's here, thought Emily, except my dear William, who is so far away...yet somehow present in his beautiful and mysterious painting that looks down on us from above the mantel!

She bowed her head, prayed earnestly for his safety, and held his image close to her heart as Albert read passages from the Bible, and they all sang the old hymns they knew from memory.

The prayer that Sophronia raised in closing the service was so heartfelt and trusting that it seemed to undergird them all...and to prepare them to face yet another week of the awful uncertainty that gripped their lives.

Chapter Eight

April 16, 1862

It was Wednesday morning when Emily again felt an overpowering urge to get out of the house. "I can stand being inside, if that choice has been mine," she said to Elizabeth. "Otherwise, I just won't endure it!"

"Seems to me you've been out quite a bit. You've been to Mrs. Elliott's and over to the Bolton's to take Addie Virginia's dress to her. Where are you headed now?" asked her sister.

Emily was tying on her bonnet. "I'm going to Mary Elizabeth's to see if she's heard from Richard. I'm anxious about William!"

Elizabeth nodded. "Now that there's no mail, and no newspaper, since The Democrat ceased publishing when Withers Clay left town the night the Federals took over--our world seems so shrunken. It's depressing!" She paused. "Are you taking Mattie with you?"

"Yes, and Bessie, too...if you'll trust me."

"Of course, I trust you! However could you get that idea?"

The sentry stationed on the opposite side of Holmes did not so much as glance their way, when they started toward town.

"Mama, I wish we could go to the Big Spring," begged Mattie.

Bessie bounced up and down. "Oh, let's, Aunt Emily!"

But Emily judged that area out-of-bounds now, probably unsafe. "Another time...when we have a man with us."

It was quiet; even the blacksmith's forge appeared to be cold. But when they turned left at Easley's corner and came in sight of the depot area, there was activity and Blue Coats visible. Emily hurried the girls along, thankful that Mary's house was near.

Their arrival was a surprise. Alonzo sketched a salute when he saw them at the door. "I'm on guard at present," he said, with a grin. "Grandpa Tinable's restin'. Mama feels the need to keep one of us on watch, for we don't know who might try to get in!"

Hearing their voices, Mary came into the parlor with her arms stretched wide. "Oh, Emily! I'm glad to see you and the girls! I've been worried every minute. Of course, Albert's so kind to check on us. He even sent word about the flour, and Alonzo got some. It's candles we're short of now!"

Emily gave her a hug, while the little girls offered cheeks to be kissed. "Candles? Why, we may have extras! If we do, I'll send some by Lucius. Albert has loaned the boy to us as home guard and helper." She handed Mary a small package of dried peaches.

"Peaches!" cried her sister-in-law. "What a treat! I'll see if Laola can manage to make us a pie!" Raised eyebrows seemed to indicate considerable doubt as to what her servant might do.

Loud giggling came from the children's room adjoining, where Bessie and Mattie were being received. Mary rose to quiet things, but Emily protested, "Do let them laugh, Mary dear! For this awful war is depriving our children of so much!"

Tears came to Mary's eyes. Although she quickly brought out her handkerchief, Emily had seen enough to cause her own sorrow to thrust to the surface. Soon they were crying together, two miserable and frightened women who had seen their husbands leave for a war they scarcely understood.

"If only I could get word from Richard!" Mary whispered.

Emily tried to collect herself. "I would so like to know if my William is having to fight with a stick, instead of a gun!"

Mary wiped away her tears and said, "Neither of us ever dreamt we would have to endure anything like this, did we?"

Shaking her head, Emily quickly changed the subject. "Lately, I've starting teaching the young ones at our house to print their letters-- and to sing a tune." She laughed. "The girls love to sing, but Archie simply detests it!"

"Bless his heart!" said Mary. "Grandpa told us how fascinated he became with the tin shop, the day they visited it."

"Oh, yes!" agreed Emily. "Tin being cut, or iron shaped on the blacksmith's forge are his interests--also, my sewing machine."

"How are you liking it?" Mary asked.

"It's the greatest time-saver! I get along twice as fast! Most of my work right now is in reducing the yardage in skirts to make children's clothes from the savings. Have you some old thing that could be made over...maybe get Laura Ann a dress?"

Mary thought for a minute. "I do indeed: an old lawn dress far too tight in the bodice. In fact, the whole dress could be ripped up and made into things for Kate and Laura Ann."

When Emily insisted, the dress was produced; measurements were taken and carefully noted down. As the little girls ran from the room, giggling at the prospect of new dresses, Emily had a sudden idea. "Mary, do let me take Kate home with us for a few days. It would be such a treat for our girls. Mattie's in my room now, and Kate could sleep with Bessie. And she could come to our school!"

Mary's face glowed with pleasure. "Oh, Emily! What a joy that will be for Kate! I'll go right now and get her ready."

As her sister-in-law left the room, Emily moved to the hall to ask Alonzo, "You're not working for Mr. Heap?"

He shook his head. "No! Mr. Heap's afraid that if the Yankees find him makin' tin things, they'll take over his shop. Anyway, Mama needs me here, and I'm sure that's what Papa would want."

Emily placed her hand on his shoulder. "Listen, Alonzo, if the soldiers bother your mother, or you need help of any kind, I want you to promise me that you will slip through the backyards toward our house and let us know. Promise?"

He nodded. "Thank you, Aunt Emily. I do promise!"

Just then, Mary Josephine came from the back to say, "Aunt Emily, I wish we could offer you a cup of tea...but we just don't have it. Could you drink some buttermilk?"

"No, thank you." Emily placed her arm about the thin frame and said, "You are growing fast? Do you hate being cooped up?"

"I don't mind. There's so much to do that I don't have time to miss going out."

Saddened to see this child of eight too involved in adult problems,

Emily said, "Let me take your measurements, too, and make you a dress from some material Aunt Susan Knox gave me."

Delight flooded the little face as she whispered shyly, "Thank you, Aunt Emily! Mama doesn't feel much like sewin' right now."

Just then, Kate came running out to hug her aunt. "Mama has me ready, Aunt Emily. Thank you for asking me."

Emily hugged her and took her bundle. "Is the dress I'm to rip up in here?" she asked Mary.

Mary nodded, as she drew Kate aside for a goodbye kiss.

"I'm sorry to see that cows can no longer enjoy that wonderful pasture opposite," Emily said to Alonzo, as they were leaving.

He shook his head. "We're all afraid to show our cows!"

What a sad situation we are in, thought Emily. Afraid to stick our heads outside! Afraid of starving! Dreading what awful thing may happen next! Mind astray, she moved forward along the path.

"Good day!" A man's voice brought her back to reality.

Mattie and Bessie had paused to curtsy, while Kate stood watching them in surprise.

Raising her eyes, Emily saw it was the Yankee officer who had searched their home the previous week.

When she smiled and nodded, he paused and, with a teasing glint in his eyes, asked, "Did your baby develop measles?"

Emily felt shame wash over her. He knew she had been shamming!

Oh, well! she thought, and looked him straight in the eyes. "No, thank goodness! That was a false alarm."

"I'm glad," said the officer. Then with a grin, he touched his cap and turned, sending one low word floating back, "Charming!"

The girls moved on, and Emily followed.

"Who was that, Mattie?" asked Kate curiously. "Mama told me to pass on by those Yankees without speakin'!"

"Bessie and I always curtsy to them. We like their coats!"

Emily laughed to herself. So that was it! But she hastened to explain, "Kate, dear, that was the officer who came to search our house. He was just as nice as he could be about it, and we were grateful."

"Oh," said Kate. "Well, we had three at our house--and none of them were nice. Mama said they poked around and stared at things, like a bunch of idiots. Of course, Grandpa was there. And he has a gun, if he has to use it."

Hastily, Emily interrupted, "Don't tell anybody about the gun, Kate! Don't even mention it...and you girls forget about it. Your mama, or your grandpa, might get in trouble, if it were known."

Kate clapped her hand over her mouth. "I know. Mama told me, but I just forgot." She looked up at Emily. "Of course, Grandpa has it hid away. None of us know where."

Emily smiled at her little niece and drew her back to walk beside her. "You are growing, Kate. You seem a bit taller than Mattie. We'll measure you both after lessons in the morning."

Kate looked up eagerly. "I want to learn to write all of those letters. I only know a few that Josephine showed me. Mama let me bring along an old slate an' pencil."

Uncertainty had eased enough for gardening to be resumed, with both Lucius and Archie welcomed to the group. Under the guidance of Uncle Pompous, the plot of ground was showing promise. It had that morning produced a bunch of onions that Sophronia termed as, "Fit fer anybody's table!"

"'Nother week an' we'll have turnip greens," promised Pompous proudly. "But a good soakin' rain'd help."

Archie, whose assignment had been to train pea vines up sticks tied upright to the rail fence, said eagerly, "Little pods are on the vines...and if we don't get rain soon, I'm going to take them some water from the well!"

Edward, who had hated the garden so fiercely at first, was now anxious for it to make its workers proud. "Wait till you see our radishes! And the beets!"

"The green tops a' beets is good eatin', too," Sophronia told them. "But what we needin' most is some cornmeal to make bread, fer it corn bread what dress up vegetables best!"

Everyone agreed. But meal--or even dried corn--was unavailable in town. Stores had none; farmers were afraid to come in for fear their wagons and produce would be taken by the soldiers. Then, of course, nothing was shipped on the railroad for the town's use.

It was Lucius who hit on an idea. He expressed it to Romeo one afternoon while on guard at the front door. "Tyler's Grist Mill's just no ways away--between Pulaski Pike and where Pinhook curves around."

"I know that, Lucius! It's been there for years!"

"Well, I could wade across the creek while it's low, and not let that sentry on the bridge see me, and get us some meal!"

"That's a good way to get shot!" warned Romeo in a voice loud enough to carry into the sitting room where Emily was busy at the sewing machine. She rose immediately and stepped into the hall to ask, "What's a good way to get shot?"

Both were silent long enough to convince her that their reply, whatever it was going to be, would not be the whole truth.

Lucius seemed stricken dumb, but Romeo came up with a story he told with some conviction, about two boys from Mill Street who had crossed the tracks. "We watched them from the garden."

"Too risky!" was Emily's mild comment, though she doubted the tale was true. "We're not supposed to go beyond the city limits unless we get permission from General Mitchel. Albert thinks a provost marshal soon may be granting passes. If so, I hope Alvah or Edward can come from Maysville to say they're all right!"

Romeo turned to her, concerned. He adored his Babcock uncles, who came to see their sisters whenever they were in town. Edward, their older brother, was a trusted employee of William Stewart, a large landowner in the Brownsboro-Maysville area. Stewart owned a cotton gin on the Deposit Road, and also a tannery.

"I wager Alvah will get here to see you soon, no matter what!" Romeo stated with certainty.

Emily recognized the truth of that. For their younger brother, Alvah, had never been backward about taking risks. "I do pray he won't try it right now!" she said.

"I venture it's not hard to slip into town from the east, down the mountain slopes," Lucius said. "It's wooded all the way."

Shaking her head, Emily went back to the sewing machine, where she was busy completing alterations on the Beeman girls' dresses.

She was anxious to finish the job and collect her charges.

Kate's visit was a great success. She happily joined in school each morning with Mattie, Bessie, and Magdalena. Archie, too, was released from his gardening duties for one hour. And, much to the children's delight, Emily also had invited Addie Virginia.

She came for the first time on Thursday, wearing her new dress and with a slate in one hand and a single pink rose in the other. "Ma sent you this rose, Miss Emily," she said. "It's off the bush she brought from Georgia. And look! Ma's lettin' me use her slate from when she was a little girl!"

Magdalena promptly raised her slate. "Miss Em'ly give me mine an' a pencil. They's the proudest things I own!"

Mattie offered her stool to Addie Virginia, saying, "Just rest your slate on your lap. I'm used to writing on the floor."

A review was necessary for the benefit of the new students. It was a delight for Emily to see how eagerly everyone tried to help the newcomers. Addie Virginia received a variety of advice on how to make her A, but she learned fast and soon had her slate almost covered with wobbly efforts at several other letters.

Although Kate already knew some letters, her big K was new for everyone.

Finally, Emily said, "Spelling is over. Let's sing now!"

Archie jumped up in such a hurry that he tripped over Bessie's feet and fell headlong into Magdalena's lap.

"Boy!" she warned. "Watch where you go! When you hears anybody say 'sing', you act like somethin' wild after you."

"I'm busy!" he called, straightening himself at the door. "The pea pods need watering, or they'll wither up and die!"

Addie Virginia rose at once. "I can help carry water. I water Ma's rose bush every day. 'Course I don't wear my good dress."

Emily leaned over and urged the little girl to sit down. "This is something Archie wants to do on his own. He feels responsible for the pea pods. But thank you anyway, my dear!"

After they had sung do-re-me, Emily decided to teach a real song. She chose Three Blind Mice. Kate had a low voice, rich for her age, while Addie Virginia's soprano was steady and true.

Their love for that lively, old air sparkled in their singing, and soon Elizabeth and Sophronia were applauding from the door.

Another voice could also be heard: Enoch's! Emily motioned to Elizabeth to take her place as leader and hurried upstairs. "I do think you'll be a singer someday!" she said as she picked him up. His cries ceased, and he said one word, "Papa!"

But that was enough! For it brought to Emily's mind such vivid memories of William singing hymns that she could only collapse in her rocker, cradle the baby close, and try to keep her tears from dropping on his face.

It was not until Friday morning, that Emily had cause again to remember the conversation she had partly overheard between Lucius and Romeo.

As the men were hitching up Old Joe, Albert noted the overcast sky and told Uncle Pompous, "You and the boys let the cows out of the stable, one at a time, so they can nibble a bit of grass. The grass by the wellhouse looks good! But listen now! Keep a lookout every minute, at least two of you looking in different directions and if you catch sight of soldiers coming, hustle the beast back into the stable and out of sight!"

Uncle Pompous took charge, appointing Lucius and Romeo to look during the first hour. "Then Edward an' me'll take over." A quick glance skyward and he continued, "It's gonna pour down 'fore the mornin's over. My ol' bones am tellin' me fer sure!"

Archie, busy carrying water to the pea vines, looked up at the sky briefly, but kept right on with his chore, apparently in disbelief of any messages sent by aching bones.

Eventually, Uncle Pompous declared the hour assigned to Lucius and Romeo as up. Lulu Belle was led into the stable and Fire Fly ushered out to the feast. Then the herdsmen changed.

A few minutes later, Addie Virginia crossed Mill Street, slate and pencil in one hand and a large black umbrella clutched in the other. In the kitchen, she announced, "I brought Pa's umbrella to shade my slate in case it's pourin' when I go back. Ma liked all my letters so much I don't want a one to slide off in the rain!"

As Emily met her in the hall, Addie Virginia glanced at her to ask, "Where's Romeo and Lucius goin'?"

Puzzled, Emily shook her head.

"I seen 'em runnin' across those fields where you used to take Lulu Belle to eat grass. They were headin' to the rail tracks for sure! An' there's Blue Coats over there! Those boys should've had me go 'long to help 'em, Miss Emily!"

Emily's heart gave a great lurch as pieces in her memory began to fit together. She gave Addie Virginia a hug and whispered, "Oh thank you for telling me! Please don't mention this to anyone, for I'm going right now to see about it!"

In the schoolroom, she said, "This is review day. Each of you teach Kate and Addie Virginia more of the letters you know. I'll ask Magdalena to keep order."

Back in the hall, she hesitated. What to do? Tell Elizabeth? Try to catch up with the boys? That might mean crossing Pinhook, for she was sure now that they were headed for Tyler's Mill in hopes of buying meal. Lucius probably had a little money.

She reached the kitchen without deciding.

"Whar's Romeo?" inquired Sophronia, busy at the churn. "Miss 'Lizbeth done give him this chore."

"Where is Elizabeth?" asked Emily, in turn.

"She got that head pain jes a mite. An' I tell her if she res' upstairs fer a bit, maybe it go way."

Emily sighed. It was best not to bother Elizabeth...but she'd have to tell somebody! And who else but Aunt Sophia, steady as a rock. So she tried to say calmly, "When Addie Virginia came over, she saw Lucius and Romeo heading west toward the railroad tracks. I think they're going to try to get some meal from Tyler's Mill!"

Sophronia flung up her hands and cried, "Lawd, save us!"

"Now listen, Aunt Sophia! I don't want you to say a word about this. Of course you can tell Elizabeth, if she comes down feeling better. But please don't tell Edward or the children!" Reaching up, she took down the big shawl they kept at the kitchen door and draped it over her head. "I'm going after them!"

105

"Oh, no, Miss Em'ly!"

"Don't worry! I'll take care." She was removing her hoopskirt. Motioning to it, she said, "Please hide this, Aunt Sophia!"

In order to keep out of sight of the herdsmen, Emily went east and around the house. Once out the gate, she ran west on Holmes, feeling sure that she would not be recognized under the shawl.

Turning north on Spragin's Alley and cutting across the fields toward the northwest, she was soon in sight of the tracks. Hidden by a clump of bushes, she peeped out. There was no one in sight!

The railroad embankment was steep, but, by raising her skirts, she managed to cross. Now she was on open ground where any sentry might spot her. I'd best try to walk along casually, she thought, and not look like I'm trying to flee the town.

At last she reached the stream only to find that the banks had been gouged deep by unnumbered years of floods sweeping down from north of town and were now too steep for her to descend. Tears of frustration came as she saw the shallow creek below. I could wade it so easily, she thought, if only I could get down there!

On the far side of the creek, a little to the north, she could see the mill with its huge wheel that was turned by water flowing through the mill race. The wheel was still: possibly for lack of water to turn it, but probably for lack of corn to grind.

But where were the boys? Not a human being seemed to be moving in the vicinity of the mill. Could I be wrong? she wondered in consternation. Why was I so sure the boys were headed here? Would they have crossed the creek when the wheel was not turning?

She waited, shading her eyes to see in that direction. Clouds were lowering, and a stiff wind suddenly came from the northwest! Just as it whipped the shawl from her head, she glimpsed the boys coming around from the west side of the mill. They were examining it from all angles, probably wondering why it wasn't running.

Just as she raised her arm to wave, she saw a blue-coated sentry no more than ten feet away. Quickly, she moved her arm to grasp the shawl instead of waving.

The sentry pointed at the sky. "It's going to start raining in a minute, ma'am. What are you a-doing out here?"

Her heart sank, while her mind raced. In seconds it gave her a glimpse of a jail cell, of Albert's shocked face, her pupils with their mouths agape, and in a final frame one word..."Blackberry"! For that word she gave thanks, and raising her eyes, tear-filled, she said to the sentry, "It's my nephew! Lost again! Archie is not seven yet, but he's got a mind for venturing!"

To her surprise, the sentry smiled slightly. "Ma'am, I had one that was the same way. Still is, now that he's a man grown!"

She nodded. "I was peering over to see if he could have fallen down in there, but I think not!" She turned. "If you're headed back toward the bridge, could I follow along? Just to be sure he's not hiding down that way."

"Well," said the sentry, "you're beyond the town limits, but I reckon under the circumstances..."

"Thank you," she said, and gave him her sweetest smile. The moment he turned, she darted a glance over her shoulder. The boys stood on the opposite bank, their mouths open in horror. At least the sentry had not seen them! Swiftly, she motioned up towards the sky, down toward the creek, and then beckoned.

At that moment, a gust of wind came whirling from the north to doff the sentry's cap and send it over into some bushes up ahead. He scrambled in to get it.

While this was going on, the boys waded the creek, and started up the bank. But Emily raised her hand to hold them back. As a distraction, she let her shawl flap in the wind, but the sentry was still trying to rescue his cap.

Turning, she motioned. Romeo, first up the bank, was told, "Go home the way you came. Run! Tell Aunt Sophia to bring Archie down Holmes toward the bridge. No one else knows about this!"

Hurriedly, she swung around, let the shawl billow, and ran after the sentry. "Wait for me!" she cried. "The wind almost got my shawl!"

He laughed. "My cap, too!" And jammed it on his head just as the clouds released their downpour.

By the time they reached the bridge, Emily was wetter than she had ever been in her life. Her hair had fallen down and her skirt was soaked. "Wait till I find my nephew!" she shouted. "He's going to rue this day!"

"I wager he will!" replied the sentry. "I'd better see you get to your door."

There was nothing to do but trudge on ahead, hoping that Romeo had understood her message. "I'm nearly fagged out," she told the sentry, as she walked slower and slower.

They were in front of Rison's before she saw Aunt Sophia start their way. She was ushering Archie with a firm grip on his arm.

Emily began with the best threats she could think of and ended with, "and I'm going to see that you don't get any dinner, or any supper either!..."

"It's boys like you that gets into trouble," the sentry added sternly, as water dripped from his cap. "Believe me, for I know! Don't let me hear of you giving your aunt here any more trouble!"

Not understanding such persecution, Archie began to cry.

"An' I don't wanta hear any that racket from you, boy!" Aunt Sophia warned. "It all be you fault!"

At that the wails increased mightily.

Emily turned to the sentry. "You've been kind," she said. "And if you don't mind going around to the back with us, we'll be glad to give you a cup of hot soup!"

But he shook his head. "I better not. It'd be worth my life if I left my post, and the lieutenant found out!"

"Stop in another time then," urged Emily.

Saluting sharply, the sentry turned and ran for the bridge.

As they hurried around the east side of the house, Emily tried to comfort Archie. "Hush now! Please! None of it was your fault!"

Once on the porch, they squeezed all the water they could from their clothes. "We'll hang that wet shawl here," Sophronia said, pegging it to the porch line. "You all go in my room, Miss Em'ly, an' I'll fetch in some towels an' dry things. Miss 'Lizbeth still sleepin'."

"Thank goodness for that," Emily said, guiding Archie into the little back room used by Aunt Sophia. There, she gave him another hug and tried to explain what had happened. "Now, Archie, I don't want you talking about this, please! It's just between us! Seems that Lucius and Romeo hoped they could get some cornmeal at the grist mill Mr. Tyler runs across the creek. They didn't tell us they were going, but I found out and went after them. That is how the sentry caught me, and I had to think up a good excuse. I knew he might do something awful to Lucius and Romeo...who should have known better...but he wouldn't hurt you. And he didn't! You saved our necks, and I thank you."

Archie sniffed. "Where's Romeo and Lucius now?"

"I don't know at the moment. But they got back safely, and I'm going to see that they thank you properly. But, Archie, if you do tell anybody else about this, it will only cause trouble. Lucius and Romeo thought they were doing a brave thing. But they should have asked a grownup first!"

When Sophia came in with a clean shirt for Archie, Emily dried his hair. "Run up and comb your hair now," she told him, "and you can go back in the schoolroom. I'll be along in a minute."

As the door closed after Archie, Sophronia whispered. "Pompous say those boys out there in he cabin, Miss Em'ly. He got a fire goin' to dry 'em off! An' when I pass Miss 'Lizbeth room, to fetch you some dry things, she was startin' to get up!"

Swiftly, Emily toweled and rebraided her hair, and put on what clothes Aunt Sophia had brought. It seemed she had been away from the schoolroom for hours, but it had probably been less than half an hour. As Addie Virginia caught her eye, she smiled and nodded in return. Bless the child! she thought. I will start her another dress this very day!

They were all working away on a word to surprise her. The word was cat, spelled KAT. Thinking what a confusing language English is, she set about correcting their spelling. "I like it better as you have it with a K," she told them, "for it makes the word look more mysterious, like a cat is. But it's really spelled with C!"

Elizabeth was standing at the door.

"Come in, Sister," invited Emily. "I want the children to show you what they've accomplished today."

Slates were held up, explained, and admired.

"Can we sing Three Blind Mice?" Bessie asked.

As Emily said, "All stand!" she was pleased to see Archie rise with the others. At first he sang tentatively, but soon, joining in the fun of the song, he forgot himself and sang out freely.

"Tomorrow is Saturday," Emily announced when the song ended, "but we'll have school anyway, so that Kate can have one more day with us. It has been nice to have her and I hope she comes back."

As Addie Virginia was getting ready to leave, Emily gave her a big hug and whispered, "Bless you! Don't tell anyone, but I got the boys back without harm. They went across the creek, thinking they could surprise us with some meal!"

"Pa says that mill ain't got a bit of corn to grind now!" the little girl whispered back, "but if I hear that its wheel's turnin', I'll let you know."

Sophronia went to the east porch to raise the big umbrella for Addie Virginia. Emily watched as she crossed the street, holding her precious slate safely out of the rain.

In the kitchen, Elizabeth was expressing surprise at the rain. "I am so thankful!" she murmured. "For it's saved our garden!"

So am I thankful!" echoed Emily from the door. For she knew it had been the wind and rain--coming just when it did!--that had sent them all safely home!

Chapter Nine

April 18, 1862

Loud knocking on the east door roused all the adults! It even woke Emily, off in the east front bedroom upstairs.

What time is it? she wondered, as she hastily donned a wrapper and ran into the hall. Surely no more than ten o'clock! The need to save candles had lately sent them all to bed soon after dark.

Downstairs, she could hear stirring and Sophronia's, "Law, Mr. Albert! If it's them Blue Bellies, I'm gettin' ma stick!"

"Don't be alarmed, Aunt Sophia. I'll see who it is right now!" came Albert's voice, calm and steady as always.

All kinds of visions raced through Emily's mind. Was the Union Army making night inspections now, or could there be a fire! Heavens! Surely they weren't burning the town!

Now another voice joined in--a pleasant voice, and recognized! "Alvah! Alvah Babcock!" In a few minutes she was downstairs to be enveloped in his great hug. Tears of joy came at the sight of this very special younger brother.

"I can't believe it!" Elizabeth added her welcome. "You are a sight for sore eyes!"

Alvah laughed, a happy sound. "Sorry to disturb your slumbers, but t'was the only chance I had. Edward wanted to come along, but he just couldn't. Mr. Stewart depends on him so, what with things being so unsettled." A grim expression quickly replaced the smile on his face. "Unsettled isn't the word! It's bad times over those mountains! Hard to believe all the loss and suffering that Union soldiers have brought on our neighbors, mostly poor folks who had no say in what's going on."

111

"You're right, Alvah," agreed Albert. "These are awful times we're in!"

Aunt Sophia's low voice melted into the silence that followed, "We do be needin' the Lawd to show us the way out."

Alvah said, "Amen! Aunt Sophia," and turned to hug her.

"Law, Mr. Alvah! You done broke ma ribs!"

He laughed. "I brought you something I hope you'll like."

Aunt Sophia said, "If t'ain't gold, I prays we can eat it!"

"It's sure not gold!" He turned back to the side porch. "Will you give me a hand, Albert?"

When they returned, each bearing a sack over his shoulder, Albert said, "We were all wishing for cornmeal. Here it is!"

"Meal!" The shout reverberated around the kitchen.

"Must be near two bushels!" Aunt Sophia marveled. "You's wrong this time, Mr. Alvah...that am GOLD to this fam'bly!"

That wasn't all! There were sides of bacon, besides a ham, in the sack. "And here's some dried butter beans," added Alvah.

"However did you bring all of that?" asked Elizabeth.

"Well, I was lucky."

Albert spoke up. "Why don't we all sit down while you tell us? Aunt Sophia, is there any of your peach pie left? And what about a cup of coffee for Alvah?"

While she bustled around, Alvah continued, "A fellow who works at the tannery got word that his folks were near starving! Seems they don't have much of a place down on Triana Road."

"Oh! That must have upset him terribly!" said Elizabeth.

"It did. 'Specially since he's the only son left, his brothers all gone to fight. So he was fixing to walk across the mountains, carrying a sack of meal and some bacon on his shoulders, when his plans came to the attention of Mr. Stewart--that good man (for he is solid sterling!) up and loaned one of his carts and a mule!"

"What a kind gentleman!" Emily could not help interrupting.

"He is that, Sister! Anyway, that's where I came in, for I saw no reason to take all that risk with the cart half-loaded, when I knew you must be suffering for edibles. I wish I could have found more, but folks are holding on to what they've got hidden away."

112

"How was the journey? What road did you take?" asked Albert.

"We came by that old road from Maysville and straight through the Gap. Jim knew some byways--rough going, but less traveled. To be on the safe side, we had to pull off time and again!" He laughed. "Once, it was a near thing, for we were almost hanging off the cliff edge while Blue Coats passed and passed. Luckily, our old mule never so much as twitched his ears! Of course, those passers couldn't have heard much over their own racket!"

"What would have happened had they found you?" asked Emily.

"Most likely they'd have taken what we had: cart, supplies, even our mule! They don't call it thievery, but it is!"

Albert nodded. "Those that stole one of my mules from the shop sure fall in that class! But how long did the trip take?"

"Nearly two days. We'd hoped to make it in one, but were less than halfway when darkness got us last night. All we could do was pull off the road. We had food and water, so we climbed into the cart for the night...sort-of a squeeze, but snakes are out this time of year, and they're nearly as bad as the Federals!"

"Did you get rained on?" asked Emily, recalling the downpour.

"That we did! We pulled off again, checked our tarp to be sure everything was covered in the cart, and, since it was daylight, crawled underneath to wait out the storm. A blessing, that rain was to the poor farmers needing it so bad!"

"Amen!" said Albert. "Our garden was wanting some!"

"We could have come on in town late this afternoon, but seemed best to chance it after dark," continued Alvah. "Besides, we had no idea how many patrols were around the edge of town. As it was, we had to draw off plenty, or I wouldn't have got here so late!"

"I hope your friend makes it home safely," said Elizabeth.

"Oh, he will! Jim's a right cagey fellow! Knows some byways to get to the Triana Road." He grinned at his older sister. "This is real coffee! If I'd known you were living so high, don't guess I'd have bothered with such common things as meal and bacon."

A chorus of explanations greeted that remark. And after Alvah had heard how Littleton Figg got the coffee...and about the theft of Barnabas, Albert suggested bed. "Due to dependence on candles, our

113

working hours are dawn to dark." He rose. "I'll take you back to sleep in the house behind. When you mention the word MEAL, the men will welcome you with open arms!"

"How long can you stay?" asked Emily, hoping for several days.

"Until Jim gets back. Probably two days. I have a long list of things to try to find in town for Mr. Stewart." He turned to grin at Aunt Sophia. "You're still the best cook I know!"

Kate's visit had been a great success and treat for all of the children. She was to leave Saturday after school, with Elizabeth as escort.

"I'm so glad you're going!" Emily spoke from her chair at the sewing machine. "I guess Alvah's still resting?"

Elizabeth smiled. "He just came in, and Aunt Sophia's feeding him batter cakes and molasses, some freshly cooked slices of side meat, and another cup of coffee. Lucius and Romeo are hanging on every word he has to say!" She paused. "Alvah's going up to the Marble Yard for a while before he starts on Mr. Stewart's list."

Emily wondered if Mr. Stewart knew how scarce and costly those things would be! A sound in the hall interrupted her thoughts.

Mattie's voice drifted in. "Before you leave, Kate, we'll all go in the parlor and look at Papa's painting."

Skirts swishing, they filed inside, leaving the door ajar.

Silence for a while; then Addie Virginia's light treble, "That is a pretty picture! Where did your papa get it, Mattie?"

"Why, he painted it himself!" the answer came in a chorus.

"Oh!" marveled Addie Virginia. "He's a good painter!"

Kate spoke up, "Uncle William is a real artist! My papa always said so."

"What's that Indian doing?" Addie Virginia asked curiously. "Is there another side to that lake? I can't see it."

"The Indian's all ready to paddle his canoe," Bessie answered this time. "See, he's got his paddle raised to dip in the water!"

Mattie took it up. "And the other side of the lake's where war is-- so Papa said. It's a long ways away--farther than Athens!"

"Lots farther!" added Kate. "Papa wrote us that it was all the way over in Mississippi! I guess that's a long ways."

Skirts were swishing through the doorway; and the door closed.

"Can I see that picture again some other time, Mattie?" Addie asked. "I liked it! If I had a boat, I'd go out on that lake!"

Emily sighed and tried desperately to bring William's face to mind. Oh, my dear! she thought. We all love and cherish your fine painting, but it's you we need here with us now!

When Emily stepped into the hall to tell Kate goodbye, she saw that Elizabeth had a little package. "It's candles for Mary," her sister said. "For I realize how awful it would be to have a child sick in the night and not a single candle to light!"

As Emily turned from the front door, Alvah was coming down the hall. "Come in and see my new sewing machine!" she invited.

"That's a treasure sure enough!" he remarked, after he had examined it closely. "Ed'll be glad to hear you've got one. He told me about Mrs. Stewart's machine and how fast it sews!"

Emily snipped the thread, released the material, and turned to him with a smile. "The Stewarts must be nice people!"

He nodded as he dropped into the nearest chair. "They do think the world of Ed, too. Mr. Stewart trusts him to help with all his affairs at the tanyard. He was so glad to get a man with some education." He paused. "But how about you, Sis? I know it was bad to see Bill go off like that--and everything so uncertain!"

Emily nodded, not trusting herself to speak for a moment. But finally, she said, "It was--and is!--awful, Alvah. I try to keep busy, give thanks for our children, and trust William is safe."

Wordlessly, he got up to kiss her on the cheek. "Ed and I pray for Bill. It's a terrible time--and who knows what is to come? As you say, we just have to trust." He moved toward the door. "Well, guess I'd better get started looking for those things Mr. Stewart is needing--and the things Mrs. Stewart is wanting!" He laughed.

"They may be disappointed!" she warned. "And Alvah, don't forget to drop in on Mrs. Elliott for a minute."

Alvah's visit was all too short. He spent most of Saturday in an almost fruitless effort to find things for the Stewarts. "Sad tales is mostly what I heard!" he told them at supper that night. "Of course,

I'm not much surprised. But what really got to me was the sight of Blue Coats everywhere about the town. Just does not seem right! Of course, I guess I shouldn't be saying it, being as I'm from New York myself, but I'm not liking the sight of them!"

"You're needing to be on your guard downtown," remarked James Conway. "Those lads think they're after owning the whole town and will as soon push you off the pathway as not! There've been times when I could scarcely refrain from laying me out a Blue Coat!"

"It's hard to take," agreed Albert, "but we try not to offend them. It's not like you can go to an officer and complain!"

"Why not?" asked Elizabeth. "I thought an officer was there to keep his troops under control!"

Albert sighed. "Depends a lot on the general, I guess. In this case, I hear that Mitchel permits his troops to rampage around the country, stealing and terrorizing folks."

"While I was downtown, I heard the Confederates had Nashville! Wonder if it's true?" Alvah said, taking another piece of ham.

"Mary Elizabeth didn't mention it today," said Elizabeth. "She may not have heard. Her folks, the Stainbacks, are there, and she was very concerned when the Union Army first captured the city."

"She's probably heard by now," Albert said. "Mr. Tinable gets around and knows what's going on, I'm sure of that!"

"It must be awful to live in a city with a battle being fought all around you!" Emily said thoughtfully. "I guess we are lucky, after all." Suddenly, she smiled. "Elizabeth, your bread is good, as always!"

Her sister laughed. "Thanks go to Alvah for the meal."

"And the ham!" came from several throats.

"Thanks to Mr. Stewart, too," said Elizabeth. "I'm sending him a letter by Alvah; Emily and I are both writing to Edward."

Alvah had the letters in his pocket when Jim came, after dusk. With the cart lightened of its load--except for the few purchases for the Stewarts--they expected to return in one day.

"I'll see you again, soon as I get the chance," he promised as he gave his sisters a final hug. "May the times be better soon!"

Better times were what they prayed for--and if those could not be, then strength was sought to help them endure what must come.

Emily had resolved to work at her dressmaking more regularly, but in spite of all efforts, sewing jobs continued to accumulate, and even overflowed to a small table brought in by Elizabeth.

"I am so embarrassed, Sister, because of the clutter I've made in this room," Emily confessed. "It is such a pleasant sitting room for all your family to enjoy--and I am filling it up!"

Elizabeth smiled from her rocker where she was knitting socks, a type of handwork she preferred and one that lately was becoming more and more necessary. "It doesn't matter about clutter--that's what a sitting room's for. Whenever we have company who are too highfalutin for ordinary rooms, we'll use the parlor!"

"Just seems I can't catch up!" Emily continued. "Ripping takes so long, and pressing out the old seams; then trying to cut along the straight of used material...."

"Why don't you take an apprentice?" asked Elizabeth.

"An apprentice?" gasped Emily. "What a good idea!" She thought for a minute. "And I think I know the very person, if only she agrees...and her mother, too!"

"Who?" asked Elizabeth curiously, her needles clicking.

"Why, Susan Pollard! She's such a biddable, eager child, and I do admire her." Emily paused. "Besides, she'll be a stylish lady someday, and it would be to her advantage to learn dressmaking!"

"The very one!" cried Elizabeth. "Why don't you go on straight across the street this minute and get that settled?"

And it was settled! Almost as soon as mentioned.

Susan's face shown at the idea. "Oh, Mrs. Elliott, I'd love to learn to sew! An' to have somebody as smart as you teach me! Oh, Ma, may I?"

"I see no reason why not!" Mrs. Pollard agreed. "Soon as your chores are done for the day, you may be free to help Mrs. Elliott in whatever way she needs you." She smiled at Emily. "It's a good chance for her to learn somethin' durin' this terrible time--when she can't even go to school! Then, I have Tildie and her daughter both helping me--if they only stay!--so I won't need Susan."

"Miss Emily," Susan spoke up. "What time may I come tomorrow?"

She thought for a minute. "I believe one o'clock would be just right. You know I'm teaching a little class of beginners to learn their letters for an hour each morning, starting at nine. Maybe you'd like your little Mattie to come to that, Caledonia? She is six now, isn't she? There's no charge."

Mrs. Pollard clasped her hands in pleasure. "Yes, I would! How nice of you, Emily! There's no hope of getting her into a school any-time soon. May I send her in the morning?"

So it was arranged. The other children welcomed "Mattie P." as they decided to call her. She came in wearing the dress Emily had made from some of the width taken from one of Mrs. Pollard's summer dresses. Over this, she had on a neat white pinafore.

Pinafores are such a good idea! thought Emily. All the little girls need those to keep their dresses clean.

Mattie, acting as hostess, seated their new scholar on a stool brought from upstairs and asked if she liked to sing. "We're all learning Three Blind Mice."

Nodding, Mattie P. said, "But I can't sing like Susan!"

"That's all right," she was assured. "We're just learning!"

"Where is Addie Virginia?" asked Bessie. "She's late!"

"I expect she was delayed for some reason," replied Emily, who had never known Addie Virginia to be tardy. "Let's begin today by re-viewing. Will you show our new scholar how to make an M, please Mattie, since it's your letter, too? Then we're all going to make a B. I'm drawing it here on my slate, and you can pass it around to try on your own." Then nodding to Magdalena, she went down the hall to-ward the kitchen.

Elizabeth was examining turnip greens from a big basket at her side. Scanning them leaf-by-leaf for bugs, she pinched off stems be-fore dropping them in a dishpan for Sophronia to wash.

"Greens!" cried Emily, sniffing their pungent odor.

Elizabeth smiled. "Our first from the garden!"

"Pompous an' Edward jes brought 'em in!" Sophronia added. "An' they do say as little turnips is already formin'."

From the back door, Emily could see the two now, still back in the turnip patch at the far end of the garden. Lulu Belle was enjoying her morning feast of spring grass, while Lucius and Romeo stood guard. But Addie Virginia was nowhere to be seen!

"Mama, just look! Mattie P. has already made a nice M!" Mattie reported excitedly. "Show her your slate, Mattie P.!"

The little girl's face lit up at this praise. "It's because my sister, Susan, showed me M, but I don't know many other letters!"

"We'll learn them soon," promised Emily. "Have you all written your B?"

Slates, proudly held up for inspection, revealed the letter in all possible shapes and sizes.

"Miss Em'ly," Magdalena whispered, and when Emily turned, gestured to the door.

In the hall stood Addie Virginia. Motioning, she moved toward the front hall.

"I didn't want to upset the others, Miss Emily," the child whispered earnestly, "but there's been an old Blue Coat hangin' 'round in the alley behind your stable. I been watchin' him, is why I'm late. He tried the stable doors on the alley side!"

"My goodness!" Emily said, shocked. "With Uncle Pompous--those boys, too!--right out there. Didn't they see him?"

"No, ma'am. The back buildin' was between him and them. I was hidin' in the bushes a-watchin'. The old sneak never saw me!"

Turning, Emily said, "I'll go right out there and see!..."

But Addie Virginia caught her arm, saying, "He's gone off down Mill Street toward the railroad, but I wanted you to know!"

"Thank you, my dear," Emily gave her a swift hug. "I will warn Uncle Pompous and the boys to watch out for him." She turned to lead the way into the schoolroom. "Mattie Pollard's here today."

"This is the nicest place in the world to learn your letters, Mattie!" Addie Virginia assured the new pupil. "Why, just look at this!" She held up her slate and pointed to one corner. "That's a letter C my little brother, Charlie made. Pa was so proud that he made me promise not to rub it off. So I drawed a line 'round it!"

Everyone looked at the wobbly half moon in surprise and Archie came over to examine it more closely. "That's good, Addie! Course little boys catch on mighty quick!"

"So do little girls!" spoke up Magdalena. "An' I don't want to hear you sayin' one word 'bout boys bein' smarter!"

He looked abashed. "I didn't mean...."

"Of course you didn't," Emily backed him up. She still felt a bit guilty for having treated Archie so shabbily on the day of the storm. "Can you think of a word beginning with the letter B?"

But Archie had to shake his head.

"If you make a B, then O, then A, last a T, that spells BOAT!"

"Like the boat in Papa's picture?" asked Mattie.

All the little girls looked up to hear the answer.

"Exactly," Emily replied, as evenly as she could.

"I wants to try that word!" Magdalena set right in. "It am a long one!"

"I'm going to have a boat some day," Archie said, struggling with his slate pencil, "so I can paddle off down Pinhook Creek, and see where it goes."

"I'll go 'long with you," promised Addie Virginia.

Looking at the heads bent low over their slates as they formed this "long" word, Emily felt a special pride creep in to warm her heart. Bless them all! she thought, for they've come to mean so much to me. Reaching over, she gave Magdalena's hand a squeeze in recognition of another soul that she knew felt the same.

The afternoon sewing sessions with Susan as helper began after one o'clock. Emily was immediately pleased with the young girl's desire to learn. She was soon able to rip seams. Together they cut out a second dress for Addie Virginia and several pinafores from an old white sheet.

Elizabeth came in with her knitting. The talk was about sewing methods and the meaning of various terms, all of which Susan must learn. Finally, she was introduced to the sewing machine.

As the afternoon flew by, not once did Emily think of the Blue Coat that Addie Virginia had glimpsed skulking in the alley.

The grass on the east and west sides of the house, and also in front, was growing tall. "I would like for Magdalena to spread a quilt on the west lawn, and take the little ones out in the fresh air," Elizabeth said to Albert at breakfast next day. "But how is she to do that with the grass so long?"

"No problem to fix that," declared Albert. "The boys can bring out the sickles and cut all that area. The cut grass, when raked and dried, will make good hay. We can't afford to waste it!"

So it was decided that, as soon as the herding and garden work were done for the day, cutting could begin. "I think Mrs. Elliott will let you boys mow her front yard and rake up the clippings," Albert said. "They only have one animal to feed--not three!"

"If you begin on the west side of the house," mused Elizabeth, "then Magdalena can take the children out this very afternoon."

It was a plan welcomed by all--with the possible exception of the workers themselves, who knew they had no choice anyway. As a result, the younger children enjoyed a good outdoor frolic.

When Susan left at five o'clock, the boys had moved across to Mrs. Elliott's front lawn.

A little later, Emily found Magdalena in the kitchen preparing to feed Alvah some soft bread and milk. "You know, I think I will see if Enoch will take some of that!" she said.

So Baby Enoch had his first food from the table! Watching in fascination, Mattie cried, "He likes it, Mama! You do like it, don't you, Buddy?"

In reply, the baby opened his mouth and spit on Mattie's white pinafore, worn that day for the first time. "Oh, Buddy!" she protested, looking down at the mess.

"Never mind," Magdalena consoled her. "Jes you wait a minute an' I clean you up so you an' Bessie can have yer supper." With a glance out the window, she added, "Looks like a few draps of rain might fall. Whar's Archie?"

Elizabeth said, "I believe the boys are finishing sickling the grass at Mrs. Elliott's." She turned to Magdalena. "I'll take the baby, and you go on to the cow shed."

"Whilst you washin' you hands, I'll get the buckets ready," offered

Sophronia. "Wonder where that Pompous is?"

"I saw him down in the west end of the garden a while ago," volunteered Elizabeth.

Sophronia spoke up, "Miss Em'ly, if you can watch this supper a-cookin', I'll light the lantern an' go out with Maggie."

"No need!" Magdalena protested. "Give me the buckets. The lantern can hang on that hook inside the stable door. I reckon Uncle Pompous be 'long in a minute, an' Lulu Belle an' Fire Fly has both already started a-bawlin'!"

Emily, hurrying to clean up both Mattie and Enoch, said, "I'll be out myself in just a second!"

But Magdalena was already gone.

Untying the baby's bib, Emily said, "I'll put him in the playroom. Mattie, you can go in and watch him for a few minutes." Placing Enoch Carlton on her shoulder, she started for the hall.

And it was at that moment that Magdalena began to scream...two ...three times, with the last one cut off abruptly.

"Lawd, have mercy!" cried Sophronia, hastily shoving pots back on the stove and grabbing the butcher knife from the rack.

With Baby Alvah under one arm, Elizabeth ran to open the door.

It took only seconds for Emily to place Enoch on the hall rug, cry, "Mattie, watch your brother!" and dash out after Sophronia.

The lantern swinging on its hook, sent a grotesque shadow across the shed, where a blue-coated soldier had Magdalena flung across a pile of hay. Above the big hand clamped over her mouth to still her screams, Magdalena's eyes gleamed with terror.

At the sound of their entrance, the soldier threw them a quick glance, jerked a knife from his belt, and jeered, "You ladies try something and I'll split this pullet from stem to stern!"

Gasping, Emily turned to grip Sophronia's arm. "Don't do a thing," she whispered. "I'm going for help!" But where? The boys could never handle this! Nor could Uncle Pompous! She ran towards Mill Street. Surely some man was around. Mr. Bolton? If only the men from the shop! Dashing to the front of the house, she saw not a soul coming from town. O God, help us! she prayed urgently, as tears of fright nearly blinded her.

122

It was then she saw two Union officers. They were coming along Limberg Street at a near trot. In a few seconds, she was standing in front of them, not even aware of how she got there. "Help us!" her voiced cracked, "A soldier has a woman down in our cow shed, a knife at her throat!"

"That'll be the bird we're after, Ed!" cried one officer, "so toot your whistle. Show us quick, ma'am!"

While the whistle blew three times, Emily ran back through the front gate and east yard, thankful for the sound of running feet behind. All stopped at the cow shed door.

Aunt Sophia, her cheeks damp with tears, stood leaning weakly against the outside of the building.

Motioning Emily aside, the officers drew their swords and went inside.

"Well, McCuther, it looks like you got yourself in a big fix!" one officer said calmly. "If you so much as move a muscle, you're going to lose your head in one whack of my sword!" He paused, and added, "You ready with two whacks to get his feet, Ed?"

Maybe I better get them first," said Ed. "They're closer. Are you ready? Then, here goes!"

But the culprit made a lightning choice, flung his knife into the hay at one side, and scrambled to his feet. He wasn't talking and his eyes looked wild.

"March!" commanded Ed, jerking him roughly out of the shed and into the care of several waiting soldiers.

The other officer turned to Magdalena, extended his hand, and said, "I trust that scum didn't injure you, ma'am!"

Magdalena tried to smile. "No sir, not over much...but he sure scared me near to death! I thank you fer comin' when you did!" A smile widened as she added, "Miss Em'ly, it were lucky the pails was empty...or all our milk would've been spilt." She picked up a pail and prepared to sit on the milk stool. Then she thought of her hands and said, "I best go in an' wash. Some dirt has touched my hands!"

Suddenly, the officer raised his cap, laughing, "You're a calm one, ma'am! I'm glad you weren't hurt--and be sure I'm taking the source of that dirt right to the lockup!"

As Sophia went with Magdalena to the house, the other officer could be heard directing the return march of the search party. To the officer who had helped Magdalena up, Emily said, "We owe you thanks from the bottom of our hearts for your prompt help. I was nearly frantic! Besides that, I blame myself, for I heard only yesterday that a soldier was back in the alley, skulking around. But I didn't know how to report it!"

"You can tell any officer, ma'am. There's some of us usually about!"

"Won't you come in and have some supper?" Emily heard herself with some surprise, and wondered what Elizabeth would think.

But the officer raised his cap and said, "Thank you, but I'll have to see to the prisoner. Goodnight, Mrs. Elliott."

"Mrs. Elliott?" Lucius and the other boys, ready with sickles and rakes, stared at her in surprise. "How did he know your name, Aunt Emily?"

She could only shake her head and reply, "I have no idea! But he was kind, and helped us when we were truly desperate!"

"I was coming!" cried Edward earnestly. "I could have chopped that old soldier up with this sickle...in a minute or two!"

Emily sighed. A few drops of rain were falling, and, suddenly, she had had far too much of the situation they were in!

Chapter Ten

April 28, 1862

Mondays were wash days! So far as Emily knew, or could recall, all women considered this the way to start the weekly schedule of housewifely duties. Any homemaker who failed to observe wash day, preferably on Monday, but at least some day in the week, stood in danger of being thought lazy by her neighbors, who were in good position to make the judgment...for wash day produced evidence on backyard lines: clean linens and garments waving in the breeze.

At the Baker home, no evidence had waved to neighbors for over two weeks. Their washerwomen, Kianna and her daughter, Tresh, had not appeared on the scheduled day, or on any other.

"They have to walk from out on Pulaski...then cross the bridge over Pinhook Creek," Emily tried to excuse the women. "Maybe they don't dare to pass the soldier stationed there." She recalled how nice the man had been to her; but how would he treat Negroes?

"That ain't no reason a-tall!" protested Sophronia. "They has got a payin' job...an' oughta find a way to get here to do it!"

Emily shook her head. She could imagine how confusion and terror of the present situation might cloud any Negro's thinking. How sad it all is! she thought.

"If Kianna doesn't show up soon," Elizabeth said as she set the table for their early Monday morning breakfast, "we are going to do the washing ourselves. Goodness knows, we've had plenty of experience! Why, back in New York state, we knew nothing else!"

Emily agreed. "I'm ready to start any time."

"Well, whilst y'all eatin' a bite, I'll jes light a fire under the boilin' pot in the yard," offered Sophronia.

Elizabeth shook her head. "You go ahead with breakfast and eat something yourself. Uncle Pompous can do that, and I want him to graze the cows by the garden fence--away from the clotheslines."

"Then, I'll run up and fetch our dirty things...wake the girls up, too," Emily said, going briskly into the hall.

"Pile everything on the side porch," ordered Elizabeth, "where we can sort it." She turned toward the dining room. "The men can add their dirty shirts and pants to the stack."

With no laundry in town, Elizabeth had always encouraged those men Albert brought from New York to put their dirty things in with the rest of the family. It was for this reason they employed two washerwomen. It still sometimes took them two days--or three, even--to wash and iron all that had accumulated from the previous week. Many times, Kianna brought one or two more daughters (from among her seven) in order to finish more quickly.

"I be thankful iffen it's a sunny day," declared Sophronia, as she vigorously stirred the breakfast mush. "We gonna have plenty problems widout havin' to peer at the sky fer a chance of rain."

"No fear of that!" Elizabeth said, almost gaily. "Sun's coming up now." She was getting out the crock of soft soap and the long wooden paddle for stirring white clothes as they boiled in the big black-iron wash pot.

"Then you an' Miss Em'ly gonna want you sunbonnets!"

Magdalena, who had apparently suffered no lingering fears from the attack on her the previous Friday, was already out milking.

This matter-of-fact attitude on the part of the young nurse amazed Emily, in whose mind the awful episode was still vivid. As she led two sleepy little girls into the room, she thought of the scene again and asked, "Who's out there with Magdalena?"

"Pompous be!" replied Sophronia promptly. "At the shed door!"

A sudden clatter on the stairs, and Edward dashed by, calling, "I'm going to guard Magdalena!"

"Mama," inquired Mattie, her voice as near to crossness as she ever came. "Why did Bessie and I have to come downstairs so awful early? And you pulled my braid too tight. It hurts!"

"We're early because it's wash day," replied Emily, as she began to loosen Mattie's braid. "There'll be jobs for everyone."

"Where's Kianna?" asked Bessie, yawning widely.

"Looks like she can't get here," Emily said. "So we'll all get to work and do the job ourselves."

"Aren't we going to have school?" asked Mattie, concerned.

"At nine o'clock," her mother replied. "But that's three hours away. You can consider helping to wash as part of school, because it's something all little girls must learn to do."

Bessie giggled, "I think it'll be fun!" and grabbing Mattie by the hand, began singing off-key, "Wash Day! Wash Day!"

"That 'nuff of that! You sit right down here an' eat you dish a' hot mush," ordered Sophronia. "Then find you sunbonnets, 'fore you thinks a' goin' outside!" She was loading a tray with bowls of hot mush, while a platter of fried meat waited to be served. "I'se a-fixin' eggs this mornin'...got a dozen extra!"

"Two for me!" cried Romeo, leading in a sleepy Archie.

"One only!" Elizabeth called from the dining room door. "Emily and I will serve, Aunt Sophia, while you start on the eggs."

Emily lifted the heavy enamel coffeepot that she knew held the imitation brew they all hated. At least it's hot! she thought, as she went in to greet the men and fill their cups. "I hope you've all brought over your dirty things for us to wash!"

One of the men laughed, "About all we have's dirty. There's a mountain of clothes piled out there! Sorry about that."

Albert got up to peer out on the porch. He looked at Elizabeth in concern. "Don't try to do all that in one day!"

"Oh, we won't," Elizabeth assured him. "And everyone--boys and all--are going to help! Eggs this morning!...so I'm coming around to see how you want yours cooked."

There were grins and remarks, "Thank you, ma'am. You do us all proud! No man could ask for better, I do declare!"

By the time the eggs had been served, the procession from the milk shed started to file in. "Y'all jes as well leave the milk out on the well house shelf till after breakfast. Whar Edward? He needed at the table!"

"He right here, Aunt Sophia." It was Magdalena. "Been helpin' us tote the milk. Them cows give extra! It be that fresh grass!"

"They're getting good herding!" Edward stated his view.

"Good herdin' or not, you wash yer hands an' head to the table quick," ordered Sophronia. "Yer Ma's done sat down!"

"Archie's gone back to sleep," Bessie pointed to her brother, whose head was resting on the kitchen table.

With her hand on his shoulder, Magdalena said, "Wake up, boy! Aunt Sophia's cooked you a' egg. Then you gotta help wash!" Archie blinked and declared, "My pea vines need watering!"

"There'll be plenty rinse water fer that garden," Aunt Sophia told him.

Elizabeth and Emily came in from the dining room.

"Why don't you dish up your own breakfast, Aunt Sophia?" asked Emily. "You need to sit down and take your time eating. You must have been rushing around since before dawn!"

"Yes, do!" urged Elizabeth. "The men are hitching up Old Joe. I told them their dinner's ready to be put in the wagon."

"They bowls an' spoons an' bag a' corn bread's in they basket ready." Sophronia pointed to the table by the back door. "They pot a' vegetable stew am settin' on the well-house shelf. It'll be bes' iffen they heats it up good 'fore they eats it." With a mighty sigh, she eased herself into a stout chair at the table.

Emily looked at her in concern. "I want you to sit there, Aunt Sophia. I'm going up to finish getting our dirty clothes together and find my sunbonnet...also, I plan to shed all the petticoats I can and put them in the wash!"

"First, we have to get organized," Elizabeth said to the group of helpers gathered around her. "Edward, you can stir the washing in the pot." When she heard him groan, she added, "You don't have to stir every minute. Step back to cool off."

"Romeo, your job will be to fill and empty the rinse tubs. See if Pompous thinks that rinse water can go on the garden. If not, then spread it on the west yard to help the grass grow."

Her eyes fell on Bessie and Mattie. "You girls pick up all the sheets and pillow slips out of that pile on the porch. Bring them to the wash pot when needed. It holds four sheets or about ten or twelve pillow slips."

She looked at Archie for a moment. "You help Romeo draw water, and carry it to the kitchen to be heated on the stove."

"Uncle Pompous, maybe you and Lucius can move two work benches from the storage shed. Put them here close to the well house so we can place our tubs on them. Then, I'm wondering if you can't string at least two more lines from one of the back sheds to the house. We're going to be short of line space."

After thinking a moment, she continued, "Magdalena, you might sort out all colored things. Then, soon as some of the water has heated on the stove, you can start washing them in the tubs that will be here on the benches." She paused, out of breath.

"Seems to me," suggested Emily, "we'll need more tubs, to make much progress."

Elizabeth nodded. "I know. Looks like we'll have to borrow!"

"Maybe Mrs. Bolton," suggested Emily. "I'll go across and ask, and we'll need more clothes pegs, too, if we put up more line. I will try to borrow about two dozen of those."

Archie stepped out the back door just in time to go help carry the borrowed tubs.

"The water in the pot is boiling, Mama!" announced Edward.

So Elizabeth called to the girls to bring four sheets. Lugging two each, they made it to the pot in time to watch her scoop some soft soap from the crock for Edward to stir in the boiling water. "Now, we'll carefully drop in the sheets one at a time, as Edward stirs." She held up her hand in caution. "But remember! Only your Aunt Emily or I can dip these hot things from the boiling water! It is so easy to get scalded, if you aren't careful!".

Emily and Archie were walking back across Mill Street carrying some tubs between them, and were followed by Addie Virginia, with a good-sized cloth bag. "Ma said just use all these clothes pegs you need. We can tell ours, for Pa made an extra groove near that top knob!" She drew one from the bag to show this distinction.

"So clever of your pa!" Emily said, taking one to examine.

"Three more tubs!" cried Elizabeth. "Your ma was kind to lend these, Addie Virginia! I'm going to tie a little piece of rag to the handle of each by way of identification." She turned to Emily to say, "That makes seven tubs in all. We'll reserve one for here by the iron pot to drop the boiled clothes into. So, now we have two lines for colored things, with two rinse tubs per line."

Emily laughed. "I believe you've got a better setup than most laundries!"

"No!" declared Elizabeth, in exasperation, "for where are tubs to rinse the white things?"

"That's right! But why don't we get two big dish pans from the kitchen to use in one of the colored lines--those clothes are not so large," suggested Emily. "Then you'll have the larger tubs for rinsing big sheets."

"Why, sure!" agreed Elizabeth. "We'll use the clothes basket for things ready to be hung on the line."

"Where do I fit into this?" asked Lucius, grinning. "Should I bare my feet and step in the tub and tread on some of these dirty things...the men's work clothes, for instance?"

"Why, Lucius!" gasped Elizabeth. "What an idea!"

Emily laughed. "Well, Sister, that's the way it once was done! And not so long ago." She paused. "Or either women beat the dirty linens on a rock at the water's edge."

"I notice you say WOMEN!" Lucius spoke up. "I'm out of place!" Still grinning, he stepped to one side.

"None of that will get you out of work!" laughed Elizabeth, "I can see that you'll fit in perfectly washing dirty shirts!"

Lucius groaned, as he held up a dirt-streaked garment. "Looks like this shirt is ready for treading on!"

Washing went on, with Romeo and Archie kept busy drawing water for rinsing or heating on the stove. Between times, they emptied used rinse water on parts of the garden chosen by Uncle Pompous, who was as particular as ever. "There! THERE! Not whar you done dump it! No need in drownin' ever'thing."

Inside the kitchen, Sophronia had occasion for loud complaint, "You boys am jes makin' a big mess on ma kitchen floor! Here, you take this mop an' keep that sloshed-out water clean up!"

Romeo accepted the mop reluctantly, but had hardly gripped its handle before he said, "I hear babies crying upstairs!"

"Lawd-a-mercy!" moaned Sophronia. "Archie, you go out an' tell Miss Em'ly...She have to see to that baby or he raise the roof!"

By the time Emily had dressed and fed the babies, she was surprised to see that it was eight o'clock. "Oh, my!" she said. "Why didn't I cancel school today?"

"You got a hour yet!" Aunt Sophia pointed out. "Go on out, an' I watch the babies. They ain't no worry, long as Enoch not cryin' an' Alvah not backin' down them stairs like he done yes'tiddy!"

Shocked at that, Emily hustled back outside and was greeted by her sister, "Those colored things can be hung on the line. It's a little more shady over near the fence."

Emily picked up the loaded basket. "Are these shirts some of those you trod on, Lucius?"

He grinned at her. "No shirt-trodding allowed in this yard!"

Mattie and Bessie, summoned by Elizabeth, ran over to help Emily at the lines, and garments soon began to wave along them.

"Aunt Emily," said Bessie, tugging at her sleeve, "that girl's wanting to see you at the fence!"

Sure enough, there stood a tall young girl, smiling shyly.

Emily went over and said, "Good morning."

"And a good morning to you, ma'am!" came a return greeting in a soft Irish lilt. "I'm Bridgett O'Casey, myself. We be living around the corner yonder on Arms. It appears you might be needing a bit of help with your week's washing?"

Emily could not help but laugh. "It is really more like three weeks' washing!" She glanced over her shoulder. "We are needing help....There'll be ironing, too!"

"I'm more'n willing," said the girl, flicking a red pigtail over her shoulder as she hastened on, "for it's work I'm needing, to help Ma. She's bad off for money now Pa's gone."

"Oh," said Emily, not knowing whether to offer sympathy.

The young face took on a look mingling sadness and shame. "Our pa, the poor soul! It just wasn't in him to avoid a fight--so he marched to war, and it was only this last month that Ma got word: he'd died a-fighting!" She glanced away sadly before continuing, "We were all struck with the thought that it must have been some awful battle to down Pa!"

"I'm so sorry," said Emily, truly touched.

And Bessie and Mattie, both listening, declared their sorrow.

"Well, Ma said if it hadn't been the war, it'd been some other thing, for it's no lie that Pa's fighting and carousing was bound to bring him to St. Peter soon anyway!"

As Emily unlatched the gate and invited Bridgett in, she saw a look of relief sweep the young girl's face and bring a smile. "Do step this way," she said kindly. "My sister, Mrs. Baker, will see you. And this is Mattie, my daughter, and her cousin, Bessie Baker. I'm Emily Elliott."

Seeing the little girls' polite curtsies, Bridgett gave both a smile, and said, "What sweet lassies!"

Emily was not surprised to see Elizabeth accept help from this appealing young girl. She saw Bridgett had already begun on one of the washing lines. How interesting it would be, she thought, to get to know, and perhaps help, this deserving young lady!

Mattie, handing up a blue shirt and a clothes peg, whispered, "Mama, I'm going to see what this little boy at the fence wants."

Peeking under the line of wet clothes, Emily saw Mattie greet a little boy about her own age, "Hello! I remember you! Your name is Jason." Then, glancing quickly down Mill Street, she inquired, "Are your big brothers with you?"

Jason shook his head. "No. They've gone off somewhere. That's my sister Bridgett a-working over there!"

"Oh, you're Bridgett's little brother!" Mattie said, sounding pleased. "Mama, here's Jason, Bridgett's brother. I already know him. It was his big brother called you a Yankee woman that day!"

Emily smiled at Jason and said, "We're glad to have Bridgett helping us. There's an awful lot to do today."

"Ma sent her over a piece of bread, so's she wouldn't starve." He held up a thin piece wrapped in a bit of paper.

Shocked at the sight of such a small piece, Emily gazed at the little boy. "Maybe you can eat that yourself, for we are planning to ask

Bridgett to have dinner with us." She turned to Mattie and said, "I expect Jason would like a cup of milk to drink with that bread."

When Mattie was gone, Emily opened the gate. As he stepped in, he looked up at her and asked, "Be you the school-teaching lady?"

"Not really a schoolteacher," Emily told him. "I am helping a few children to learn their letters."

"I can make an O!" he said, proudly. "Addie Virginia taught me how, 'cause it be my letter."

"Of course," said Emily, not a bit surprised to hear of any of Addie Virginia's works of kindness!

Mattie moved along slowly, trying not to spill a drop of milk. "It's good!" she told Jason earnestly.

But when he had the cup in his hands, carefully held, he still did not raise it to taste. Instead, he looked up at Emily. "I was thinking," he said timidly, "if you don't care, I'd take it to my little brothers, Donny and Jim, for they be always a-crying after some milk, but Ma...."

Reaching out to close the gate, Emily took the cup and led the boy over to the back steps. "Sit right here," she urged, "and eat the bread and drink all of this milk. When you've finished, we're going to send your ma a whole bucket of milk for your family."

He looked up at her unbelieving, but Mattie sat beside him and said, "We have plenty of milk right now." She told him about the cows and promised that as soon as he had eaten, she would let him meet Fire Fly, who was contentedly munching grass near the garden fence.

Walking to where Bridgett was carefully rinsing a shirt, Emily said, "I'm so glad to meet little Jason! Mattie already knew him, but I didn't realize until now what a fine little fellow he is!"

The young girl looked up, smiling. "Ma and me think the world of Jason, Mrs. Elliott. He's the only lad I ever knew that never has a thought for his ownself. I'm thanking you for giving him a whole cup of milk. 'Tis few drops of that he ever gets!"

"He brought you some bread," Emily continued, choking back the deep concern swelling up inside her, "but I insisted he eat it...for we're expecting you to have dinner with us today--or any time you're here."

Bridgett smiled shyly. "And I be thanking you, ma'am."

Elizabeth, next to hear the story, put Lucius in charge of the boiling water, and drawing Edward aside, told him to wash his hot face and hands. "Then you can walk home with Jason, the boy there on the step with Mattie, to carry a bucket of milk to his mother, Mrs. O'Casey. Tell her we had an extra amount today and want her little children to have some of it. Also tell her that Bridgett's such good help, and we'll probably need her for several days, and will give her a good dinner each noon."

Bessie was calling from the back steps, "Aunt Emily, it's five to nine and Kate and Mattie P. are already here."

Sighing, Emily turned to Elizabeth, who was wringing hot water from a clean sheet. "I hate to leave, Sister, but I did not have the foresight to cancel school for today."

"Why, I wouldn't have consented for you to do that anyway, and you know it! What you're doing for the children is too important in my eyes. We'll work along, maybe stop to rest for a bit."

Emily smiled her thanks and turned to Mattie, "When Jason has finished, don't forget to introduce him to Fire Fly. Then as soon as Edward takes him home, you can come in to school."

Emily and the others who had been helping to wash felt a bit untidy, but had one of the best school days yet. On Archie's insistence, they wrote the word EGG--though Mattie P. declared that delicacy made her sick. Then, they thought of so many words using E and G that Emily finally had to say, "I must send you home now, I'm very busy helping with our washing. All stand."

As they stood up, Kate came over and said, "Aunt Emily, I can spend the day--Mama said, if you don't mind--and Alonzo will come for me at five?" Wistfully, she looked up, awaiting the answer.

"Why, of course," Emily said with a smile. "I'm afraid we are all working today, but I know Mattie and Bessie will welcome some help."

Happily, Kate held out a small sack. "Mama sent you some real good tea. Grandpa Tinable got it somewhere."

"Oh, thank you!" cried Emily, grasping the sack in both hands. "What a wonderful gift!"

Addie Virginia was the next to speak. "I've got to hurry! My job today is watchin' Charlie while Ma cooks. See you tomorrow!"

As soon as Mattie P. had gone, Emily said to the others, "We'd just as well go out and join the festivities!"

Magdalena hesitated. "Should I come too, Miss Em'ly? The boys be wakin' up any minute now! An' I done hear 'bout Alvah crawlin' down them stairs by heself. Made my heart lurch!"

"Don't think of coming back out," urged Emily. "Maybe you can give Aunt Sophia a hand until you hear Enoch screaming." She added, "Try feeding them both some bread and milk."

She paused in the kitchen. "We'll be having two more mouths to feed for dinner, Aunt Sophia. I'll count how many in all and come in in time to set the table." Smiling, she held up the paper sack Kate had brought. "Tea! Real tea! Sent by Mary."

Elizabeth was pegging up a tablecloth so long it had to double back on a second line. Over near the fence, the little girls were moving from line to line, carefully feeling the bottom edges of each colored garment to see if it was dry.

"Here's one!" cried Kate, tugging at a little boy's shirt. "I can't reach the peg, though!"

Emily went over. "Bring a clothes basket, Mattie. There may be several dry things here. In fact, most are dry!" Waiting for the basket, she said, "I'll hand the pegs to you, Kate. Drop them in the peg bag. And Bessie, you and Mattie, fold each piece so it'll fit into the basket."

Elizabeth came over. Emily, noticing how weary she looked, was inspired to say, "Aunt Sophia needs some advice about dinner--and while you're in there, I want you to rest for at least an hour. I had an hour off and feel like a new person!"

But it seemed a long time before Aunt Sophia called, "Time to wash up for dinner!"

Since most of the white things had been boiled, Uncle Pompous was ordered to let the fire die down. Then Emily told the boys to go around in the east yard and wait until the girls had washed.

135

Mattie and Bessie came to show Bridgett the outhouse, behind a lattice of vines. The others lined up to wait their turn. There was much splashing in the wash pans on the well-house shelf. But, finally, the girls finished, and the boys could be summoned.

In the kitchen Bridgett was introduced to Sophronia, who said, "Miss, you'm got the purtiest red hair of all I ever seen. It do be a glory red!"

The color spread quickly to Bridgett's face, then receded just as fast when she was introduced to the babies. "Now right there's a sweet sight!" she declared. "Just look at those fat cheeks!"

"Papa!" shouted Enoch.

"Mama!" Alvah took his turn, adding, "Pooh!" followed by a big shower of milky crumbs.

"There! Don't be a-wasting your food, child!" Bridgett cried. Realizing what she'd said, she clapped one hand over her mouth.

Emily stood in shock at the thought of the value that could be placed on a teaspoon of food or a few drops of milk.

But Magdalena knew what to say, and didn't hesitate, "Shame on you, boy! When you gonna start learnin' manners?"

"Let's go in and sit down," urged Elizabeth. "The boys will be in soon, I'm sure."

There were bowls of hot greens, corn bread, radishes, and a small platter of thinly sliced ham. Emily felt sure the ham was at Elizabeth's order. There was also a dish of dried peaches that had been stewed with honey to eat on the bread.

As heads were bowed for grace, Emily saw Bridgett swiftly make the sign of the cross, just as did James Conway. They must be Catholics! she thought. And here's a case that James...in all the kindness of his heart!...needs to know about.

After they had eaten, Elizabeth announced that everyone was to rest for half an hour, and then they would work until three. "It seems a miracle," she said, "but I believe that will only leave a few work clothes that need soaking. We'll do those tomorrow. You have all been good workers! Thank you!"

"An experience like this makes you value your clean clothes so much more!" admitted Emily with a laugh.

"I, for one, enjoyed it every bit!" spoke up Bridgett, "and in my whole life, I never ate no better food than this!"

Elizabeth smiled. "Uncle Pompous and our boys have worked hard on the garden this year, and it is really beginning to pay off!"

"My pea pods will be ready soon, Mama!" Archie said proudly.

"The beets, too," added Edward.

Romeo, not to be outdone, announced, "There are little string beans about an inch long down one whole row!"

Sophronia stuck in her head and asked, "Want me to put them sad irons on to heat, Miss 'Lizabeth?"

Elizabeth hesitated, but Emily said, "Yes, please do! Susan's coming over, and I'll give her some lessons on the correct way to iron sleeves from a dressmaker's viewpoint. Between us, we should be able to get some shirts ironed."

"I'm a good ironer, myself," spoke up Bridgett, "and willing!"

Elizabeth smiled at her. "You'll get plenty of opportunity!"

"An', miss!" Sophronia added. "I be keepin' a plate of food as was left from dinner for your ma. So don't forget it!"

"Forget it!" cried Bridgett, aghast. "How could I do that?"

Emily, noticing that tears stood in the girl's eyes, rose to say, "Mattie, why don't you girls show Bridgett around the house? And then all of you rest a few minutes."

It was a day somehow unique in many ways! Emily realized that they had all had a lesson in what it means to be destitute. Also, they had been reminded of how much hard work goes into washing, and that was a lesson that would surely pay off as everyone tried harder to keep their garments clean.

When James Conway heard at supper of the pitiful situation of the O'Casey family, he promised that friends among the Catholic community would call on Mrs. O'Casey and offer help.

Though Emily's heart rejoiced over this, it now bore a heavier weight. For when Alonzo came for Kate, he had handed her a short note from Mary. It told of receipt of a letter from Richard, delivered that morning in person by A.T. Schrimsher, who had walked several days from North Mississippi in awful conditions.

Mary wrote: "Richard said that William was out on patrol when the opportunity came to write, and so missed it. He said both are well, and he thought you'd be glad to know, Emily, that William has escaped the fever that others have come down with."

That word 'fever' brought an awful fear to Emily's mind. The one thing she had dreaded most, she now knew as a real danger.

Depression claimed her and could not be dislodged. It engulfed all the darkest hours.

In addition to her fears for William, Emily was disturbed by noises from the railroad lines behind the house. Was there a big movement of troops under way? Surely not a withdrawal?

As she lay there, worried and sleepless, her thoughts also led to Mrs. O'Casey and her desperate plight. It's almost useless for us women to hope and plan, she told herself sadly...for our needs and desires count for so little in this awful mesh in which we're caught. Only God knows how it will ever be solved!

Chapter Eleven

April 29, 1862

At breakfast next morning, all the talk was about the previous night's traffic on the railroad. The noise had kept them wakeful and disturbed by its implications.

"Our lodging being a mite closer to the lines, we were treated to a cruel dose of the racket," reported James Conway. "I even stood by the north window for a spell, hopeful of learning what was up. But the puzzle could not be solved there."

"Sure sounded like the whole kit and caboodle of 'em was going on," someone added. "But I reckon that's too much to hope for!"

"I was wakeful and wondering, too," admitted Emily, trying not to yawn.

Albert nodded agreement. "It might be something to do with the news I heard yesterday: that General Mitchel was furious because the Confederate Cavalry has chopped down telegraph poles and torn down lines--even prized up track in places, and then picked off Union soldiers while they were trying to make repairs."

Conway laughed. "I'm thinking old Mitchel's scorching because he can't catch those Confederate daredevils that come a-riding in a-striking like lightning itself. I am speaking truth when I say nobody can best the Southerners when it comes to horsemanship!"

"It's true!" added another voice. "And they ain't slouches at sharp-shooting either! I hear many learned to hunt when hardly out of the cradle--and not having ammunition to spare, they soon came upon the way to get a turkey or a deer with one shot!"

There were nods of agreement around the table.

"Daring they be," agreed Conway, "still I'll be after thinking their big need is guns and all. Poor brave lads!"

"What I fear most now," another added in a worried voice, "is reprisals against all us unlucky folk penned up here in town!"

Suddenly unable to bear any more of such talk, Emily rose from the table and fled to the kitchen.

"I wuz jes comin' wid hot coffee." Sophronia held up the pot, but before she could reach the dining room door, it was opened by Elizabeth, who stepped through vigorously shaking her head.

Sophronia, taking note, said, "Menfolk!" in a disgusted voice, and sailed into the dining room to finish her remark. "What y'all mean by sich talk here at the break a'day! You done driv Miss Em'ly an' Miss 'Lizbeth clean out the room!"

Mouths were opened in surprise; shamed looks exchanged.

"I guess we got carried away by all the goings-on last night," Albert said, pushing back his chair. "Don't know what came over me! I'll go and apologize."

But a loud chorus of protest greeted that. "I'll say my own apology! Ladies, forgive us rough fellows! Come on back! We never meant to upset you!"

Glancing at each other, Elizabeth and Emily could only return, take their seats, and smile in forgiveness at these men they knew meant them no harm. But Emily warned, "Don't offer me another cup of that so-called coffee. One is plenty to ruin my day!"

Sophronia peered in to announce, "Here Miss Bridgett, come to help wash!" Flinging open the kitchen door, she called, "You best come on in, chile, an' have a cup a' coffee!"

Bridgett asked, "Can you spare milk? 'Tis more to my liking."

Turning to pour a cup of milk, Aunt Sophia complained, "Don't know how we ever gonna get rid this coffee!"

"Maybe Uncle Pompous will drink it," suggested Emily.

"Huh! Not him!" scoffed Aunt Sophia. "He got high taste when it come to coffee!" With no further comment, she placed a bowl of hot mush, the molasses jar, and a pitcher of cream near Bridgett, whose eyes gleamed. Pretending not to notice, Sophronia asked, "Whar them little girls an' Archie? I do declare, I can't get ma breakfas' serve at no decent time! It near six o'clock!"

Lucius came in to speak to Bridgett. "Did we nearly wear you out yesterday?"

She looked up at him saucily. "You're knowing better'n that! I'm not after being one of those delicate lassies."

Lucius started to laugh, but sobered up. "I never took you for anything but an honest girl with both feet on the ground."

"I'll not be knowing exactly what that means--still, I'm after thinking 'tis better than hopping on one!"

He roared with laughter, and Emily, overhearing the exchange, quickly recognized a girl with plenty of spirit.

"Get on wid you, Mr. Lucius," Sophronia ordered. "You hangin' 'round in here like you didn't know yer job a-waitin' outside!"

When Elizabeth entered the kitchen, Bridgett rose courteously. "Good morning, ma'am." From her apron pocket, she drew a wrinkled scrap of paper. "Ma took pleasure in sending a note to you, Mrs. Baker, to thank you for all your kindness to us." Gracefully, she remained standing while the note was read.

"What lovely words of thanks!" Elizabeth said, with a catch in her voice. "We're glad to have you with us again today, Bridgett. When you're ready, we'll go out and get started. Thank goodness, there's a little less to wash than yesterday. I will try never to let dirty clothes pile up like that again!"

The sound of children's voices on the stairs announced Mattie, Bessie, and Archie. Magdalena, following, said, "Here we all is, ready fer our mush!" Then, turning quickly, she asked, "Ain't you chillun gonna say mornin' to Miss Bridgett?"

A chorus of greetings sounded, accompanied by two curtsies.

Laughing in delight, Bridgett said, "And never have I received a sweeter greeting! A good morning to you all!" Quickly spooning up her last bite of mush, she rose, placed her dishes on the side table, thanked Aunt Sophia politely, and hastened outside.

"That one nice young lady!" Sophronia voiced her approval and turned to dish up the children's breakfast.

The morning wore on, with washing, some ironing, and school at nine. Lingering until the other students had gone, Addie Virginia voiced a request. "Miss Emily, I was wonderin' if maybe Jason can come to our school sometimes--if you think there's room for him?" She paused, then rushed on, anxious to justify her request. "He's five, an wantin' to learn bad. I know his ma would wash him up...'fore he comes!"

The memory of Jason's eager little face, beneath his thatch of red hair, rose so vividly in Emily's mind that her reply came tripping, almost stammering, off her tongue. "Room? Of course we have room for Jason! I'm glad you mentioned it, Addie Virginia!" She paused, suddenly a little breathless. "If I write a note...to Mrs. O'Casey...would you deliver it for me?"

Grinning, Addie Virginia said, "I'll be outside when you get it ready!" Then, suddenly sober, she turned. "An' if his brothers come sneakin' back, ruinin' ever'thing, I'll fix their goose!"

"Oh," said Emily, shocked. "You think they wouldn't want Jason to learn his letters?"

"Sean, he's the oldest, don't want nothin' good like school!" the child replied. "Now, I don't know 'bout Patrick. Maybe Sean just made him go 'long." She paused. "'Course they might not even come back! They been gone near a week now."

"Doesn't their mother know where they are?"

"No, ma'am. Nobody knows where they are. Jason said they stole all the money in the house an' left." Then flashing her quick grin, Addie Virginia closed the conversation with, "But don't you worry, Miss Emily! I'm gonna take care of it!"

Bridgett soon became a welcome addition to the kitchen, where piles of clothes--sprinkled and unsprinkled--awaited the pressure of sad irons, heated just right on the kitchen stove. As she set to work with a will, her polite manner and ready wit soon won all of them.

When the question of pay arose, Emily asked Elizabeth to allow her that privilege. "Do you think a dollar a day?"

"But you can't pay it all!" protested Elizabeth, who was busy dusting the shelf ornaments in the sitting room.

"Why not? I have money now from my sewing and I can't think of a better use for it! You and Albert are giving the O'Caseys milk, and

142

doing other things. So please let me!"

"I'll have to talk to Albert," Elizabeth demurred.

Smiling to herself, Emily began anticipating the joy she would feel in handing Bridgett her wages each week.

"We'll be faced with a problem if Kianna and Tresh should come next Monday," Elizabeth mused. "It's just that Bridgett suits so much better--and you don't have to handle her with kid gloves!"

Emily laughed. "Well, who knows if they'll come back? They may have found something else."

"Heavens!" cried Elizabeth, turning suddenly, her dust cloth in the air. "This job reminds me--I've completely forgotten about house-cleaning! It's near the first of May, and not a lick done!"

"That's right! Thursday will be May first...May Day!" A faint idea suddenly began to blossom in Emily's mind. But she thrust it away, for she had thought of something else. "And, Sister, do you realize that tomorrow, April 30th, is Enoch Carlton's birthday?"

Elizabeth stopped dusting to look at her. "That's so! I wonder why I hadn't thought of it!"

"Everything is so confused right now," Emily mused, wondering what could be done to impress a one-year-old on his birthday; but something must be planned--and for Mattie's sake, if for no other reason!

"Tomorrow!" cried Mattie and Bessie in delight at the news.

"Are we going to have a party for him?" asked Bessie.

But Emily shook her head. "He wouldn't understand a party, or anything like that, I'm afraid. You can say Happy Birthday."

"Mama, I want to do something more than that!" Mattie looked determined. "He's the only one of my four brothers I even have! And I love Little Buddy!" Tears streaked her face.

Mercy! thought Emily. That reminder of my lost babies--while I am so sadly conscious of their absent father--is almost more than I can bear! She grasped frantically at her first thought. "I have a new pillow for his crib. Would you like to give him that?"

Mattie looked doubtful.

"To tell you the truth, he would enjoy a new pillow to lay his head on about as much as anything," Emily persuaded.

Mattie nodded, but her mind was on something else. "Mama, does Jesus have birthday parties for babies in heaven?" Her eyes rose anxiously.

Emily had to take a deep breath to steady herself. Still, her voice trembled. "I'm not sure about parties, Mattie, but I do believe that dear Jesus fills Heaven with joy and happiness!"

Mattie nodded again, and this time she was smiling.

When the children came to school next morning, an eager-faced, and very clean Jason was with Addie Virginia.

"We are so glad to have Jason with us," Emily said, smiling at him. "I see you brought your slate, ready to learn."

Grinning, Jason held it up and asked, "Is it all right that it has a crack? My pencil's near gone, too. But Ma said for me to use it right to the end, for her hopes are to get me a long one."

"Oh, my slate's got a crack, too!"

"Just look-a here! The whole corner of mine's gone!"

"Best thing to do is just skip that cracked place!"

Emily marveled at the way the children were taking the little red-headed boy to their hearts. Archie, proudest of all, now had a buddy sitting right beside him, ready to be guided.

"I have two announcements this morning," Emily said. "Today is Enoch Carlton's first birthday. Mattie and I would like to bring him in later, when he wakes from his nap."

"I'll hold him!" offered Addie Virginia. "I hold Charlie, even though he wiggles terrible!"

Other offers followed, while Mattie beamed with happiness.

"My second announcement," said Emily, "is that tomorrow is the first day of May. It is called May Day."

"May Day! Is that spelled MA?" Archie inquired, obviously to impress Jason.

"No. You have to add a Y on the end," explained Emily. "Here's a Y on this piece of paper to be passed around. But, first, will you show Jason how to make an M?"

"He already knows M!" spoke up Addie Virginia. "I showed it to him yesterday. But he don't know A yet."

Archie set right in to teach Jason how to make A.

Everyone bent to their slates and eventually produced MAY DAY, in varying stages of readability.

"Long ago, May Day was celebrated by children dancing around a May pole," Emily continued. "I wish we had one, but we don't. Yet there is another way of celebrating. That is to make posies..."

"...what are posies?" asked several voices.

"Little bunches of flowers tied together."

"I could do that!" offered Archie. "I know all about gardens!"

Emily sighed, hoping Archie would soon tire of showing off to Jason. She held up her hand. "I want to tell you what posies are used for on May Day. They are to be given to special friends. It is done in a certain way, called a 'ceremony'."

All the little girls listened intently while Emily told of the ancient May Day custom of presenting posies. "You make a curtsy, then hold out your posy and say, 'I wish you a happy May Day.' It is such a nice thing to do. How many of you would like to? Raise hands!"

Girls' hands waved eagerly. Jason's hand, uncertain, rose only halfway. But Archie kept his clasped tightly in his lap. "Boys do not make curtsies!" he declared firmly.

Emily replied, "That is exactly why I'm going to teach you and Jason how to make a proper man's bow. Stand up. Bend your elbow, the right one, and place your arm across your stomach. That hand will be holding the posy. Now, put your left arm behind you. Then bend forward, hold out the posy, and say, 'Happy May Day!'"

Archie looked uninterested. But Emily had an inspiration, "Let us see how well you can do that, Jason!"

The little redhead bent his arms, bowed, and spoke the best he could. As Emily led the little girls in clapping, Archie was won over, and performed in turn.

"Now we must make a list of friends. Each of you name one."

"Mattie's Grandmother Elliott," came from Bessie.

"Can it be a man?" asked Archie, suddenly interested.

"I don't see why not! Who did you have in mind?"

"Mr. Tinable Figg," was the reply.

"Then I can give one to my mama, Mary Elizabeth," said Kate.

145

Emily was scribbling names. "What about you, Jason?"

"Can I give mine to Mrs. Baker?"

"She will love it," replied Emily, adding Elizabeth's name.

"I want mine to go to Jason's mother," spoke up Addie Virginia promptly. "What's her first name, Jason?"

"Margaret O'Casey, for her grandma, way across the big sea in Ireland," was the little boy's shy reply.

Next, Mattie P. chose Mrs. Bolton.

"Mama," requested Mattie. "I'll give mine to Mrs. Pollard."

"I'm not tellin' who mine goin' to. It a secret!" Magdalena declared stoutly.

Emily nodded. "I'm giving mine to my Aunt Susan Knox. That is nine posies. They'll be ready in the morning, and delivering them will be our school tomorrow. Tell your mothers, in case you are a little later getting home than usual."

They all wrote MAY DAY a few more times on their slates, while Emily went upstairs for Enoch Carlton. He was awake, and for once not screaming. She bore him into the schoolroom, saying, "Here's our one-year-old!"

Mattie jumped up to get the pillow, but when she said, "Happy Birthday, Buddy!" he ignored the pillow, grabbed her braid and jerked hard, screaming, "Papa!"

The children laughed as Mattie disengaged his hand, kissed him and explained. "He never had a birthday before, so he has to learn how to act."

Emily laughed, too. "He acted just like a one-year-old!"

All the children hugged Enoch Carlton or patted his hand, as they wished him: "Happy Birthday."

As Mattie stood by beaming, Emily thought, What a fine mother my little daughter will make some day!

After supper that night, James Conway drew Elizabeth and Emily aside to report on a visit he had made to the O'Casey home. "That poor widow," he said, "is in a bad plight but plucky with it all! Seems her husband is no more, having gone off to war for the pure joy of fighting and met his match. Then her two older boys, young and ignorant lads, took her last dime and set out on their own."

"Mercy!" cried Elizabeth. "Where would they go?"

"I wager it'll be thieving around the countryside," Conway replied, "for their ma's not hesitating to lay their bad traits to their pa's example."

"That is so pitiful," Emily whispered.

"It be that!" agreed Conway. "Then the brave lady had fifteen hens she was depending on to bring in a bit of egg money, but one night some of these upright and fearless Blue Coats crept in and took the lot! Not a single chick left! And two little lads under Jason in age! That makes five mouths to feed!"

"Makes my heart bleed," Elizabeth said, sadly. "We are giving her milk for the babies and garden vegetables. And Emily's paying Bridgett a dollar for each day she works. What else?..."

Conway shook his head. "Nothing--beyond being friends. 'Tis up to us Irish, as countrymen and Catholics, to help, and--by the good Saints!--we'll not fail the poor widow. Her hope is to raise the money to take her brood across the river to Walker County to her own folks, her pa being a coal miner."

"That doesn't sound too promising," said Emily.

"Well, the good lady can't leave Huntsville now!" Conway said. "The plans are for later."

"What a sweet May Day posy!" Mrs. Elliott whispered, burying her nose in the wild buttercups picked by the boys in the family early that morning in the big field behind the Rison home. "An', Bessie dear, you presented it so prettily! Reminds me of my own girlhood back in Petersburg, Virginia. Only we tied our May Day posy to the doorknob an' ran like the wind. Your way's sweeter!"

Happy smiles lit the faces of the children. The Elliott house was their second stop, but Emily could already foresee success.

The first presentation had taken place in the Baker parlor, as Jason had handed his posy to Elizabeth. His face flaming, he had made his bow, held out his offering, and said his piece with true Irish charm. Elizabeth had given him a kiss, and everyone in the room had applauded, Bridgett with tears in her eyes.

147

Now, as they waved goodbye to Mrs. Elliott and reassembled on the walk, boys in the lead, Emily felt a thrill of pride.

Their carefully planned route would take them straight through town to the Knox home on Green, then back to Kate's on Jefferson, left on Arms to visit Mrs. O'Casey, and finally to the Bolton and Pollard homes on Mill Street.

They were welcomed everywhere, smiled on, and applauded. In town, blue-coated soldiers even stepped off the paths to let them pass. For awhile that day it seemed as though war and occupation forces had been pushed to the background.

Aunt Susan, who appeared touched to receive a posy from Emily, was also reminded of long-ago days in Petersburg. "This is such a sweet thought!" she said, "an' lifts my spirits mightily!"

When Archie presented a posy to Mr. Tinable, that gentleman returned his thanks with a flourishing bow of his own. "I recall, as a young man," he told them, "that it was essential to know how to bow gracefully--a custom I'm sorry to see fall into disuse!"

As Mary Elizabeth gracefully returned her daughter Kate's curtsy, she said, "I agree with Grandpa! We're losin' so many of our nice old customs--just too busy an' too worried to remember."

"Mama, I'm going on with the others--until we deliver the last posy," Kate explained. "Jason's ma, Mrs. O'Casey, is next."

That lady--a clean Donny and Jim clinging to her skirts--asked them inside the house.

"There are so many of us, Mrs. O'Casey," Emily replied, "that we are only calling at our friends' doors. We are happy to be at your door. And now, Addie Virginia has something to say."

Mrs. O'Casey directed the tiny boys to, "Sit you down right on the step, now, and see what is going to be happening!" Once they were settled, she stood smiling in anticipation.

Addie Virginia came forward with all her natural confidence to extend her posy, make a curtsy, and say, "Happy May Day, ma'am!"

Dipping a neat curtsy, Mrs. O'Casey replied, "Thank you. For I feel my own heart grow warm to be accepting this posy from you, Addie Virginia, and to see before me so many new friends, with my dear wee Jason among them. My own ma told me of joys like this in the Old Country--that place that must have been heaven on earth." She suddenly buried her face among the buttercups in her hand.

Seeing the good lady almost overcome with emotion, Emily broke in, "Thank you for those words, Mrs. O'Casey. Jason gave his posy to my sister, Elizabeth Baker, and did it with such grace. We are proud to have him in our group. And now, children, we still have two calls to make before we go back to our house for a surprise."

As they waved goodbye, Addie Virginia called, "I'll be walking home with Jason afterward, Mrs. O'Casey. Bye, Donny! Bye, Jim!"

The surprise arranged for the children included one for Emily, too. After Elizabeth had served them gingerbread and milk at the dining room table, Magdalena rose, curtsied gracefully, and said to Emily, "Ma'am, I been savin' up my posy to say Happy May Day to you--for 'tis you has made ours happy!"

Surprised and grateful, Emily rose to accept the posy and hug Magdalena. "This is one May Day I'll never forget!" she told them from her heart.

It was the very next night that the word 'reprisals' was again mentioned--this time by Albert. They were in the sitting room as he told what he had heard. "Seems that General Mitchel is so mad that he's arrested twelve men in town and put them under guard!"

"My goodness!" cried Elizabeth. "Whatever are the charges?"

"He threatens to hold them until they sign a paper declaring the war illegal, and that any citizen who fires on trains, or rips up track, shoots at Union pickets, or the like, should be punished--by death!"

"By death!" Elizabeth echoed. "Those men won't agree to that!"

"Who are the men?" Emily wanted to know.

"I'm not sure I remember all of them," Albert said, "but there are old Dr. Fearn, Mr. Acklen, Sam Cruse, Gus Mastin...and George Beirne. Oh, yes! And Bishop Lay of the Episcopal Church!"

"That is outrageous!" declared Emily. "Stupid, too, don't you think, Albert? It'll make people here hate the Federals more."

"Yes, I'm afraid it will," he agreed. "And, too, word is going around about the Union Army burning houses, looting, and worrying private citizens. It's hard to believe that Union officials, or President

Lincoln, would condone it! Surely, General Mitchel has exceeded his orders!"

Both women stopped their work to stare at him in disbelief.

"I wouldn't tell you all this," he explained, "but you need to know what's going on so you can be thankful that Huntsville's not been made into a battlefield."

"Oh, surely they won't do that!" gasped Elizabeth.

Albert shook his head. "I hope that both sides realize there's little to gain by it...and much to lose!" He paused, with lowered head, as if he were making up his mind...but finally spoke, "And, another thing, business here is just falling to pieces. Folks are only buying necessities--and tombstones, mantels, foundations for buildings, and the like, are not among them! Luckily, I had a bit put aside--and then, Conway has some--or we could not keep going. Come winter, we hope to make some money from the coal mine...fuel is a necessity!--but right now we're at a dead standstill."

Elizabeth's head came up and she gave him a warm smile, "Oh, I know you'll work it out, Albert. You are so wise, and have always treated people fairly."

"Thank you, my dear. But neither wisdom nor fairness is likely to figure in this case. For this is WAR!"

Though the conduct of the Union Army in the area was upsetting and frightening in the extreme, it was hard to judge rumor from reality. And reality in the West Holmes Street area was growing a lot more bearable. Passing Federal troops barely looked their way and it seemed that the sentry was gone from Mill Street, although the one on the bridge was still there. The general atmosphere was more quiet and relaxed. Doors were kept locked, but not guarded.

On Sunday afternoon, Emily and Elizabeth sat on the east porch enjoying the beautiful May weather. Below them, on the grass, the children, too, were happy to be out-of-doors. The babies crawled about on a quilt, under Magdalena's watchful eyes. Archie and the little girls, installed on another quilt, were working with their slates. Running and playing were forbidden on Sunday.

Suddenly, a pleasant voice said, "Good afternoon!"

Emily looked up, surprised. Beyond the fence stood the Union officer who had searched their home. She rose immediately, went down the steps and said, "Good afternoon, Lieutenant!"

"I ventured to come by," he began, "to extend apology for that frightening incident your young friend there," he paused, nodding gravely toward Magdalena, "suffered at the hand of one of our insane soldiers. It was only yesterday that I learned of it."

Emily turned to smile at Magdalena. "It was really terrifying to all of us! I admit it! But Magdalena--being the brave soul she is--seems to have borne no ill effects."

"Still it was a criminal act that I deeply regret." With that remark he proffered a bundle, which consisted of two parcels tied together. "It's some sugar and coffee from our stores."

"Coffee!" cried Emily joyfully. "Oh, we never get any that is fit to drink. Oh, thank you!"

Magdalena came forward to take the bundle. "Law, Miss Em'ly!" she cried. "An' sugar, too!" She raised her brown eyes humbly. "I thanks you, too, sir!"

But Emily's face had taken on a serious look, for she had just remembered the O'Casey family. "If you don't mind," she said, "we will divide this wonderful gift with our friend, Mrs. O'Casey, a widow who lives with her four children around on Arms Street. For about two weeks ago," she hesitated briefly over the right words, "some of your men stole all her laying hens, fifteen in number. What money that family had for food came from the sale of eggs. But for the help of friends, they'd be starving! So I will..."

"...No! No!" he begged, raising one hand. "Please don't share what I gave you with Mrs....O'Casey, is it?...for I will see that she's recompensed. She lives around on Arms, you say?"

As Emily started to give explicit directions, Edward stepped forward. "Aunt Emily, I'll walk to the corner with the Lieutenant to show him which house." Always hopeful of a chance to get out, he ran along the fence toward the side gate.

But the officer wasn't ready to go. "I saw you and the little children yesterday as you delivered May Day posies," he said. "It made me think of my own twins back in Pennsylvania."

151

"Oh? What age are they?"

He paused. "Nearly six now...little girls. They are living at my parents' home. I lost my wife the day they were born."

"Oh, I'm so sorry," gasped Emily, suddenly aware of the bleak and lonely look on his face. It was as if he were baring his very soul to her! And what could she do in return? Nothing! She dared not invite him inside, for the neighbors might misunderstand! All she could do was say in a low voice, "I would like to invite you in, but...."

The sad look on his face eased somewhat as he said gently, "I understand." Then lifting his hat politely, he bowed and bid all of them a pleasant afternoon.

To Emily's delight, she saw the little girls curtsy and Archie do his best to bow properly.

"Goodbye, and thank you!" they all called, as the Lieutenant walked to meet Edward.

Turning from the fence, Emily met Magdalena's sorrowful glance and heard her say, "Law, that poor man! If he the enemy, I don't know what that word mean!"

"I will never understand it!" vowed Emily. "Never as long as I live will I understand these times we're living in! So much evil and cruelty everywhere!"

"...No ma'am!" denied Magdalena with certainty. "Oh, no ma'am! Not ever'where!"

Chapter Twelve

May 5, 1862

Emily got up the next morning resolved to put aside worries over those aspects of their situation that she could not improve. Instead, I'll think of what I can do to help, she told herself firmly. My dressmaking, for instance! With just a little effort, I can do more. People do need clothes! Children do grow!

Children's clothes, she repeated. I could get word around that I make them from excess material in overlarge skirts.

Then she thought of Susan, who was always anxious to learn and seemed to have special talent with little girls' dresses that are far easier to hold and soon finished. Bearing that in mind, she determined only to teach--not to make a drudge of!--this trusting pupil. Perhaps she should make that clear to Mrs. Pollard.

There was also Mrs. O'Casey...so deserving, bright, and clean! Could she handle the task of ripping dresses apart? What a saving that would be in my own time and eyesight! she thought. For fifty cents a dress, surely the good woman would welcome the job, since it could be done at home.

By the time the Monday morning school hour was over, Emily had decided. She would visit both Caledonia Pollard and Mrs. O'Casey.

The week's washing chore, under way out back, appeared tiny in comparison to their previous wash day. She no longer felt obliged to help--especially since she was now paying Bridgett. "Would you lend me Archie?" she asked Elizabeth, who was hanging garments on the line with the help of Mattie and Bessie. "I have dressmaking calls and would be glad of his company."

Elizabeth laughed. "He's yours! Although I fail to see that he can contribute anything to dressmaking."

"He can help me carry some things," Emily explained. "Anyway, he's good company!"

So they set off, with Archie lugging a laundry sack containing an old dress of Emily's to be ripped and a little girl's dress to show Margaret O'Casey. Every step taken with the bundle seemed to inspire him to think of a different way to mount it on wheels.

Caledonia Pollard, her hair concealed under a white cap with a ruffle, opened the door, saying, "Excuse my looks, Emily. We're tryin' to houseclean...late as it is!"

"We haven't even begun!" sighed Emily. "Archie, put the bundle on the floor and sit on the step." Then, as they were invited in, she explained, "No, Caledonia, I shan't come in. I only stopped by to report on Susan's progress--really to say how talented she is! I'm sure you know that she's willing. I enjoy having her with me and promise not to make a drudge of her. Instead, I'm teaching the best methods I know, and trying to bring out her own creative talents. Would you object if she goes with me to interview and measure a customer?"

"I don't object to anything you ask her to do," Caledonia made it plain. "She's learnin' so much an' likin' every minute. Thanks for your patience! By the way, when I was cleanin' my wardrobe, I found two old dresses I can no longer wear. Maybe Susan can rip them up...practice on them...cut 'em, or whatever."

Taking the folded garments, Emily said, "Perhaps she can make a dress for herself and something for your Mattie. That sweet child has been such an addition to our school class!" She turned, saying, "Excuse us for hurrying off, but my baby will wake soon."

They found Margaret O'Casey sweeping her steps with an old twig broom while she kept an eye on Jason and his tiny brothers at play under a mulberry tree beside the porch. "My! But you two do pleasure a person's eyes this fine morning!" she greeted them.

"It is a beautiful day!" agreed Emily. "May I sit on the steps a minute and talk to you about a job you might do for me?"

Margaret's face held a glow of anticipation, as she laid aside her piece-of-a-broom and dropped down by Emily. "A job is it? The word be sweet music to my ears!"

And Emily's explanation brought tears of joy into the woman's expressive eyes. "Ripping, is it? And for money? Why, I've spent most of my wedded years a-ripping and making over! And not a word a' thanks!--let alone cash. Yet to my thinking, fifty cents is too much."

Emily shook her head. "Some of the work will be double-seamed and very tedious." She took her own old dress from the bag and showed Margaret what to do. Then she held up the child's dress. "Here's a little dress we made from scraps taken from a lady's skirt."

"Saints alive! But you do have a neat way with sewing, ma'am!" marveled Margaret, examining the tiny seams.

"Thank you. I'd be pleased if you'd call me 'Emily'." Handing over the bag with the dress to be ripped, she said, "When you've finished, Margaret, let Jason or Bridgett bring the pieces to me in this bag. I'll send back your fifty cents--along with more work, as I have it."

Margaret smiled. "It's my best I'll be doing! For rejoicing I am to have work that can be done under my own rooftop where I can keep an eye yonder." She nodded toward the tree.

Satisfied with her calls, Emily returned to find Magdalena feeding Enoch some bread and milk. Seeing her, he spit out his mouthful and said, "Mama!"

"Now, if you ain't made a mess!" chided his nurse.

But the baby wasn't through. He said, "Papa" and then began to call, "Eeeeee! Eeeeeeeee!"

They looked at each other, puzzled. What did he want?

"Surely he doesn't mean 'eat'," said Emily, "He's doing that!"

"Eeeeeee! Eeeee!"

Magdalena's face lit up. "Law, Miss Em'ly! He's a-callin' his big sis?"

"Of course," agreed Emily. "How thrilled she'll be!"

Fetched inside, Mattie greeted her tiny brother's efforts with joy. "Oh, Buddy! Here's your sister, Eeeee, right here! Oh, Mama! I can't believe he really knows me. He knows me!" She hugged him, spilled milk, bits of bread, and all. "Now, I'll teach you..."

"...Oh, let the poor baby eat!" begged Magdalena. "He already learned one lesson today, Eeeee."

Emily sighed happily. Life could be hard, even cruel at times, but

155

there were so many blessings and precious moments to prize.

"I'm determined to start housecleaning on Wednesday," declared Elizabeth. "Just determined!"

"That sounds like a good time," Emily said. "Bridgett may have the ironing about finished so she can help. I'm sure Margaret has taught her how to clean, almost from the crib up."

"Oh, yes!" agreed her sister. "She's fine help."

Emily was sorting the work on her sewing table. There was one of Elizabeth Swift's summer dresses and two Leona Bolton had sent over to be made into something for Addie Virginia. The white one was suitable for the little dresses that Charles, aged three, was still attired in.

"I think," she said to Elizabeth, "that Susan and I will visit Aunt Susan Knox this afternoon. She may know of someone who might let me remodel a dress for material for a child's garment."

"Why, of course, my dear," Aunt Susan said earnestly. "Several ladies right in my own church...even in this neighborhood!...have small children an' would welcome a chance to get a pretty garment like this!" She was examining the cut and attractive styling. "In my estimation, it's way above what most local seamstresses would make...an' just from scraps, too!"

"That's the main point, Aunt Susan! The material removed from a thickly-gathered skirt is more than enough to make a tiny dress or a boy's shirt. Besides, the remodeled skirts are so much more comfortable to wear! Here's a sketch I made to show the style."

Aunt Susan was still admiring the little dress. "I see you've even provided extra tucks an' a deep hem. So sensible! I wonder if I might keep this little garment for, say the rest of the week, an' the sketch, too, of course. That should give me time to show them to several ladies I have in mind. What are you askin'?"

Emily hesitated. "I thought three dollars would be fair."

Not enough!" Aunt Susan stated flatly. "Make it four! Those ladies I show it to will be able to pay that. After all, they'll still have their dress--only made more comfortable in the skirt. Besides that, they'll have a child's garment."

"I'm willing!" replied Emily, and told about Mrs. O'Casey.

Aunt Susan nodded, then turned to Susan, smiling. "Young lady, I'm acquainted with your mother. She is so sweet--just as I'm sure you are! Do you know how fortunate you are to have Emily for a teacher?"

"Oh, yes, ma'am!" replied Susan sincerely. "She's taught me so much, and..." she hesitated shyly, "..she's so lovely to be with. My little sister, Mattie, is goin' to Miss Emily's school for one hour each morning."

"School?" asked Aunt Susan. "I didn't know about that."

Hastily, Emily explained, "It's not a real school. I help some of the neighborhood children to learn their letters. They have so little chance of getting any schooling. Most are girls. I started with Mattie and Bessie--and now have six more. It is truly one of the most satisfying and rewarding things I've ever done."

"Mrs. Knox," Susan spoke up, "did you notice this dress I have on?...and the bonnet? Miss Emily made them for me." And rising gracefully, she turned around to show off the outfit.

"Ummmm, yes!" Aunt Susan said. "Stylish! Also, I must say that I'm glad to see how stunnin' you are, my dear!"

As they were leaving, Aunt Susan asked, "Do you hear anything from William?"

Emily shook her head. "I've only had one letter. But Mary has heard from Richard--and William was all right then. It's so awful not to know, Aunt Susan!"

The old lady nodded and said, "I pray for them each night. My old heart beats proudly to have such brave nephews."

"What I need," mused Emily aloud, as she stitched the seams of a little dress, "is some writing paper. I don't care what kind! I must make a list of our work according to importance. And then I need paper to print the alphabet for the children to study."

"Paper?" Elizabeth asked. "You're joking! I have a few sheets I'm hoarding for letter-writing--when mail becomes possible."

Albert was no help either. "I only have a few blank billheads left--

not that it matters, for bill-paying is all but forgotten!" He rose to take a turn around the sitting room floor. "I heard some news today. Seems we're no longer confined within the city limits, but can get a pass to go out...on good reason!"

"Really!" cried Elizabeth. "I'm so glad!"

He nodded. "You have to apply to a provost marshal who is set up in the courthouse. Trouble is, I hear George Lane's there to advise the Federals on who is deserving of passes."

"Is he the famous Union sympathizer?" asked Emily.

"Yes--and he has his favorites. Doubt if I'm on the list! But I must try to get a pass to take the wagon to the mountain for us to quarry limestone. Of course, our purpose will be to get the coal mine going-- and we must keep it secret from the Federals!"

"Why don't you get Jim Pollard to go with you to the marshal?" asked Emily. "Isn't he still street superintendent? And don't you sometimes crush a little stone to fill in holes?"

Albert looked at her in surprise. "You know, I hadn't thought of that! I'll remind the marshal that I can't get stone by rail, and there are several bad places that need filling. I believe Jim will back me up! If I have to, I can tell him secretly about the mine and promise him a little coal, come winter. We plan to haul it down the mountain hidden under stone, or even wood!"

Elizabeth and Emily smiled together, happy to see him hopeful, even excited, over this new chance to save his business.

Before he returned to his chair, he stopped at Emily's side to say, "In return for that idea, I'll find you some paper!"

Albert made good his promise on Thursday night with a stack of old advertising bills. "I'd forgotten I had these," he said. "You can use the backs. They were bills printed at The Democrat office before an error was noticed, and that office passed them along to me, for they know I always need paper to work out wording to be engraved on tombstones--so I can be sure of getting it spaced right before we start to use the chisel."

"Oh, this is the very thing! I can use it for school, and for making lists...and Elizabeth, help yourself!"

Elizabeth reached to take a few sheets. "I need to list my cleaning tasks in the order I want to do them."

The next night, they were again disturbed by unusual noises on the railroad, which they found out next day was the movement into town of Confederate prisoners captured by the Union at the recent battle up in Bridgeport.

Mrs. Pollard came across to tell them that Confederate wounded from this battle were being moved into the West Clinton Street Church. "I thought you'd want to know, Emily," she said.

"Oh, I do!" Emily cried. "I do! And I must go right over there to see if I can help. Thank you, Caledonia!"

"They may need sheets," was Elizabeth's thought when she heard the news. "There are several old patched ones I've been saving to make pillow slips from the good parts."

"If I take them over there, they'll probably be ruined!"

"That's all right! Take them anyway, if they're needed."

Emily was donning a white apron and cap, preparatory to going. "Maybe I should take one of the boys with me, Sister?"

"Ummm," mused Elizabeth. "Edward will want to go, but I'm just not sure how he'll stand up to the sight of wounded men. But try him--at least he can run back here for anything you need."

It was still early morning. "I'm glad it's Saturday, and not a school day," Emily mused, as she walked with Edward along Limberg Street. "Luckily, Susan doesn't come to sew today, either."

Edward nodded very sedately, obviously aware of the importance of their mission. As he walked along carrying Emily's satchel, in which she kept a few bandages and medical supplies, he asked in a voice that was just a trifle breathless, "Do you think those Blue Coats will let us in?"

"I hope so, but, if they don't, we'll just go on back home. We can only try to help where we see a need," Emily said. "Every day I pray that some kind person will take care of William, if he is wounded or sick."

Wagons were drawn up in front of the church, and several Union soldiers were carrying in wounded Confederates on stretchers. The others hobbled in as best they could. Two local men were helping the

159

minister to put up small beds, cots, and pads along each side of the room.

The minister greeted Emily and Edward with relief, a sad shake of his head, and the information that they were going to look for more beds.

In the back, Emily found two other ladies who had come to give help, but seemed already defeated by the magnitude of the job.

"Looks like they're goin' to leave the care of these poor boys up to us," one of the ladies volunteered in a whisper. "At least, I hope so, for they won't get nothin' from those Federals! Why, there ain't even a doctor here!"

"Oh, we must have a doctor!" Emily was sure on that point.

"The minister's already sent for one," the other lady said. "An' I'm hopin' they can find some more beds 'stead of those hard straw pallets on the floor. An' where's beddin' to come from?"

"We have a few sheets," Emily offered. "And we can send around the neighborhood to ask for more." She turned to Edward. "Run on home and ask your mother if she will let you--and maybe Lucius or Romeo--walk around our neighborhood to let people know about the wounded Confederate soldiers--and that we need old clean sheets. Don't promise to return them. Be sure to go to Mrs. Elliott's!"

"An' we don't even have no water here!" said the first lady.

Emily looked at her in wonder. Apparently, these two were just about helpless. "Well, I'll soon fix that!" she said, and ran to call Edward back. "First thing, when you get home, tell Romeo to bring us two empty well buckets, a dipper, and two washpans. This lot has a well there, behind the church."

These ideas seemed to nudge the other ladies to action. "I'll go on home an' fetch towels and washrags," said one, while the other offered a broom, mop, and what clean rags she could spare.

"We may also need some paper to make notes of names...or write letters for these poor men," Emily called. Then she walked toward the nearest cot where lay a man in a soiled gray uniform. Traces of dried blood stained his face. She took his hand and leaned over to whisper, "I'm so sorry you're suffering! A doctor will be here soon to help you, and I'm going to remove that dirty uniform and bathe you and make

160

you feel better any way I can."

He raised his eyes to hers and whispered, "I thank you, ma'am! And God bless you!"

As she moved along the room from cot to cot, Emily noticed the other two women had returned with supplies and Romeo was carrying in buckets of water. He came to her to report that the neighbors were being asked for linens and he would soon be back with some.

There were two of the Confederate wounded who appeared too ill to speak, and several more nearly as bad. Wishing that the doctor would hurry, Emily suggested that they start bathing the patients who were less seriously wounded. Seeing the women agreeable, she summoned the Union orderly who had been left as guard, "Will you please undress some of these patients so we can bathe them?"

"Let 'em undress themselves!" the orderly replied, in a very insulting manner. "I ain't here to play nursemaid!"

A nearby soldier, who had an arm wound, spoke up, "Ma'am, I'll manage without askin' 'His Majesty' for anything," and began to unbutton his tunic with his left arm. "What I'm wantin' most is a cup of cool water." When this was forthcoming, he drank deeply and, sitting on the edge of his cot, began to try to take off his tunic. Emily helped him loosen the sleeve from his wounded arm, which he seemed unable to use.

Together, they managed to peel the blood-caked material off of the wound and free his tunic. Though it must have hurt terribly, the soldier's only concern seemed to be for his uniform. "I hope it's not ruined, ma'am? For Ma made it for me when I enlisted."

As he raised his eyes, Emily realized that he was only a boy, surely no more than eighteen. "Never fear," she assured him with a smile. "For I'll take it home and mend and wash it--your pants, too, if you'll just slip them off while I get your bath water."

In a short time, he was stretched out in a clean bed, with a temporary bandage on his wound, and his uniform folded to take home for washing and repairs.

"Now, I'm wanting another cup of water," he begged. "I've got a terrible thirst, for some reason."

She felt his forehead. It was burning hot. It's no telling how long

161

his wound has gone unattended! she thought. When she went to get him a dipperful of water, she paused to whisper to one of the other women, "We're in need of a doctor here!"

"More than one!" replied the other grimly. "An' a man to help out. Why, we ain't got a single chamber to offer these poor men, an' in their condition they can't go back there to the outhouse!"

Seeing Romeo come in with another bucket of water, Emily told him their need. "Try to borrow two, if you can. And, Romeo, we have no bed pillows for these poor boys to rest on."

He thought about that briefly. "Addie Virginia was asking what she could do...I'll tell her 'pillows'."

Emily nodded, confident that pillows would soon be coming.

It had grown warm in the room...and the stench of blood-soaked garments was almost sickening. So, once again, Emily spoke to the orderly at the door. "Does raising windows fall in line with your duties?" she asked, trying to sound as kindly as she could. "I've no wish to ask you to do anything you're not supposed to!"

Actually looking embarrassed at that approach, he moved around the room raising windows and propping them up with sticks. Fresh air soon began to remove some of the staleness and stench.

Dr. Sheffey finally arrived. He was accompanied by a young man who seemed very sympathetic and willing, though his left arm hung in a sling. "Got hit by a minie ball during the fighting up at Nashville," he explained to Emily. "I was lucky to meet up with this good doctor, who got me back here. Else, I'd probably be one-armed by now!"

"Here, Will!" the doctor was calling. "You hurry back to town an' get me some help. Try to get two more doctors to come. These are our own boys here, some in bad shape. An' stop by my office for bandages." He turned to Emily. "Unless you ladies have some?"

"I have enough to start with," she replied, opening her bag so he could look inside.

"Well, I see you have a few medications, too!" he said kindly. "So, does that mean you've had some experience, young woman? For I'll be needin' an assistant while Will's gone."

Emily nodded. "I'm here to help, Doctor. Tell me what to do."

At that moment, Lucius and Romeo arrived with stacks of linens and two chambers. Seeing those, Emily said to the doctor. "We're needing an orderly to go round the room with a chamber...but that one assigned here, isn't...."

Dr. Sheffey nodded. "Here, boy!" he called to Lucius. "What's your name?"

"Lucius Baker, sir."

"Well, Lucius, take one of those pots an' go bed-to-bed to see if these poor fellows need to relieve themselves. We're all human together here...an' some are sufferin' terrible!" When Emily saw Lucius take the utensil and willingly begin the menial task, she was so proud of him that her eyes grew moist.

"Ladies!" Dr. Sheffey was calling, "I need a washpan, soap an' a towel for washing my hands, an' extra water in a bucket, also, a chair, table, or something to put my instruments on."

This time it was Romeo who came forward with one of the chairs that had been put in the back to make room for beds. While Emily spread a clean towel over the chair for the doctor to lay out his instruments, Romeo set up another nearby as a washstand. "I'll be here to change the water," he said.

Emily thought the doctor moved with assurance and sympathy as he went from patient to patient asking questions and trying to assess the extent of injuries. He told her in a low voice that he would need another doctor's help in several cases, but where it was possible to clean, bandage wounds, and relieve pain, he would go ahead, with her assistance.

In spite of all the fresh air, soap, and water, the unpleasant odor lingered in the room; but they tried not to notice. It was the cries and groans of the wounded along with their requests for water that could not be ignored. Water was served. Soothing hands and comforting words were offered, and in many cases helped.

But there was one soldier who suddenly began to babble loudly about home and call his mother and a sister named Addie Mae. His eyes looked wild as he thrashed around on his cot. If Dr. Sheffey came near, he shouted, "You're a devil, ain't you? I know you! So jes stay way from me!"

"I don't think there's much wrong with that poor boy," was the doctor's assessment to Emily, as they worked with a patient under one of the west windows. "But if he keeps that up, I had best tie him down and knock him out with laudanum, for he's disturbin' the men who are really sick!"

The soldier they were trying to help had caught a shot high in his left shoulder. The doctor had dug it out and was packing the wound. Emily, straightening up to rest her back, glanced through the window and saw a handcart loaded with pillows moving slowly along the path. Edward was pulling, and Addie Virginia pushing.

In a few minutes, Addie's voice, a little breathless, could be heard addressing the guard at the front door, "These are pillows for those hurt men in there. We'll carry 'em on in, but don't you let anyone take our cart, Mr. Blue...for we had to borrow it from Mrs. Figg!"

The pillows were brought in a few at a time. Addie Virginia, almost invisible behind her load, could be heard as she asked, "Where's your bed, Mr. Soljer?"

"I'm on it, little gal. An' this here straw pallet feels good to me, after sleepin' on the ground fer nights on end! Ain't much wrong with me anyhow. Jes got a spraint ankle!"

"Well, here's you a pillow with feathers in it. Want it under your head or your spraint ankle?"

"My head, please, missy. May help my brains to rest!"

Giggling, Addie Virginia plumped up the feathers and handed it over.

"Where's mine?" asked the next patient, raising himself on one elbow. "A cannon ball done nipped me in the thigh, so I ain't got much longer in this world!"

Addie Virginia appraised him quickly, shook up another pillow, and said, "Rest your head on this while you wait."

One by one the patients on pallets got pillows. These were the soldiers least injured, and most were cheered by the attention of the children.

Next they came to the two unconscious soldiers. When Emily saw Edward trying to rouse one, she called, "Just skip those that are asleep, Edward. And that next one, too!"

But Addie Virginia, busily shaking up a pillow, already stood beside the cot of the delirious soldier.

Alarmed, Emily called, "Skip that one, Addie..."

"...Addie!" screamed the soldier, jerking erect and grabbing her, pillow and all. "My sweet little sis, Addie Mae, has come at last! Oh, ain't you soft. I'm never gonna let you go! Keep that old devil over there away from me, Sis!"

All the adults in the room stood paralyzed, except Edward, who advanced in a run.

"Get back, Edward!" warned Emily. "Stay back!"

"Did Ma come with you, Sis?" asked the soldier, his voice in a whisper. "Whar is she?"

"I don't know...you got my face caught in this pillow; how can I see? So let up, will you?...an' I'll look round." Her voice was muffled, but firm.

"I ain't lettin' you go! You're so soft, Addie Mae!"

"Quit callin' me 'Mae'!" came the muffled voice followed by a quick stab of a hard little shoe to the shin nearest.

Grabbing for his leg, the soldier lost hold of Addie Virginia, who backed out of reach. The pillow dropped to the floor.

Dr. Sheffey was there in a bound, but Addie Virginia waved him back. In a whisper, she asked, "What's his name?"

But no one knew.

"Listen, boy!" Addie Virginia said. "You lay back down on that cot. We gotta get you cleaned up. You stink too bad to be huggin' me!" She turned to the doctor. "Where's a pan of water, some soap an' a rag?"

Lucius had them there in less than a minute. He waited to help but she waved him off and motioned to Edward. "This boy's Edward, who came to help me. Now lay down!" When the soldier failed, she gave him a shove. "Lay on down, so as we can bathe you! I promise we'll do it just like your ma."

Confused, but persuaded, he swung his feet up and flopped back on the cot. Addie folded a damp cloth over his forehead and eyes and turned to whisper to Edward, "If he grabs me again, just turn the whole pan of water over his face and hold down! Go get us two more

165

rags. I'll do his top and you can do his bottom."

Seeing the doctor still watching, Emily plucked at his sleeve. "We can go back to work now, Dr. Sheffey. I believe Addie Bolton can handle anything she sets her mind do. I'll keep an eye out!"

But before they could turn to the next patient, the front door opened to admit the young man with his arm in a sling. Behind him came two doctors carrying bags. They were followed by two ladies wearing white aprons and carrying towels and some more pillows.

Seeing all this new help, Dr. Sheffey insisted that Emily take a rest. "You're the best help I've had in a long time; maybe you can come back a while tomorrow morning."

Emily readily agreed, and then watched the doctor walk over to Addie Virginia and Edward, who were gathering up their things.

"Shhh!" Addie Virginia cautioned. "He's gone to sleep! Maybe he'll be all right when he wakes up, 'cause we didn't find a single place where he was hurt."

"Thanks, young lady, for your help, and you, too, young man!"

"You're welcome, and we'll be back after awhile with some food that people are cookin'."

"Thank you again for handlin' that hard case!"

Addie Virginia giggled. "I was just lucky that Ma made me wear my shoes today, or I'd have broke my toes on his leg bone!" She looked up at the doctor and whispered, "That was the first time I ever bathed a soljer!"

166

Chapter Thirteen

May 14, 1862

"This straw matting has transformed the playroom!" Emily stood admiring the light-tan summer floor covering that had replaced the wool rug with its dark hues. "It must be so nice to sit on, cool and smooth. I wish we'd had it when we were children!" She tried to picture the wooden floors and braided rag rugs of their childhood home in New York state.

Elizabeth nodded. "Though I did like the rugs! Do you remember how we used to identify certain pieces of material in the braids, like that blue calico that was from Aunt Maria Archibald's dress?"

"I do! I remember that very piece, and always will," Emily replied. "In fact, it was probably the rugs and those beautiful quilts in our old home that made me to make pretty things of my own." She slid the toe of one shoe along the smooth matting. "The children will love playing on this, especially our crawlers! The older ones can sit on it to work on their slates, so we won't need to bother with stools around for people to stumble over."

"I know," Elizabeth said with satisfaction. For several years the tan matting had lightened the house in summer. "But it's such a job to put down! All that stretching, tugging, then tacking the strips to the baseboards! It took Bridgett and I, and Lucius--and sometimes Romeo--to get it down. Then the whitewashing!"

Emily gazed in delight at the fresh soft-white walls. "It does make such a change in this room. So light!"

"Now you can go ahead and tack up your letter-examples and the children's work on the walls, for they'll be easily repaired."

"Thank you, Sister!" exclaimed Emily. "No one is more caring

167

than you!" She paused to swallow a lump in her throat. "Our class out-of-doors on Wednesday and Thursday, while you worked in here, was nice, too. I was surprised at the things the children noticed and could figure out how to spell: BEE, TREE, and Archie wanted to learn PEA POD. Then he wrote: I LOVE PEA PODS. He is a smart boy--ingenious, too!"

"I hope so!" said his mother. "How is Bessie doing?"

"Just fine! She was the one who wanted to spell TREE. She's so admiring of trees and flowers. Oh, and Addie Virginia insisted on spelling PILLOW. At first, I said no, because we had not studied W, but then I realized she could turn her slate and just make M." She paused briefly. "All the children want to go over to visit at the hospital. I think Edward and Addie Virginia have told them of it. So I thought I'd ask their mothers if I might take them along in a group on Saturday afternoon and let them sing for the boys."

Elizabeth's face lit up. "That is a wonderful idea! And do let me go along! We could take flowers to distribute."

All that week Emily had gone to the hospital from ten until about one in the afternoon. Many days she had brought soup and bread that Elizabeth and Aunt Sophia had cooked for the patients.

She knew her help was no longer indispensable, for many others in the area had volunteered and were coming at regular times, but she had an overwhelming interest in these soldiers and wanted all of them to get well.

Addie Virginia and Edward had also come often to help feed the men. They were particularly interested in the young soldier whose name was unknown. He was greatly improved; no longer wild, but at many times confused, and no matter how hard he struggled very few early memories had returned.

One day when Addie Virginia was there, she ran over to Emily to say, "He's remembered his first name! It's Joshua! That's such a pretty name." She paused sadly. "But he still can't think of his last name. Edward an' I have been callin' out most every name we know, but none of them is right."

"What a shame that his papers are missing!" Emily said. "Still there's a possibility someone will come in and recognize him."

"But--what will happen if he never finds out who he is?" asked Edward, deeply troubled. "If he can't remember where his folks lived, he can't go back home. What will happen to him?"

Sadly, Emily shook her head.

"That's all right, Edward!" Addie Virginia spoke up. "You an' me can take care of him!"

"Sure we can! He can live with Pa's workmen!"

Emily hated to burst that glorious bubble...but knew she must! "Remember now! These Confederate soldiers are all prisoners. Only the Union Army--and the officers of that army--can decide what'll happen to them." The moment those words were said, she wanted to grab them back, for the two young faces before her registered astonishment, disbelief, and desperate sadness.

Addie Virginia--that brave little soul!--buried her face in Emily's apron and burst into tears. Guilt-ridden, all Emily could do was stand there accusing herself as she tried to console the child.

"Listen, Addie!" Edward begged, his own voice wobbling, "We have to keep working anyway...help Joshua remember!"

Slowly lifting her head, the child took the handkerchief Emily held out to her and mopped away her tears. Then she looked up to make her dignified, heartrending explanation, "I'd just forgotten they were prisoners!"

"Well, they are!" said Edward matter-of-factly. "So let's you and me go out in the yard and decide what we can do for Joshua."

At the door the children encountered Mrs. Chadick, wife of the minister of the Cumberland Presbyterian Church on Lincoln Street. She was coming in with two ladies from that church. When she saw Emily, she came to greet her, saying, "That child at the door was crying. I wonder if this sight is too much for children?"

Emily looked that kind lady straight in the face and said, "It is too much for most of us, Mrs. Chadick. But it seems to be our cross to bear just now. And if ever a child can bear it and learn from it, Addie Virginia Bolton will be that child, for she is one truly unusual person!"

Mrs. Chadick looked surprised. "How remarkable!"

"She and Edward Baker are trying to help that young soldier across the room there to remember his name. They have become very attached to him--and because of them, he has remembered his first name is 'Joshua'."

"I'll go right over and speak to him," said Mrs. Chadick. "But tell me, how is the soldier who is so very ill?"

Emily shook her head. "Dr. Sheffey fears he won't last through the night. He's been moved to the back, where we have some sheets hanging to give privacy. We are taking turns to be with him most of the time."

"Then I'll take my turn," Mrs. Chadick offered. "So will those ladies who came with me. We brought bread, honey, and jelly."

"Oh, I know the men will enjoy that!" Emily said. "I'm leaving in a few minutes. I stay from ten until one each day."

"I'll see you again, then," said Mrs. Chadick. "I am glad that Dr. Sheffey is helping. He has been such a rock and strength for us in caring for the wounded housed in Huntsville Female College! A good doctor!" She turned away to speak to Joshua.

Emily moved to the door to look for Addie Virginia and Edward. They were nearby examining the grass for something. Surprisingly, the Union Army guard was bent over helping to look. Suddenly, he straightened and held out a clover to Addie Virginia. "This one has four leaves!" he declared triumphantly.

"Thank you, Mr. Blue," Addie Virginia took the slender stem in her hand and added, "I never would've found one, if I'd looked a whole month!" Carefully holding it ahead of her, she came through the door.

Edward paused to explain to Emily, "Addie thinks a clover may help Joshua remember."

"Oh, I do hope so!" breathed Emily, as she followed them to his bedside.

"Joshua, I brought you something!" Addie Virginia held out the clover.

At the sight of it, his face lit up and his eyes sparkled. "A clover!" he whispered in a husky voice. "And four leaves! My! But they's ever'where 'round our house. The slopes is covered, an' us all tryin'

170

for a lucky four-leaf one. I mind that Aunt Martha was usually the first to find one each year. Though Uncle Matt could reach down an' pick one up most any time, but he be dead...killed at...." His eyes flew wide open, and his mouth, too!

They were all stricken, afraid to move for fear of causing his vision to vanish. He was concentrating so hard, he barely seemed to be breathing.

Finally, Addie Virginia leaned close and whispered, "Shut your eyes now, Joshua, an' hold the clover. It'll help you see back!"

As his eyes closed, they tiptoed away. The children went out, but Emily approached Mrs. Chadick and whispered, "He is beginning to remember, so it might be good to let him rest."

At home, she found Susan already at work. A fast learner, she was now able to lay a pattern correctly on the grain of material, and to cut around it carefully. Her stitches were small and neat. In fact, the two of them together had made so much progress with their sewing that it would soon be necessary to seek more work.

Housecleaning was also progressing. It had reached the sitting room. In fact, matting was being tacked down on the floor even as they came in from the hospital. The furniture, including the work table and sewing machine, had been moved either to the parlor, or the hall, and was at that very moment being polished with great vigor by Bridgett, who was working an extra day that week.

She looked up now to say, "It's promising I am, Miss Emily, to put everything back where you and Susan had it."

Romeo and Lucius were tacking down matting as their mother watched. She looked tired. "I am determined to get this matting stretched and everything back in place by two o'clock," she told Emily, as she pushed damp wisps of hair away from her face.

"Oh, but ma'am!" cried Bridgett. "Have no fear! For we'll have things in before then. Here's the furniture cleaned and polished, all ready for setting in...and that'll take no time at all!"

"We only lack one roll of matting," said Lucius. "The pictures could be hung back on the wall any time."

"You can set your china things up on the mantel right away, Ma.

Nobody's touched 'em, but you." Romeo added. "Oh drat! I hit my thumb with this plaguey tack hammer!"

"Romeo!" admonished his mother sharply. "Don't use such words before me!"

"No, ma'am. I meant to say 'heavy' tack hammer."

Lucius nearly choked at Romeo's use of the word 'heavy' to describe the light-weight tool.

Emily examined the thumb, promised to doctor it, and then told her sister anxiously, "I do hope you're not going to be too tired to go to the hospital with us at three! Why don't you go up right now and rest?"

A chorus of agreement drowned any objections Elizabeth raised, and the matter was settled when Bridgett insisted, "A-shining and sparkling is what your room will soon be, ma'am. You'll see!"

Magdalena did not want to go with the others to the hospital.

"I wish you would change your mind!" begged Emily. "Go and put on that peach-colored dress I made you! It becomes you so!"

"No, ma'am. I thanks you, but I wants Miss 'Lizbeth to go. She never get out this house! An' to walk with all the pretty chillun would pleasure her mightily!"

"I agree, but I don't see why you can't go, too. We'll be away less than an hour."

But it was all to no avail. Although Magdalena gave her reason as caring for the babies and helping Aunt Sophia, Emily knew that it was more a hesitancy to be seen with them on an equal basis. I can imagine, she thought, how bewildering it must be to feel part white and part black--not a whole of either. It was a situation without remedy, one that engaged her sympathy and caused her to be even more determined to protect and help the young nurse.

Mr. Tinable had walked down to bring Kate. "I plan to go along with you, if you've no objection," he said. "Though I see what a sad blight I'll be castin' on this charmin' party!"

"No such thing!" Emily insisted. "You cast a blight! Why, that is ridiculous!"

"I, for one, am glad you came, Mr. Tinable," Elizabeth said to the kind old gentleman. "You can squire me. This is my own first visit to

172

the hospital!"

Each of the little girls had a bouquet of flowers contributed by their family or neighbors. There would be enough for each sick or injured man to have several blossoms.

"Mama, the roses came from Grandmother Elliott," Mattie said, pointing opposite. "See! She's on her porch waving to us now!"

"So she is!" cried Emily, delighted, but not surprised, at her mother-in-law's interest. "Let's all step across to greet her. You can sing your song. It will be a good way to practice."

While Elizabeth and Mr. Tinable climbed the steps to greet the old lady, Emily arranged the children on the walk in the way they were accustomed to stand, and then asked Jason to raise his hand.

"Mother Elliott," she said, "we want you to meet the newest of our class, Jason O'Casey, who is waving to you."

"Hello, Jason!" Mrs. Elliott returned his wave. "It's nice to meet you. My! But y'all look so pretty that I think the sight of you will be the best medicine those poor soldiers could have!"

Addie Virginia quickly began a series of "Thank-you-ma'am's!"

"And now, if you don't object, we'll practice the song we will sing at the hospital," Emily said to the adults on the porch, as she mounted two steps and turned to the children. "Ready, class?" As the clear treble voices sang the intricate melody of Three Blind Mice, more people gathered to listen. Mary Ann came out, and Caroline listened from the doorway. Mrs. Jordan stood on her porch, and several passing Blue Coats stopped. They all applauded when the children curtsied and bowed. Some neighborhood dogs also joined in by barking.

Turning back toward the porch, Emily noticed her mother-in-law quickly blink away tears as she said, "Thank you, children! That was so pretty!" Then leaning toward Emily, she asked, "But where is Magdalena?"

Emily shrugged. "I couldn't persuade her to come."

When the order of march to the hospital was decided, it seemed natural for Addie Virginia to lead, with Archie and Jason close behind.

The Union guard on duty at the church halted them at the door. "What is this--a school class?" he asked Emily.

173

"Indeed it is!" she replied. "The children have come to visit and to sing for the patients."

"What are they going to sing?" he asked curiously.

Emily gave him a smile. "Three Blind Mice."

"Well, I hope they know where to quit!" he said. "For I recall from my own childhood getting lost in the windings of that song!"

"You just step on inside and listen, Mr. Blue!" Addie Virginia invited, handing him a small red rose. "This is in return for the clover!"

"I may do that!" the soldier replied, as he opened the door.

Emily could not help but reflect on the difference in attitude of the Union guards since those first days of the hospital and to wonder what had brought it about. Was it from watching the caring attitude of Southern women and doctors? Might it have been Addie Virginia's special touch? Whatever it was, she welcomed it. She welcomed anything that might put the blue-coated soldiers in a better light. For she had heard of so many of them that appeared to be failing to represent the North as she knew it!

Inside they saw eager, delighted faces turn to greet them, and many of the patients raised up in bed so they could see better.

"We've come to visit today," Emily told them. "These children have flowers for you." Dividing them, she sent one group down one side and the rest down the other. "Now, introduce yourselves!"

While Elizabeth and Mr. Tinable followed, stopping at each bed to chat, Emily made her way to the back, where she saw two ladies she knew. "I do hope we're not going to disturb anyone," she said to them. "The children plan to sing a song before we leave. First let me ask about the soldier in the back?"

"No better, Mrs. Elliott," replied one. "In fact, Dr. Sheffey says he'll not last the night. You can be sure he'll never notice a bit of singin', or anything that y'all do!"

"But the rest of them'll listen!" added the other woman. "They are just a-layin' there, day-to-day, dreadin' what's to come!"

Emily nodded, as she moved off around the room, speaking to as many as she could. The soldier whose uniform she had cleaned and mended seemed anxious to meet Elizabeth. "Are you that lady who's been sending us the good soup an' corn bread?" he asked her. "Oh, ma'am, I could live on that!"

Elizabeth, pleased, said, "Luckily, we have a big garden this year and enough cornmeal. So, you can count on getting more!"

Just then, Addie Virginia ran across to say, "Miss Emily, when Joshua saw Jason's red hair, he remembered that his own ma has about that same color hair. Only, he says she's a blind woman!"

"Poor thing," said Elizabeth sorrowfully.

"That is sad, Addie Virginia," agreed Emily, "but I am glad he is beginning to remember more! Talking to people, and seeing some different ones, may help him. And now, I think we should sing our song. We don't want to overstay our welcome!" Walking about, she gathered the children, then assembled them in their customary positions near the front door.

Without question, Three Blind Mice was greatly enjoyed! "Sing it again! Please!" came from every side.

At the end of the encore, the children bowed and waved goodbye as Elizabeth and Mr. Tinable began to hasten them outside. Emily, hearing her name called, turned back.

"Oh, Mrs. Elliott!" One of the ladies who had been in the back of the church came to whisper, "That poor soldier revived when he heard the singin', an' he sort-of smiled." She paused to collect herself. "Then he began a-swingin' one finger back an' forth with the music." She raised tear-filled eyes. "You an' those children gave him some joy in his last moments!"

Unable to speak, Emily embraced this woman she scarcely knew and hugged her tight.

That night at supper, Albert, James Conway, and all of the men seemed excited, almost jubilant. But it was not until later on in the sitting room that Elizabeth and Emily found out the reason.

"Pollard and I went to see that provost marshal today," Albert told them. "Picked a good time--just after George Lane left to go home for his dinner. Littleton Figg let us know. He can watch the courthouse doors--both of them--from his place."

Elizabeth and Emily quickly laid aside their work to listen.

"The marshal was reasonable enough, at least when Pollard

mentioned several holes along the streets that needed filling in. I was expecting him to suggest 'river gravel', and he did! But Jim convinced him that unless you sort it out, you get stones all sizes, besides a lot of gritty silt that only makes mud. Luckily, that fellow didn't seem to know a lot about gravel, so he didn't press the point."

"You mean you got the pass?" Elizabeth couldn't wait.

"We did! And all we have to do is show it if we're stopped. Of course, we'll have to crush some gravel for the street holes, and I doubt we can collect from the city. But that's little enough to pay for a chance to pass back and forth freely."

Emily considered that. "You don't think they'll follow to see where you go, do you, Albert?"

He nodded. "It's possible, but they won't find the coal mine, for it's some distance from the limestone we expect to quarry. It so happens that the coal's on forty acres near the top that we're hoping to buy from Frank Brannan. In fact, we've an option we can take up as soon as the Union forces leave here."

"That is so exciting!" said Elizabeth, her face alight.

But Emily was still trying to get it all clarified. "What you plan to do is take your men to the limestone quarry, and leave them working while you drive the wagon on to the mine?"

"Something like that," replied Albert. "Of course, we won't go on for--maybe several hours--to be sure nobody's spying on us!"

"Then at the coal mine, you'll load coal in the bottom of your wagon?..."

"...first, we'll spread a tarp to keep coal dust from sifting through and leaving a telltale trail behind the wagon. Then we'll pull the rest of the tarp up over the top of the coal before adding limestone...or even wood."

"You're going to do all this hauling with only Old Joe to pull your wagon?" Emily was incredulous.

"Not exactly," Albert said, grinning. "Pollard says we can use one of the city corporation's mules while we're furnishing gravel for the streets."

Emily clapped her hands. "Well, if I do say so, Albert, you've worked it out to the last complicated detail. Congratulations!"

176

"Better hold up on that until after we try it out next week," he suggested.

"Who is helping at the coal mine?" Elizabeth asked. "Not your own men, I hope!"

"No. Jonathan found a couple mountain men, who like the hills better than army life, and are glad to earn some money without having to show themselves down in the valleys."

Elizabeth looked worried. "I do hope they're trustworthy!"

"Jonathan thinks so. He's had 'em working for two weeks."

"Albert, how much is this coal going to sell for?" Emily asked curiously.

"Well, we don't know yet, but it'll be enough to cover all our expenses and give a profit to Broad and to our own company."

"Do you think people can pay what you'll have to ask? It looks like it would be cheaper to burn wood." Elizabeth frowned, as she puzzled over this.

"You're right! How many loads of wood have you seen passing here lately?"

The women looked at each other and shook their heads.

"That's it! None! There are so few men to cut wood now, or mules to haul it--and then they're needing a pass to bring it in town."

"People here are going to be in desperate straits come cold, winter weather, aren't they, Albert?" Emily was ashamed to hear her voice tremble as she asked that question.

He nodded. "But we're hoping--and praying!--that the Union will decide to pull out of here before that."

"Oh, dear!" Emily yawned in spite of herself. "I need to go to bed. I am so weary tonight. It really has been such a tiresome week!" Folding her work, she rose. "By the way, Albert, there is going to be a preaching service at the West Clinton Church in the morning at ten o'clock for those injured men and anyone who wants to attend. I'm not going, for I need to rest."

"And indeed! You must rest!" insisted Elizabeth, concerned.

Albert rose, too. "I'll attend the service," he promised. "And both of you rest! For you've been helping those poor fellows all the week, and I'm ashamed to say I haven't even called by."

"One of the men is not expected to live," Elizabeth said. "You should inquire about him!"

"And speak to Joshua," requested Emily, "that poor boy who has forgotten his last name." She paused, with a worried look. "And, Albert, pray for all those men, for I very much fear that any day now the Union Army is going to ship them off to some awful prison camp!" Passing into the hall with her lighted candle, she called back, "I just can't bear the thought of it!"

Albert helped Elizabeth to her feet and hugged her close.

"For some reason," she whispered, "I am so worried about Emily right now! I don't know why, Albert."

"It's an awful time!" he agreed. "But, pray God!, we will come through it somehow!"

Chapter Fourteen

May 19, 1862

Emily, Addie Virginia, and Edward were walking near the end of the long procession that wound toward the cemetery east of town.

The horse-drawn hearse bearing the body of the soldier who had died at the hospital on Saturday night could be seen far ahead of them. Since none of his family lived in town or nearby, the citizens of Huntsville had tried to take their places.

There were carriages and other vehicles in the procession, and among the many people on foot were some of the prisoners from the West Huntsville Church building, for Gen. Mitchel had surprised everyone by giving permission for them to attend the burial.

"I wonder where Joshua is?" Addie Virginia whispered.

Edward peered ahead. "I see two wagons with soldiers from the hospital. He may be riding."

"I hope you won't get too tired, Addie Virginia," Emily looked down at the spunky little girl at her side. "We're about half the way there." They had crossed Lincoln Street and now were walking east on Randolph. "Albert told Uncle Pompous he could harness Wego to the carriage and drive us, but I had never walked before in a funeral procession and somehow felt a need to do that."

"Why, I'm not one bit tired, Miss Emily!" insisted Addie. Then she added in a low voice, "It's just 'cause I'm doin' somethin' grownup an' important."

"That's the reason!" agreed Emily. "We're doing what we should do--and no matter how hard that is, it makes you feel good."

They were whispering, conscious of the solemn occasion. And it was indeed a solemn one! As the procession had wound its slow way

179

through town, many men had paused to stand at attention in honor of this fallen soldier, who, though unknown to them personally, had given his life for the Confederate cause.

We, as women, have our part to play, Emily mused, but how very limited it is! We can only watch our menfolk go away to fight, nurse them when they are injured or sick, pray constantly for them, and honor them when they die. And, of course, we'll rejoice mightily when they return! But there could be no rejoicing today.

The procession wound its way up Randolph Street, as it climbed toward the cemetery grounds. Dust from the creek gravel underfoot almost obscured the hearse up ahead. Finally, they could see the cemetery fence with its high wooden posts and six cross-rails designed to keep out animals. Grass already stood fairly high along the fence row and into the grounds themselves.

Conveyances were drawing up to allow their occupants to alight and pass on in through the gate. The press of the crowd, many of whom were women in hoop skirts, completely blocked the view of the open grave. There was only a distant murmur to indicate that the service had begun.

Addie Virginia, who had never attended a funeral, wanted to go closer. "I can squeeze through," she whispered.

But Emily was afraid to let go of her hand for fear they would be separated. "We can bow our heads right here," she said, "while we pray for this poor soldier's family and friends...who probably do not even know he is dead...or where he is being laid to rest." And suddenly, that thought seemed so awful, that, even though her eyes were closed, no words would come. What is wrong with me? she wondered frantically. I can't even pray!

At last the service ended, and the crowd began to disperse.

Yet Emily was unwilling to leave the cemetery without visiting the graves of her three tiny babies. When the crowd had thinned, they began to search in the tall grass for the small markers that stood near the grave of their grandfather, Enoch Elliott.

But even with Edward's help--and Addie Virginia looking at the tombstones in hopes of seeing the letter E--success did not come. "I know it's right along here," she insisted over and over, while her mind offered a blank, lost feeling, almost of disorientation. I feel as if I were stumbling in the dark, she told herself, more than a little frightened.

Edward, however, offered an explanation for that when he said, "Aunt Emily, it looks like it's going to storm!"

"Mercy!" she said, studying the darkening sky. "Let's hurry along and find some shelter!"

Carriages were pulling away, their wheels crunching the sparse gravel and raising more dust from the parched ground.

People on foot, released from the mood of a graveyard, started to call cheerfully to one another. A rumble of thunder sounded in the distance.

"I should have brought an umbrella," Emily said, as she rushed the children down the sloping lane to Randolph Street. "Though we can stop in at someone's house, if we have to."

Just ahead of them were several people on foot, including two or three soldiers from the hospital.

"There's Joshua!" cried Addie Virginia, pointing.

Emily sighed. Now that so many of the injured soldiers were able to get about, she was sure their removal to a Federal prison camp must be imminent. She glanced at the little girl, who had such a deep concern for this nameless soldier, and asked, "Why don't you and Edward run and catch up with Joshua? I'll follow as fast as I can."

They were off in a second, and as she saw Addie Virginia reach Joshua's side and take his hand, Emily felt the weight of anxiety over the parting that must come soon. Tomorrow, she told herself firmly, I will write down what Joshua has been able to remember about himself and also Addie Virginia's address, and pin the note to his pocket. Maybe some kind soldier will help him write to Addie from prison. Surely that will be allowed!

A raindrop splashed her cheek; others spattered nearby. The odor of sprinkled dust rose sharply. "Edward!" she called.

He turned and saw her motion to the right. They were near the corner of Greene Street, less than two blocks from Aunt Susan's. Crossing to the Methodist Church side, she waited briefly for the children to run back to her. "We'll try to get to Aunt Susan's!" she said, as she took their hands.

But the rain beat them by about half a block, so that when the steps to the Knox porch were reached, they were all soaked.

Uncle David opened the door, as welcoming as always. "Step right inside," he urged. "It doesn't matter that you're wet. For you look good to us any way!"

Aunt Susan and the girls were there in a minute with towels to dry them off. "We're just ready to sit down to dinner," they were told by Aunt Susan. "And since chance seems to have brought you, you must not leave before you eat!" She looked at Addie Virginia and asked, "And who is this child, Emily?"

"I'm Addie Virginia Bolton," the child spoke for herself. "We live 'cross the street from Miss Emily...an' I'm in her school learnin' my letters." She then added solemnly, "We've been to the cemetery to bury the dead soljer."

In the surprised silence that greeted this statement, David Knox could be heard urging Edward to come inside. Instead, Edward called, "Aunt Emily, I'm already wet, so I'll just carry my shoes and run on home. I can tell everyone where you are."

"All right," said Emily. "but be sure to tell Mrs. Bolton! And if it hasn't stopped raining by one o'clock, ask Uncle Pompous to hitch up Wego and come for..."

"...No!" interrupted Uncle David. "Don't do that! The Federal soldiers are collecting as many horses as they can find! You best try to hide Owego, Edward! We'll lend Emily an umbrella."

Eyes popping at the threat of horse-stealing, Edward removed his shoes, tied the strings around his neck, and set off running.

Inside, Addie Virginia was deep in her tale of the soldier who had died at the hospital. "Miss Emily's been helpin' to nurse the hurt ones," she explained. "But Edward an' me are tryin' to help Joshua remember his name."

Seeing everyone spellbound with curiosity, Emily said, "I will explain it all later, but don't let us delay your dinner. There's little Josie waiting!" The child sat in her highchair, banging on the tray with a spoon and calling out a few words. "She has grown so fast...nearly two now, isn't she?"

182

Mary Ann smiled fondly. "She'll be two come September. Here's your Cousin Emily, Josie, and look at this little girl who is goin' to sit beside you!"

"Hello, Josie!" said Addie Virginia, wiggling on top of two thick books placed to raise her to table level. "My name's Addie Virginia. Can you say 'Addie'?"

"Addeee!" screamed Josie, beating with her spoon.

Her mother quickly grabbed her hand as David Knox began to ask the blessing. Sue rose to pass several dishes of vegetables and corn bread. One of the vegetables was rice in a cream sauce that contained small pieces of diced ham.

"What a delightful dish!" exclaimed Emily. "And a really good idea for making ham go a long ways."

"I'm goin' to tell Ma 'bout it," Addie Virginia said, "just in case we ever get any ham. Right now, we ain't got a bit of meat, but Pa's hopin' to find some soon."

"Where does your pa work?" asked Uncle David.

Addie Virginia looked at him solemnly. "He used to be an agent at the railroad, but those Blues wouldn't let him come back. Now he's just got some carpenter work. Pa can write so pretty! Miss Emily's tryin' to teach me, and I'm teachin' Charlie, my brother, who's only three...but he can make a good big C!"

"Well, I'll say this!" exclaimed Sue. "Emily's mighty lucky to have an eager pupil like you!"

"No, ma'am," insisted Addie Virginia. "I'm lucky havin' her to show me...for I ain't never had a chance to go to school."

Aunt Susan smiled. "I think you're lucky to have each other!" She turned to Emily, "It seems almost providential that the storm brought you here today, for I was goin' to get word to you that I have two orders, an' several other ladies want you to call."

As she thanked the kind old lady, Emily felt a little spark of excitement rise to brighten the sad and uncertain day.

While Addie Virginia played with tiny Josie, Aunt Susan showed Emily two dresses to be made over. "When you make a child's dress from the savings, make each one the same size as the sample left with me and they'll fit. Here's your sample back!"

183

Arrangements were then made for Emily and Susan to return the next day to visit the other two prospective customers.

Aunt Susan said, "You attract such charmin' people to you! I'm especially delighted with Addie Virginia!"

"She is a rare one!" Emily agreed. Glancing toward the window, she rose. "It has stopped raining, so we must go."

But Addie Virginia wasn't quite ready. She was explaining how she could buy flour. "An' if you need any, Mr. David," she said, looking up at him. "I'll get it for you. It's a dollar a bucket, if you take your own bucket."

"Papa," Sue broke in. "Do let's get some. We're about out!"

"Yes, indeed!" her father agreed. "Here's two dollars. But you are too small to carry it, Addie Virginia!"

"Edward always helps me!" she assured him. "We'll go tomorrow! We've got some clean buckets."

"Then when Susan and I come at one-thirty tomorrow, Edward and Addie Virginia can come, too, and we'll bring everything!"

Addie Virginia had run back to hug little Josie. "I'll be back tomorrow," she whispered.

"Addeeee! Addeee!" The child's cries followed them down to the corner, where they turned to wave.

Emily hastened to deliver Addie Virginia to her mother, and to explain, "The rain caught us, but we had a nice visit at the Knox home, and Addie Virginia has had a good dinner that she will tell you about."

Mrs. Bolton threw up her hands, saying, "But I don't worry one second when that child's with you, for I know she's all right an' learnin' things I could never in this world teach her!"

"She charmed the Knox family!" Emily said, smiling. "And she's offered to do them a favor that she'll tell you about. But I must hurry on...my feet are a little damp. Addie's may be, too!"

The moment Emily entered the kitchen, she knew that Edward had stirred up all the excitement he could over the chance of Owego's being taken by the Union Army.

"Law, Miss Em'ly," begged Sophronia, busily drying a wet dish. "I

184

jes hopes you can tell us the straight 'bout Wego havin' to go off wid them Blue Bellies!"

"Mama! Mama!" Mattie catapulted into the room. "You just can't let Wego go off to war! Remember how he pulled us over to Athens that day?...splash!...splash!"

"Oh, Aunt Emily!" Bessie was at her heels. "Where can we hide Old Wego? Papa won't want him to go to war!"

Elizabeth came in more sedately, but with a worried frown. "I would've sent word to Albert, but I know he's on the mountain. Do you think it's true?"

"Yes, I do, for Uncle David told me. Soon as I get these damp shoes off, we'll talk about it."

It was Lucius who thought of a possible solution for rendering Wego invisible. "Well, not exactly invisible," he admitted, "but, at least undesirable! We've got to make out that he's cut his leg real bad...bandage it up, and all!"

Elizabeth was the first to speak. "It might work! We need some salve to spread on it...and old rags for bandages."

"And a dab of William's dark red paint to look like blood," Emily suggested, grinning.

Lucius regarded her with admiration. "That'll do it! We'll depend on you for the paint, and Aunt Elizabeth for the rags. I'll get Mr. Beeman to give us some salve...make him think it's for a real cut, on some wire!"

By the time Lucius returned, Emily was in the stable with rags and some dark red paint. And Uncle Pompous, having been told the plan, added a valuable bit. He inserted a rock in the horse's hoof in a place he declared would make him limp.

Lucius came back, warning, "Mr. Beeman said there are some soldiers in this end of town right now--looking for horses."

Frantically, they spread the salve and tied one bandage. Then Emily decided to dampen the next layer so the red paint would seep through it to a top layer and look more convincing.

"That salve stink so, don't know how Wego gonna stand it," complained Uncle Pompous.

"Between that and the rock in his hoof, he is in for a bad old time," agreed Lucius. "Maybe save his life, though!"

"Let's go and wash up," Emily suggested. "And you keep Wego in the stable, Uncle Pompous, until I call you to lead him out. For we sure don't want soldiers going inside and finding our cows!"

They had just finished cleaning their hands at the well-house shelf, when Mattie and Bessie ran around from the east yard where Magdalena had the children out in the air.

"There's some soldiers wanting in, Aunt Emily," cried Bessie.

Lucius went toward the gate where stood two Blue Coats.

"We've already curtsied to them, Mama," said Mattie. "But I'll do it again, if you want!"

"No, darling! Once is plenty."

Bessie fled inside; and Sophronia, hands behind her, suddenly appeared at the back door.

Heaven help me! prayed Emily, or we'll have an incident right here. "Good afternoon!" she said pleasantly. "Can we help you?"

"Not unless you got a horse we can use!" one of the men, gruff of voice, declared.

Emily, thinking to hold out as long as she could, spoke shyly, "But you've already got our good mule, Barnabas!"

"Makes no matter!" exclaimed the other soldier, who had a scar over one eye and a bad squint. "Where's your horse?"

Lucius!" Emily said. "Please ask Uncle Pompous to bring Wego. He's awfully old!" she explained in a shaky voice. "My sister's husband brought him down when we moved from New York state...and now he has this bad cut on his leg. I tried to doctor it. Maybe you gentlemen would be kind enough to take a look at it, too?"

"Not me!" cried gruff-voice. "I ain't no horse-doctor!"

The soldier with the squint tried to open his bad eye.

Uncle Pompous stepped from the stable leading Wego, who limped at every step and whinnied at several. The odor of the salve soon enveloped them all. Both soldiers retreated speechless, for paint had spread through the bandage in a very convincing manner.

"Oh, Mama," sobbed Mattie. "Poor Wego!"

"Don't cry!" begged Emily.

Lucius added a valuable bit. "Mr. Beeman said he'd come down, soon as he can get free...see if he can save him!"

The soldiers retreated still further, and squint-eye said, "Go on, Waige! Ain't nothing here for us. I'd say that animal's ready for the glue factory, ma'am."

Wego whinnied loudly several times as the soldiers left, with Lucius following to wire the gate shut.

Uncle Pompous led an angry Wego back into the stable, where he and Lucius got the horse calmed down enough to remove the stone.

In the kitchen, Sophronia was quivering with laughter over every inch of her vast body. "I do say one thing!" she declared when she reported the incident to Elizabeth. "That horse sure did act he own part!"

In the yard, Emily was trying to soothe Mattie and Bessie, and still not give anything away. The other boys, who had been out in the west garden through it all, must never be told about how they had tricked the Blue Coats. Only Albert would hear of it.

"Tell me about the funeral this morning," Elizabeth requested, as she settled down with her knitting. "Was there a big crowd?"

"So big we couldn't see the grave or even hear the minister! Because of the crowd and the rain, I was glad I hadn't taken any more of the children." Emily hesitated before she went on, "It was strange, but while we were in the cemetery I just felt so lost! I couldn't find the grave of William's father, nor even our babies. It was like a bad dream, all dark and confused."

"You didn't feel sick or dizzy, did you?"

"No. Just lost. But we had a good time at Aunt Susan's. She's already found me some new customers. That reminds me! I must note them down in my book." She picked up her pencil, asking, "Is this the nineteenth of May?"

Elizabeth nodded. "I'm sure it is, though days seem so much alike now, it's hard to be sure of dates."

When Albert came in and heard about Wego's close shave, he was both relieved and amused. "I'm glad to see the Blue Coats bested any day!" he declared. "Now, if we could only locate Barnabas! I sure need him the worse way for hauling from the mountain. Just can't believe he's gone for good. Then, old Ebon's been downcast ever since that thievery. Blames himself, though I don't."

None of them guessed that, no more than a week later, the lost mule would be spotted, in--of all places!--Beeman's smithy. Then simply because Archie insisted on stopping there.

Emily had gone to deliver a finished dress and taken Archie to carry an extra bundle. On the way back, they could hear the ring of the anvil long before they reached the shop.

"Oh," gasped Archie, as if the gates of heaven had opened just for him to glimpse inside! "He's shoeing a mule, Aunt Emily!"

Of course, she stopped. "That's a big strong mule!" she called to Archie. And the way the animal was standing, she could plainly see a long scar on his left buttock--a scar that she recognized immediately as having been made by the razor-sharp edge of a piece of falling stone. Here was Barnabas! The lost was found!

Gasping, Emily grabbed Archie's arm and forced him back out of sight of the open shop. "Listen," she said. "I think that mule is Barnabas. You run fast as you can to the Marble Yard and tell Mr. Conway, or your pa, whoever is there, to come over here quick."

Standing where she was, beside the porch of the Beeman's house and out of sight of the smithy itself, Emily tried hard to listen for sounds that indicated that shoeing was still going on.

Behind her, she heard a door open and a voice asking, "Are you coming to visit us, Mrs. Elliott?" It was Sarah Beeman.

"How fortunate!" Emily cried, as she ran up the steps to tell Sarah the situation.

The young girl smiled in excitement. "Never fear!" she urged, "For I'll tell Papa to hold the man as long as he can." And with that, she dashed around the back of the shop, calling her pa. In a moment, the blacksmith himself came from behind his smithy long enough to raise crossed fingers high in the air for Emily to see.

When Sarah returned, she exclaimed, "Pa felt he recognized the mule. He promised to hold him and the man, as long as he can."

It seemed forever before Archie and James Conway came. By this time, Emily was standing with Sarah on the Beeman's porch, where she wanted to remain, if there was going to be a confrontation.

Conway looked her way briefly and gave her a wink before going into the shop. His greeting was cheerful, "Well now! Old lost Barnabas has shown up. How are you, dear craycher?"

"Whoa!" Mr. Beeman was shouting. "Hold up there! He sure 'nuff recognizes you, Mr. Conway. I thought I knew that old scar! Made by a stone fallin' on him one time, if I recollect?"

"What yer mean?" the supposed owner asked indignantly. "That's my mule. I bought him fair an' square!"

Conway laughed. "You might have bought him 'square', but, sure wasn't 'fair'! Albert Baker did the raising of this craycher, and has worked him many a year since...and is a-needing him bad!"

"Be you Albert Baker?" asked the man, his words quavering.

Mr. Beeman's loud voice rang out. "This here is James Conway, Mr. Baker's partner in the marble business. To make things plain, sir, I recognize this mule and know he was stolen from their shop not quite two months ago, if I remember correct."

"The twelfth of April, to be exact," put in Conway. "So now the question remaining is: Where did you get him, lad?"

Emily could tell by the man's voice that he was visibly shaken and could hardly answer. "I bought him offen a soljer as told me he wuz an army mule that weren't no good fer the life!"

"Well, it'll surprise me if there's an army brand on him!" was Conway's reply. "You see one, Beeman?"

"There ain't none!" the blacksmith boomed. "No sir, he's just a stolen animal that has found his way home!"

"Saints alive, lad!" Conway said, his voice suddenly hushed in awe. "Tell us what the thief asked for a sweet craycher like this one? Why, you could've got that bird for horse-thieving!"

Silence for a few seconds.

"Speak up, lad!" Conway insisted. "For I'm not overflowing in patience right now!"

"I give the soljer a good-sized pig, along with most all our chickens. My wife near killed me fer that!" Now his voice changed to begging for understanding. "You know fer a fact, mister, that I wuz lucky to get the mule, or anythin' else. That Blue Coat could've wiped us

189

clean out an' left nothin' a-tall!"

That last thought hung in the air awhile.

When Conway finally spoke, it was in a softer tone. "I'm not doubting the truth of that, lad!"

Seeing hope, the man forged ahead, "Since I near lost my leg fightin' up at Nashville, I've had trouble jes gettin' 'round. Near had to crawl at first. But with the mule, I seen a chance a' cuttin' wood an' haulin' it to town for sale. I got one boy 'bout fourteen can help."

"How far out do you live?" asked Conway.

"Oh, jes a ways yonder toward Chapman Mountain, maybe two mile or so. So I snuck in town this yere mornin' an' went to see that marshal in the courthouse, an' when I told him how we'd been robbed, leavin' out the part 'bout the mule, he wrote me out a paper says I can go back an' forth through the lines to sell wood. Look a-here! You can read it fer yourself!"

After Conway had studied the paper, he mused, "So the sad tale is: though you got a wagon and a son to help you cut wood, and a genuine pass for hauling, you're still lacking a mule!"

"Looks that a-way, mister! It's a bad blow fer my hopes!"

"Well, many's the time I've been hit my ownself, so don't give up, lad! If Beeman's finished with Barnabas, why don't you heist yourself up on his back and ride with me over to our Marble Yard? For it's thinking, I am, that my partner and I can give you and your son a job cutting wood and hauling it along with stones, and such, from the mountainside, using your wagon, your pass, and our mule. What do you say to that now?"

"I hafta say as I'd be mighty pleased!"

"Well, then, what's your charge for shoeing our old lost mule, Beeman? I'll pay it myself!"

The blacksmith's great laugh rang out. "No charge a-tall! Mark it down as my part in a fair-made deal!"

As the clip-clop of Barnabas' hooves sounded going away, Archie came from around the front of the shop. His eyes were nearly as big as saucers, and he hadn't found his tongue.

Sarah smiled at him. "That was just like watching a play, even if we couldn't see the expressions on the actors' faces!"

"I must go around and thank Mr. Beeman for helping us get that mule back," Emily said. "And, Archie, if you hadn't insisted that we stop here, I would've walked right by and never recognized Old Barnabas!"

With the return of Barnabas to the fold, it seemed fortune had smiled. Albert's spirits rose perceptibly. "The thing is, besides getting our good old mule back, we got the use of another wagon, and a man with a pass!"

"What's the man's name?" asked Elizabeth.

"Smith--Lamperson Smith. Says his ma's folks were among those first settlers up in Tennessee."

"Then I guess he's used to working."

Albert nodded. "In my book, any man that's hampered by a stiff knee, but still keeps trying is a good man. His boy's a biddable one, too. Name of Jackson."

"So now you've two wagons to load!" said Elizabeth.

"That's about it! We're going to put Old Joe to Smith's wagon. It'll have coal in the bottom, all covered with a tarp. Then, on top of that'll be wood that he and his boy have cut. Won't be as heavy as our wagon that'll have coal with limestone on top."

"What will happen if the guards stop Mr. Smith?" asked Emily.

"Probably nothing. Most of the guards aren't smart enough even to care. But, just in case, we got a lease drawn up and signed so the burden will fall on us."

"Looks like you have it all worked out," Elizabeth said.

"The Smiths will drive Old Joe and stable him. They have lots of hay, by the way, and will let me have some. Barnabas will come here to our stable at night." He turned to Emily. "You'll be glad to know that I gave Archie a dollar."

Emily laughed. "No doubt he'll save that for the firedogs he wants Mr. Beeman to make him."

"I don't know how you knew, but that's it!" Albert said.

"You and Elizabeth have some interesting children," Emily said softly. "They never cease to delight me!"

191

Chapter Fifteen

May 31, 1862

With Susan's help, Emily's dressmaking was progressing beyond her expectations. By Saturday morning, she could note in her book that all orders but two had been delivered and paid for. Proudly, she told Elizabeth, "I had twenty dollars left over after I paid Margaret and Bridgett. What do you think of that?"

"I think you're smart enough to be my sister!"

"This clean room has helped. It has made me feel more cheerful and not so lost and confused as I did for a while. The weather is so pretty, too," Emily said, as she glanced through the front curtain at green trees tinted with early morning sunshine. "It'd be nice to have a little outing for the children down to the Big Spring, where they've been begging to go!"

"I might go along," offered Elizabeth. "We could take the boys with us for protection."

"Mama!" Mattie had heard the plan. "Can I take my pawasol?"

"I don't see why not, darling."

"Papa would like to know that I'm using it. You could write to tell him--and I'll make my kiss mark at the bottom." Suddenly the little voice paused, then changed tone. "Mama! What's wrong?"

Emily was silent, staring in awful dread at the two figures at the front gate: Alonzo, supporting his mother, Mary Elizabeth, who held a handkerchief to her eyes.

Elizabeth was at the door in a minute. Emily could hear their whispering, but for the life of her, could not let go her frantic grasp of the curtain.

"Mama! What is it?" Mattie kept insisting. "Please sit down in your rocker and tell me!"

Between them all, they got her placed where they thought she'd best be to take the news...that awful news she knew was coming!

"Oh, Emily, my dearest! I'm so sorry it's me has to tell you!" Mary Elizabeth was trying to talk between sobs. "But a soldier just brought a letter from Richard...and, Emily! Oh, dear God! How can I tell you this?...He said William's gone! The doctors did all they could for him. It was typhus fever!"

In the doorway Sophronia broke into a wail and was soon joined by Magdalena. Elizabeth went that way in a hurry.

But Emily only felt an overpowering calmness. She was certain that this was only a dream! And in the dream, she asked, "When?"

"On Monday of last week...the nineteenth of May. He died in the hospital at Lauderdale Springs, Mississippi, and they buried him right there. Oh, Emily, do you understand? William's buried way over in Mississippi. Our brave William!"

Emily nodded. She remembered the nineteenth of May--that black day she had been lost in the cemetery! She was back there now, lost again and unable to speak--not even to dear Mary, who was so anxious and upset!

Out in the hall, Elizabeth was saying to Alonzo, "Please go to the garden and round up the boys. Tell them to come in the house. I want one of them to find Albert right away. And send Magdalena here!"

It was Mattie sobbing on her lap that finally brought Emily to her senses. She stroked her little daughter's silky hair and said into her ear, "We'll just have to bear it, darling. Nothing else can be done." Looking up, she saw Magdalena, her face streaked by tears. "Will you try to comfort Mattie?" she begged. "Take her in where she can see her papa's painting. Let her look at it as long as she wants to. Mary and I are going over to tell Mrs. Elliott."

"Oh, no, Emily!" Elizabeth protested, wringing her hands as she gulped back a frightened sob. "Don't go this very minute!"

"But, we must!" insisted Emily, rising. "For William has been gone nearly two weeks...and it's time his own mother knew it!"

Mary Ann threw open the door for them. Her eyes questioned; no words came.

Emily extended a trembling hand and asked, "Has Mother Elliott dressed?"

"She's seated in her rocker. All of you come on in!" Mary Ann spoke with a choked sniff that became a little hiccup of anxiety.

Mrs. Elliott, her smile fading, gazed upon the group before her: Mary Elizabeth sobbing, Alonzo concerned, Mary Ann about to burst into a scream, and Emily composed to the point of stiffness.

"Which of my sons is it?" Her quavering voice rose with a note of dread as she gripped the chair arms.

Emily came forward to kneel at her side. "It's William, Mother Elliott. He died on the nineteenth." She looked lovingly at this strong old lady, whose face--in spite of an heroic effort--seemed to be dissolving in grief. "He's been gone nearly two weeks...and none of us even knew!"

Mary Elizabeth, kneeling on the other side, repeated, between sobs, what Richard had said in his letter.

Mrs. Elliott turned to face Emily and murmured through her own shock, "It's just as you feared...about the fever!" And suddenly, a concerned look crossed her grief-stricken face. "Can't you find any tears?"

Emily shook her head. "I can't find anything--and I've lost my feelings...somewhere strange!"

Mrs. Elliott stroked her arm in sympathy. "You'll cry later. I know how it is. There's somethin' about losin' your husband that cuts so much deeper than tears."

Seated in the parlor that afternoon in her only black dress, too hot for summer wear, Emily felt separated from everything and everybody by some murky, impenetrable curtain. Although she moved by habit and responded politely by habit, she could neither feel, nor cry.

But Mattie had enough tears for them both. She had stopped her sobbing, now it was just an occasional drop that fell on her blue muslin dress. Seated on a stool at her mother's side, she watched Emily anxiously and finally asked, "Mama, don't you have a single tear inside you?"

Emily did not reply immediately. She was trying to think of an honest answer. It could only be, "Yes, darling, I have bushels of tears, but they're all stuck right in here." She pressed her hand flat against her breast. "And can't...can't find the way out!"

"Well, I wish mine would get stuck!" declared Mattie. "I'm so tired of them rolling down my face all the time, and making spots on my dress." She looked up anxiously. "Mama, I picked this dress to wear 'cause it was the one Papa liked."

Emily looked at it and agreed. "Yes, he did. He was partial to blue. Liked to paint blue skies."

Mattie raised her eyes to the painting over the mantel in puzzlement. "But that sky's not very blue! Why not, Mama?"

Why not, indeed? Emily groped for an answer. There must be one somewhere. And then, out of the murk, it came shining. "It's just because that's a sunrise. Your papa painted a sunrise!...the most glorious part of the day! Remember that, Mattie."

A glow of understanding spread across the sensitive face. She smiled. "Of course, Mama. Papa's gone to that sunrise. Isn't it where heaven is?"

"I expect so, darling. It must be somewhere there." Suddenly, she drew an involuntary breath. A ray of hope had come. Her eyes were suddenly damp.

"Mama!" cried Mattie. "I see a tear!" Her handkerchief ready, she asked, "Want me to wipe it off?"

But Emily shook her head. "No, leave it! It may coax out a few more!" Rising, she went into the hall where Elizabeth and Albert were talking in low voices. "I'm thinking of that good photograph of William that's in our room," she told them. "I'd like to have it in the parlor."

"Why, sure!" Elizabeth's relief that Emily had asked for something--anything!--was evident in her face.

"And what do you think of inviting Mother Elliott and all over here to sit with us?" Emily inquired. "It seems wrong for us not to be together!"

"I agree," Elizabeth replied. "Food is being brought here--and plenty for all to eat when we feel like it."

"And one more thing!" requested Emily. "I can't bear it in the parlor with the shades down and all these hot candles! Maybe it's not the thing, Sister, but can't we raise the windows and let in some fresh air?"

"I see no reason why you must go through anything, only for form's sake, Emily!" Albert said emphatically. "I'll take care of the windows right this minute! And also get William's photograph."

And I," added Elizabeth, "will go right across to invite Mrs. Elliott and her family."

For Emily, the next two days passed in a blur of callers; mere acquaintances...neighbors...relatives. In fact, so many called that Elizabeth commented, "Only a few months ago, soon after war broke out, we were all anxious for fear some here would call us 'Yankees' and not want us in their midst. How wrong we were!"

Emily agreed. "So many kind friends! I will never forget. Why, even those ladies I worked with at the hospital have called!"

"And they brought such beautiful flowers! One of them brought a cake. Where would she have found ingredients for that?"

"I can't imagine. But the flowers were from the patients over at the hospital," Emily pointed out. "Let's give part of those to Mother Elliott."

"Of course! I'll do that now. Most of your school pupils have come in this morning..."

"...they have? What day is it?" asked Emily, as she tried once more to pierce the murk that was slowly thinning to a haze. "Then I need to go on in and...."

"No!" Elizabeth was emphatic. "This is only Tuesday. You must stay here ready for visitors for another day or so, Emily. People would expect it, you know. Besides, I'll sit with the children in your place. If you don't object?"

"Object! I'm simply delighted! Why, Sister, the children will love having you...and you will be amazed at the joy you'll get in return! Thank you. But...but I would like to see any of them who want to come in here."

In a few minutes, Mattie came in with Mattie P., whose sweet little face mirrored her uncertainty and concern.

"Mama," said Mattie seriously, "Mattie P. said she didn't know any words to say to you, but she wants to give you a hug."

Touched, Emily held out her arms. "No words are needed, Mattie dear--anyway your parents and Susan have all been so kind to come over. They brought something good to eat and told us they were... sorry."

"You see, Mattie P.?" interrupted Mattie triumphantly. "That's what everyone says!"

The child raised her face, now bathed in relief, and whispered softly, "I'm sorry, too, Miss Emily."

"Thank you," Emily replied, forcing back tears that threatened at this moment, when she didn't want them. "I know my sister is enjoying being teacher today!"

"Yes, ma'am! She knows all the letters, too!"

Archie escorted in Jason, whose face flamed as red as his hair while he stood there searching for words. Unsuccessful, he placed his right hand on his stomach, his left behind him, and executed a very credible bow.

"Thank you, Jason," Emily acknowledged the gesture.

Thus encouraged, he executed another, even deeper, that seemed to free his tongue. "Ma told me what to say," he gasped. "But now I've forgot it!"

"You don't need to say anything," Emily assured him. "Your bow said it all. Your mother came to see us Sunday afternoon, and all of us appreciated her courtesy. She brought some of the best gingerbread our family has ever tasted."

Jason's face lit up. "Addie Virginia got us some flour over at the mill, and Mr. Conway gave us a bit of sugar."

Emily's heart smote her as she realized what a great sacrifice the O'Casey family had made to give up such a rare treat. Briefly she closed her eyes in humble thanks for such friends. When next she opened them, the little boys were gone and Addie Virginia was coming in.

Here was a child who needed no escort, nor any prompting as to the proper words. Her words came from her heart. She dropped down on the stool beside Emily to say them, "I'm so sorry, Miss Emily! I just wish I'd known Mr. William better. I do 'member seein' him walkin' along. Oh, there's his picture, isn't it?"

"Yes, and it's a very good likeness--though I think he looks a little sad. But then, people don't smile in photographs." Hearing herself in astonishment, Emily realized that she had never before thought of William's sad expression. But it was true!

Addie Virginia looked up at her seriously. She hadn't finished all she had to say. "Miss Emily, do you remember the day we were in the cemetery an' couldn't get close enough to hear? You wanted us to pray for that poor soljer's family? Well...I been prayin' for you an' Mattie an' Enoch. I wanted you to know. An' somethin' else! Charlie prayed for you, too! After he said, 'I lay me', he said, 'God bless Miss Em'ly'. He said it on his own...."

"Bless his heart!" quavered Emily, pressing her hand hard over her own heart, which seemed about to burst. There was something bursting! It was the dam that had held back her tears! They came gushing now, wrung out by great sobs that shook her body.

"Miss Emily!" moaned Addie Virginia, patting her back. "Please don't cry so!"

But the wrenching sobs only grew worse. It was hard to draw a breath. She rocked back and forth in the effort.

Alarmed, Addie Virginia ran from the room. In a few moments, Elizabeth was there, and Sophronia holding a wet washrag. At the door, Mattie stood sobbing, "Mama's found her tears!"

They tried placing the damp rag on Emily's brow, but it would not stay, she was shaking so! Alarmed, Elizabeth dashed out in the hall to find the children and the boys gathered. "Lucius!" she said, "run across and tell Mrs. Elliott that Emily is crying, and we may need her help. Try not to alarm her!"

Seeing the anxious faces of the children standing in the hall, Elizabeth gulped back her own tears and urged, "Don't be upset! It will help her to cry and soon be over. Edward, please take the class back in the schoolroom and teach them how to make an S."

Reluctantly, the children followed Edward, who was glad of a chance to try some of the teaching methods used by Prof. McCay.

While she was in the grip of the paroxysm, Emily was conscious of nothing except the effort to breathe. When this eased, she became aware of Mrs. Elliott seated beside her, holding her hand, or perhaps it was she who was gripping the old lady's hand. "It's hard for me to believe I made such a spectacle of...hiccup!...myself...hiccup!"

"Don't try to talk!" instructed Mrs. Elliott. "You're feelin' better now. Elizabeth, you might get some scissors...or somethin' cold to put down her back to stop the hiccups!"

"That's all right...hiccup!..."

"Don't talk now!" begged Mrs. Elliott. "Try to breathe deep!"

Trying, Emily said, "Hiccup!"

The next instant, she felt something cold pressed hard against her back and gasped. The gasping seemed to help, so she gasped again, and gradually felt herself relaxing. The hiccups departed. And now she yawned...not once, but several times.

Mrs. Elliott was smiling. "That's good! Now you are better! I expect you'll feel sleepy. Have you been sleepin' at night?"

Emily shook her head as she tried to drag the memory of recent nights from the haze that had enveloped her. "Not much."

Mrs. Elliott rose. "What she needs is to go right to bed. Magdalena, why don't you help her? Be sure Enoch is downstairs so he won't wake her!" She turned to Emily with a smile. "I slept well last night, so I'll take my turn here in the parlor, in case callers come." She put her hand out to help Emily rise, promising that a deep sleep would work miracles.

Submissively, Emily allowed herself to be led upstairs and put to bed. Reality dropped away. When it returned, after unnumbered hours, she was so deep in lassitude of body and mind that it took more effort than she could find to even stir. Sound was audible; voices almost meaningless.

"I know it's rest she needs," Elizabeth whispered, "but I keep worrying about her not eating!"

"Law, Miss 'Lizbeth, don't you fret!" murmured Sophronia. "It God am takin' care of her now. He healin' her. Just let Him go a little longer!"

Mattie's voice had a frightened catch, "Mama's not dying, too, is she Aunt 'Lizabeth? Oh, Aunt 'Lizabeth!..."

"No, no, child! She just needs to rest. She's been pushing so hard...trying to be strong...."

On Thursday morning, Emily finally awoke refreshed and anxious to get up. She was received downstairs with relief--and an almost overpowering amount of attention.

"I'm ashamed of myself for giving up completely!" she admitted to Elizabeth. "It was weak and disgraceful!"

"You needn't say that--or even think it!" Elizabeth protested.

"Why, Mrs. Elliott was here both days! She enjoyed seeing people, and it did her a lot of good. We all loved having her with us."

"I'm so glad. She is a darling! But tell me who came."

"The Beeman girls, all three, and they said they would come again soon. Then Uncle David drove his carriage down, with all their family in it--even tiny Josie, to the delight of our little girls. By the way, Aunt Susan brought you a whole bolt of black, summer-weight material--in on your sewing table--to make yourself a summer dress and one for Mrs. Elliott. Aunt Susan requested you not to make a black dress for Mattie! She disapproves of mourning clothes for children. And so do I!"

"Why, I wouldn't dream of putting Mattie in black! But a whole bolt of black...and thin material! Oh, I wish I had it made right now! This dress is so hot! Who else came?"

"Andrew and Viora Bolton came over the night after you...er... had that spell. Addie Virginia had told them about it. That dear child was frightened to death for fear it was something she had said that caused it! Anyway, they were really anxious."

"I hope you reassured them," Emily said, trying to recall what Addie Virginia had said. It was something about...Oh, yes! It was about little Charlie praying. "I'm sorry for frightening all the children," she added now, "but if I hadn't let go soon, I'd have just burst with all I was bottling up!"

"I agree," Elizabeth nodded. "By the way, William Halsey drove his carriage down Tuesday afternoon and brought Martha and four of their daughters. I was glad that Mrs. Elliott was here, for I did not know them very well--in fact, it had slipped my mind that she is Martha's aunt."

"They live out on Meridian," Emily explained. "I like them and William had such respect for Mr. Halsey's work." She paused. "Did anyone else come while I was sleeping? Most neighbors had come in on Sunday."

"Yes, but several came again, when they heard you had..."

"Did Mr. Tinable come?" asked Emily.

"Oh, yes! Every one of them came, more than once. They were so concerned about you. I've the names written down for you, in case I forget. Oh, one more! The Union Lieutenant brought another sack of coffee and some more sugar."

"He did! I wonder how he learned of William's death?"

Elizabeth shook her head. "I don't know, but when he heard you were resting, he left his card, for he said he would be away from here for a while. Now where did I put that? Must be in the parlor someplace."

When Emily held the card in her hand, she looked up. "Are you sure this is his?"

"It's the one he gave me--and wrote something on the back."

"Dr. Aaron Langhowe Fraser! My! I never dreamed he was a physician!" She turned the card and read: "My deepest sympathy! Sorry not to see you in person, but your little daughter spoke so beautifully for you!"

Emily was puzzled. "Well, what did Mattie say to him?"

Elizabeth smiled. "She took him in the parlor to see William's painting. Then she explained very carefully about the sunrise and its meaning. It was so touching, Emily...so touching! Tears were in his eyes when they came out."

"I'm not surprised!" Emily said thoughtfully. "He told me that his wife died at the birth of his twin daughters. I'm glad Mattie told him about the sunrise!" She was still studying the card.

There was something about it! The date: June fourth? What day is this?" she asked hesitantly.

Elizabeth smiled. "Why, the fifth of June...but now don't you fret!"

"Fret! Of course I'm going to fret! My little daughter's fifth

201

birthday was yesterday--and I slept right through it!"

"Well, Mattie wasn't a bit put out! The children wanted to say 'Happy Birthday' yesterday, but she made them wait until you were back downstairs."

"Then we must have Mattie's birthday celebration today!"

Elizabeth looked a little shocked. "Is that appropriate?"

"Yes!" Came Emily's certain answer. "It's appropriate! For she needs to have it, and that is very important to me! Do you think Sophronia can manage some kind of cake?"

Elizabeth nodded. "She has the ingredients already put aside!"

"Then we can all walk down to the Big Spring for awhile...it's what Mattie wanted to do! And come back here for cake." Glancing at Elizabeth, she could sense disapproval. She went on to explain as best she could, "Mattie is very sensitive, and I don't want to have her suffer. It won't bring dear William back! Nothing I can do will bring him back. My heart's near to breaking just thinking of it. Please try to bear with me, Sister!"

Elizabeth rose, her arms outstretched. "Of course, I will bear with you! And help you all I can. Surely you know that!"

By the time they left for their four-block walk to the spring, their party had increased considerably. Besides Elizabeth, Mattie and all the school children, it included Edward, Romeo and Mr. Tinable-- and even one younger, for Addie Virginia had asked to bring Charlie. "I'll hold his hand every minute!" she promised.

Emily had also invited Susan to enjoy the treat with them, and it was she who made a count as they assembled on the front stoop and overflowed into the yard. "Fourteen! If I'm not mistaken."

"Oh, Mama!" cried Mattie, her hands clasped excitedly over the handle of her parasol. "It's a real party! Thank you!"

When Emily glimpsed the joy on her little daughter's face, she felt a tiny lessening of pain in her own heart.

The sun was warm and inviting. The women and little girls wore long-sleeved summer dresses and sunbonnets. As they walked along, Mattie shared her parasol with any who wanted to walk beneath it. Her invitation was spurned by all the boys except little Charlie, who giggled his delight to his sister, "Look at me, Addie! Here I am!-- under Mattie's big tent."

Once they had persuaded Archie to pass Beeman's, where the anvil was ringing mightily, they turned south for the two blocks on Gallatin Street to the spring. At the Baptist Church corner, they crossed West Clinton Street to the rough road that led sharply downhill behind the new Huntsville Hotel's stabling lot.

"Whichever way you come, it is hard to walk down to the spring on account of being so steep and these awful rocks underfoot! Be careful, everyone. Don't fall!" Elizabeth warned.

"Fountain Row and that lane south of the hotel are still worse than this!" declared Mr. Tinable. "Much steeper, seems to me."

"What I'm concerned about," whispered Emily, "is if there'll be a bunch of Blue Coats down there."

But they were lucky. The area was unpopulated, except for one Negro patiently watering his horse in the stream from the spring that flowed unbridged across Gallatin Street.

Thankfully, they turned left onto the flat, grassy verge along the runoff. Here, the strong flow from the spring had cut fairly deep, but the water was so clear that they could see the smallest pebble in the stream bed. In several places, long fronds of moss waved slowly under the water, to the delight of the children.

"What is that?" asked Charlie, straining to get closer.

"It's moss waving," replied Addie Virginia, trying to restrain the eager child. "You step back or you'll fall down in an' drown! 'Cause I can't swim to save you."

They got him back by calling attention to the high cliff that hedged them in on the east. "See those houses way up yonder?" Edward, self-appointed guide, pointed upward. "That's just their backs. Their fronts face the courthouse."

"Why?" Charlie asked curiously.

"So people can get in their doors. Nobody is going to climb up that cliff from down here. Besides, the street's up there."

This was too much for Charlie even to comment on. Anyway, all his attention had been caught by a mule-drawn wagon coming along Gallatin from the south. Wheels grating on the rough gravel, the equippage hit the stream at a good clip, splashing water in every direction. Charlie squealed in delight.

Addie Virginia looked up in dismay. "I'm sorry he's actin' so bad, Miss Emily!"

"He's really not acting bad," Emily consoled her. "He's just a little boy--curious, of course, and, I'd say, very bright for his age."

Relieved, Addie Virginia allowed Romeo to take Charlie's other hand and help answer his questions.

Archie was curious about the brick building on their left, and when he learned that it was the city gas works, was overcome by a need to know how the gas was made.

"I don't know," Emily told him flatly, "but I expect your pa will tell you all about it, if you ask him tonight."

On their right, across the stream, stood the new building that housed the city water works. This substantial masonry structure, which held the pumping equipment, was partly over the stream with a bridge that made access possible to the other side. Naturally, all the children wanted to cross the bridge.

Emily could understand their eagerness to look down from above the stream, and as the bridge was securely railed, she said, "All right, but before we go out on the bridge, you should know what's in the building. It's a pump that forces water up through that big pipe that rises up the cliff behind the bank building. Raise your hand, if you can see the pipe."

Satisfied that everyone understood--with the exception of tiny Charlie--she continued, "After the water gets up the bluff, it is forced through more pipes to a big reservoir--that's like a great big lake with sides--then into more pipes until it reaches houses where people need it."

The little girls gave her their sweet, mystified smiles, while the boys delved into the complications of pumping water, an operation that Mr. Tinable was able to explain very clearly.

It was Addie Virginia who asked the obvious question, "Where's that lake--whatcha call it?--that holds all the water?"

"The reservoir, something like a huge pot with a cover," Emily replied, "is up on a hill east of town."

The crossing of the bridge was accomplished with many comments at the sight of the clear water below. Once across, they circled the building so they could see back into the crevice in the cliff on which the courthouse was built.

"That is where all the water comes from," Elizabeth went ahead with the tale. "I don't know how many thousands of gallons a day flow from under those cliffs! Huntsville is so lucky to have this wonderful spring of pure water! Bad water makes people sick!"

As they were recrossing the bridge--and pausing, of course, to look down--the sound of band music suddenly surrounded them. They listened in amazement. It seemed to be coming from the courthouse square.

"Oh, Mattie!" exclaimed Bessie, in delight. "Just listen! That music is for your birthday!"

The lovely sound--so exciting to their unaccustomed ears--held them motionless on the bridge. It seemed to Emily that time stood still a few moments to allow them an unforgettable experience, as they stood there over the beautiful stream in the lovely, natural bowl of the Big Spring, with music all about them. "My!" she said finally. "How very strange!"

"I heard the Blue Coats were goin' to get a band in town!" Mr. Tinable remarked, "and we got here just in time to hear it."

The music accompanied their walk back along the stream to Gallatin, at which point Edward halted the party. "There it is!" he said, indicating a large two-story house on a rise to the west of Gallatin, just beyond the intersection of Fountain Row.

They all looked that way to see what "it" was.

"That's McCay's School, where Pa makes Romeo and me go!" Here he paused to entertain a hopeful thought. "Of course, it might be that Prof. McCay won't start up again when the Blue Coats leave!"

"Edward!" admonished his mother. "I'll declare, I never heard such a lot of nothing! The McCays are excellent teachers, and you are lucky your pa can afford to send you there! I'm confident the school will reopen. Still that reminds me, you both should review some this summer so you'll be ready for the next term!"

Edward's mouth fell open in consternation, as Romeo directed a reproachful look his way. "Well, I didn't mean to say anything against the school!" he blurted.

Addie Virginia stepped heroically into the breach by pointing the building out again to Charlie, "There's where you'll be goin' to school, Little Brother, after you learn to write your letters! Then, you'll be as smart as Edward and Romeo!"

Emily dared not meet Elizabeth's gaze, for she knew they would both explode into laughter. How delightful--and how trying!--our children can be, she thought, as she got the group started up the uneven gravel path to West Clinton Street. Then, suddenly, as she turned for one more glimpse of the spring, she was visited by the memory of walking with William there in the early days of their courtship. The brief vision was so unsettling that she would have tripped had not Susan been there to assist her. In an effort to bring herself back to the present, she mentioned the summer black material. "I hope to measure Mother Elliott this very afternoon, and get started on our dresses," she said, her voice wobbling.

Susan responded with interest. "I'll help all I can. I'm sure the dress you have on is hot!"

"Fiercely!" admitted Emily with a sigh. Up ahead she could see her little daughter giving tiny Charlie another opportunity under the parasol. Our Mattie! she thought proudly--sweet and unselfish child! So much like her father!

From behind, came the clatter of galloping horses and rattling wagons as a Union Army contingent swept by. The noise of their passage seemed to echo and re-echo in Emily's mind, penetrating much deeper than sound. It hit at the core of her being, and completely shattered in one moment the one precious picture--so long held inviolate-- of William, the children, and herself, all secure and happy together. Not until that one awful moment had she been fully aware of her loss.

"William is gone!" Instinctively, she spoke those words aloud. "And now everything in the world is changed for us!"

Susan looked up at her, confusion and sympathy clearly written on her face. She reached out her hand in a motherly way and whispered, "I hate war so awfully much!"

"So do I," Emily agreed brokenly. "Beyond words to tell!"

Chapter Sixteen

June 6, 1862

For the next five or six days Emily suffered silently, as if a wound had been opened in her heart, almost a mortal wound. Will I ever recover from the blow this awful war has dealt me? She asked herself this question repeatedly, and found no answer.

It was Mrs. Elliott's discerning eye that first detected a problem. "Are you feelin' well today?" she asked solicitously. "I do hope you're not comin' down with somethin'!" Her tone changed suddenly to one of alarm. "I've heard there's smallpox about among these Union soldiers. Pray God you're not!..."

But Emily hastened to reassure the kind old lady. "I'm well enough physically, Mother Elliott. It's just that...How can I say it?...Like something has chopped me into little fragments!" She had been kneeling to adjust the skirt of the black dress. But all at once, her hands fell away and she sat back, her head bowed low in discouragement. "I sometimes wonder if I will ever get myself patched together again. I'm trying so hard, Mother Elliott!"

Studying the bowed head in sorrow, her mother-in-law hesitated for a few seconds. When she finally spoke, it was in a soft, yet firm, voice. "Maybe you're tryin' too hard...thinkin' too much about it. That won't help what is! Try to let it go; just don't allow that broken feelin' to creep in. Right now, you're angry at the war an' at William for goin'. No reason to feel ashamed of that. It's natural. Just try to put it out of your mind--for now. I know that seems heartless, still it's the thing to do. Later on your feelin's will soften an' change. I promise it!"

Emily raised her tear-streaked face and whispered, "Thank you.

I'm sure you're right!" As she rose to hug the dear old lady, she made up her mind to try to follow her wise advice.

"Just go on in your sweet, kindly way," Mrs. Elliott said, and changed the subject. "Appears to me this skirt fits well enough. Do you need me to do any handwork on it?"

"No, Mother Elliott. Susan is looking forward to finishing the hem. She would be disappointed."

Later, as Emily walked toward the front gate, her arms full of black material, she was aware of feeling better. Unconsciously, her eyes strayed to the violet beds bordering the path. Their delicate purple and blue blossoms had gone now...for their season had ended. Only the leaves remained, somehow grown broader on stems that seemed to stretch toward the sun as if they pleaded for more light...another chance!

Pausing at the gate, she raised her eyes with her own plea for more: more strength, more patience, more knowledge of the way her own path should lead.

Early next morning, as Barnabas was being hitched to the wagon and the men were preparing to leave for the shop, Albert summoned Romeo and Edward to the backyard. He motioned toward the stable. "Boys," he said, "this is stable-cleaning day!"

They both groaned, but only slightly, for they knew their pa's no-nonsense voice.

"I want that empty stall between Barnabas and Lulu Belle to be cleaned slick as a whistle! And while you're about it, why not do the same for the other stalls. You can clean while Uncle Pompous is pasturing the cows on the side lawn."

"Oh, Pa!..." Edward, attempting a complaint, cut it short at sight of the expression on his father's face. Instead, he struck at the ground with his heel, thinking what a hard time he and Romeo had now that Lucius was again working at the Marble Yard.

"When do you want the stalls cleaned?" Romeo asked, hoping for a date far in the future.

"Why, today, of course! Any reason you can't do it?"

"Oh no, Pa!" both boys chorused weakly.

"Be sure you do then!" Albert warned. "For when we drive in to-night, we'll be bringing something to put in there."

Edward's mouth flew open to ask, but he soon thought better of that. Yet, mystery hung in the air of the stable, along with bits of straw, and all kinds of debris raised by their brooms.

Later, when Elizabeth came out and saw the clouds of dust, the mystery was passed on to her, and she promptly passed it along to Emily. "Albert's having the stable cleaned for something he'll be bringing to put in it. Mercy knows what!"

"At least he had the foresight, when he built that barn a year ago, to make it large enough for needs that might arise!"

"That's true," admitted Elizabeth. "Albert always thinks ahead as far as he can."

The mystery was solved that night when Barnabas pulled the wagon into the yard and, after several tries, got it situated for unloading. The sides had been boarded high and appeared only to contain a big load of hay. It was when part of the hay was forked off, or pushed to one side, that the real mystery was revealed.

"Coal! COAL!" The astonished cry burst from Romeo and was amplified by Edward, whose excitability had no bounds.

"Don't shout!" begged their father. "Why tell everybody? We're hoping to keep this quiet. So I don't want to hear THAT word! You understand? I want you both to promise me that you'll not tell a soul what's in this stall. We can't afford to have it get around that we have fuel. So be sure you don't mention it to Archie or Bessie...or to any other children coming here. Or to anybody!"

Solemn promises were made, but Edward had to ask, "What can we do if they find it out for themselves?"

"That's not likely to happen! The stable's going to be locked from now on. Your ma will see to that, for she'll have the key."

In the sitting room that night, Albert explained to Elizabeth and Emily the necessity for keeping the coal a secret. "I'll not be able to supply everyone in town--only a few who will keep it quiet. For if word leaks out, the Blue Coats will be trailing the wagon to the mountain. And, once they find the mine, I know what will happen. They'll take it over and operate it...just like it belonged to them!

Maybe force Conway and me to take 'The Oath' to keep the Marble Yard going. It's a perilous time right now. So hard to tell which way things will turn!"

"I'll do anything I can to help," Emily volunteered. "Should I quit having the children come to the house for their schooling?"

Albert turned to her in surprise. "Why, no! Don't change that! The stable will be locked. Anyway, the children won't go there."

"What about Archie?" asked Emily. "He has more curiosity than any ten children I know."

"That is certainly true, Albert!" agreed Elizabeth, looking up from her mending. "Are you going to warn him?"

But her husband shook his head. "That may be the worst thing I could do. Let's just hope he stays in ignorance. The coal will be covered with a tarpaulin, with hay on top of that."

"I'll keep the key on my belt," Elizabeth promised.

"I know that's an added burden for you," Albert admitted, "but seems it's necessary right now."

"It's a task I can help with, if need be," offered Emily, from the side table where she was sorting materials.

"There'll be a load of wood coming soon from Lamperson Smith. He and his son have cut one for us. That Lamperson--even though he's stiff-legged--is turning out to be a top-notch worker, and dependable with it. He's taught Jackson to work, too, and the boy's not expecting to do anything else. He's a sharp boy--likes wildflowers, and seems to know a lot about them, such as the ones that are good for doctoring ailments. Said his ma taught him!"

Emily looked up from her sorting to say, "I wish I had some of that knowledge."

"No doubt Mrs. Smith knows plenty of helpful things, since her family were pioneers to these parts," added Elizabeth.

"No doubt," agreed Albert as he returned to reading an Atlanta newspaper that had been left in the Nevill & Figg Coffee Shop and was now being circulated among friends.

"Mrs. Elliott knows so much plant lore," Emily added. "I can't understand why I'm not writing it down! Why, I could use the back of some of those fliers Albert brought us. I'll try to start that in the morning when I go over to take her black dress."

"Oh, is it all finished?" asked Elizabeth.

Emily nodded. "Susan put the last stitch in the hem late this afternoon. I do hope the thin material will be enjoyed as much by Mother Elliott as it has been by me! And, Sister, the best thing is that I have enough of the material to make another dress!"

"Maybe you can design the next one a little fancier."

"What a good idea!" agreed Emily, feeling a sudden interest in sewing that had been lacking during the recent difficult days. Do help me look through Godey's Lady's Book for a pattern!"

As Elizabeth laid her work aside and joined Emily in a pursuit they both enjoyed, Albert stepped out in the early dusk. He felt more worried than he cared to admit. Money owed him was not being paid, and, with the Federal Army in control, it was dangerous to ride through the countryside trying to collect debts. He feared the day when he might not be able to pay his men. It all seemed to hinge on their getting coal from the mine, secretly delivering it, and being paid in cash--maybe as much as ten dollars a load.

He paused in his walk to try to calculate what it cost them to dig and deliver a load. But there were too many variables. Every day brought new problems, new risks. Care of his men was of first importance. God grant they don't get hurt! he prayed, or stopped by the Blue Coats! There was even a possibility of being robbed, for there were said to be deserters from both armies lurking in the mountains.

He thought of James Conway, his hard-working, congenial friend and partner, who was risking money in their venture, and wondered what would happen, if....

"Albert, we're going up to bed!" Elizabeth called.

With a mighty effort he thrust back his worries. Once inside, he began his rounds of locking and bolting every door. Night was here and rest needed, for no telling what emergency the next dawn would bring.

"I jes don' know as I'se ever seen a June month wid any colder nights an' hotter days than this here one!" Uncle Pompous said, as he worked his hoe along the corn row. "The crops don't like it one bit.

Jes looka here at them corn ears! Nothin' but nubbins!"

Romeo and Edward, both toiling nearby, stopped to glance at an ear.

"How long are they going to get?" asked Edward curiously.

Uncle Pompous rested on his hoe and looked at his young helper in disbelief. "Why, near twice what they is an' filled out nice and plump, wid plenty juicy kernels."

Romeo hastened to show his ignorance. "How will we know if an ear is ready, Uncle Pompous?"

"Law, boy!" Astonishment crossed the old man's face. "It ain't a-gonna shout 'I'm ready!'. See all them silky hairs a-growin' out its tip? Well, they gonna turn brown. Then you kin peer in 'tween the shucks an' see how big the kernels has got." Taking a quick jab with his hoe, he mumbled, "A person got to use he brain to be a gard'ner!"

"You need the right weather, too!" Edward put in bravely.

"Hmmmp!" Uncle Pompous spat.

"R-o-m-e-o!"

Hearing his mother's call, Romeo dropped his hoe and started for the house.

"Come back here, boy! Pick up that hoe!"

When Romeo swung around, he heard the rest, "An' clean it with a sharp stick, 'fore you puts it up...."

Elizabeth and Aunt Sophronia were seated on kitchen chairs near the well house happily sorting through several big baskets of ripe peaches.

"Jes you look at what we got this mornin'!" Aunt Sophia said, grinning widely.

"Where in the world?" Romeo gasped, as a vision of fried peach pies rose to delight him.

"All through the kindness of Mrs. Lamperson Smith," his mother explained. "Mr. Smith brought them in. And not only that, but they sent a crock of honey." She pointed to a big crock standing on the well-house shelf. "Their son, Jackson, found a bee tree!"

Romeo whistled. In his heart he nourished a desire to learn about bee trees, gardening, and such things that other people just seemed to know instinctively.

"This basket of peaches is for Mrs. Elliott," his mother said, indicating a nearby container. "Go wash your hands and get ready to take them over. You may have to make two trips, for I want to send along some of the honey as soon as I can get it divided...."

"I'll do that," offered Emily from the doorway where she stood tying on an apron. "Lift the crock and bring it inside, Romeo, so I can remove the cloth cover. Flies are awful out there!"

"They've already got word of the peaches," sighed Elizabeth.

Aunt Sophia nodded. "It do be fly season, an' some a' these is old horse flies, too. I hates 'em nasty, buzzin' things! Got to be puttin' up some more flypapers coated with 'lasses, a-hangin' from the kitchen ceilin', and trap me a bushel or two!"

"Mrs. Baker!"

They turned at the sound of a strange voice. A tall boy waited at the east fence. He was grinning widely beneath an enormous hat made of straw; his arms were full of clothes.

At sight of him, Romeo called, "Hello, John! Hold on until I can unlatch the gate. We wire it closed to keep our cows in."

Elizabeth rose, as Emily came down the steps to greet the newcomers, for there were two. A little girl, also carrying some clothes, stood nearby.

"It's John Hardie, isn't it?" asked Elizabeth.

"Yes'm," he replied, his grin widening, "and this is my little sis, Alice. This load we're a-totin' is just some old dresses of ma's that she wants made over for her little ones. They're all about out of clothes!"

Emily hurried forward to take Alice's armload. "Hello, Alice! I'm Emily Elliott, the one who sews for people."

"Is Mattie your little girl?" asked Alice, in a sweet treble voice, her face uptilted. "I played with Mattie over to Addie's."

"Of course," Emily replied quickly. "We all know your parents, and that you live just up the street from the Swift's corner."

"How is your mother?" asked Elizabeth. "I haven't seen her for a while."

"That gal that's been helping Ma for so long, just up and went off, to goodness knows where," reported John, in obvious disgust, "and now Ma can't hardly get out to do anything!"

213

"She had meant to come with these clothes." Alice's voice was full of concern. "But the baby was carryin' on so, she couldn't."

"Did she tell you what she wants done?" asked Emily.

Nodding, the little girl fished from her pinafore pocket a bit of paper, much folded. "She wrote it down, ma'am. I can't read it but I 'spect you can, as you're a teacher."

Taking the folded note, Emily said, "Why don't we go inside so we can look at the things you brought?"

"Go ahead," urged Elizabeth. "We'll get the honey divided--and the peaches taken care of. I want to send some to Mrs. Hardie."

Romeo stepped up to take the pile of clothes from John. "After I put these inside, will you give me a hand to carry some peaches across to Mrs. Elliott?" he asked, seeing a possible chance to be away from garden work for awhile.

"Just so as I get back pretty soon, I can," agreed John. "Ma's got me choppin' in her bean patch today."

Romeo sighed, reflecting that the lives of most boys were well beyond their control.

In the kitchen, the younger children, who were finishing their breakfast, greeted Alice in surprise and delight. "Let's all play dolls," suggested Bessie.

But Alice only said, "I didn't come to play. Ma sent me with a few things for Mrs. Elliott to sew."

The things turned out to be three summer dresses, a nightdress and two petticoats, each of which looked to contain yards of good material. "Ma says she can do without these," Alice said. "An' we are all goin' to have to wear made-over clothes from now on!"

"I know," Emily said. She was having some trouble deciphering the dim writing on Harriett Hardie's note. But, eventually, she understood that she was being given a free hand to make what she could for the children at her usual charge. The note closed with a question: "What is your charge for schooling? I want Alice to learn her alphabet! She's already seven and can't read a word!"

Alice, standing patiently by...almost with tears of anxiety in her eyes...breathed a question, "Did you read the last words?"

Emily smiled at the little girl and gave her a quick hug. "Yes I did,

Alice! And we'll be glad to have you come with the others at nine in the morning for one hour. I'm not a real schoolteacher so there's no charge at all. But I'll help you learn your letters and how to put some of them together to make words. You will need a slate and pencil. Do you like to sing?"

"Oh, yes, ma'am!" The little head went back, the eyes closed, and the tones of Sweet and Low filled the room, flowed into the hall, and soon attracted an audience.

"Oh, Mama!" Mattie was the first to speak. "That was pretty!"

"It truly was," agreed Emily. "What a blessing your voice will be, Alice! And, children, she is going to come to our school!"

Delight over this was evident in all their faces.

But Alice did not start to school that day. She had to go home to help care for the baby so that her mother could do housework and cooking.

Before she left, Emily took her measurements and wrote them in her book, a process that impressed Alice mightily. "All my old dresses are about torn up," she said. "My sister, Florence, is big for four years, an' she rips ev'ry one she puts on. Ma sews 'em up, but Florence just goes ahead an' rips 'em open again!"

"We'll have to do something about that right quick then!" said Emily cheerfully. "Maybe I'd better walk home with you to measure Florence and any of your other small brothers and sisters."

"Yes'm," agreed Alice brightly, "an' be sure to write them all down in your book!"

With enough peaches for a pie and a cup of honey, Emily walked with Alice along West Holmes to the Hardie's house.

She told Elizabeth later, "I do admire Harriett Hardie! There are six children. I couldn't tell their exact ages! But the child Florence-- they say is four--could hardly be still long enough for me to measure her!" As she spoke, she was busy pinning notes onto various garments to be ripped. "Bridgett can take these along to her mother tonight. In the meantime, I'm going to try to get one dress for Alice from some material I already have."

"I wish I could do something for Harriett," mused Elizabeth. "When I think of having to do all of my work while trying to care for six children, I feel so thankful for all the willing hands in this household! I understand John Hardie is a builder. Wonder if he's getting work?"

Emily nodded. "I think he's probably helping at the new hotel. According to Littleton, they're continually needing repairs, for many of the Union officers are staying there. One hundred rooms in it, you know!"

"By the way, when Romeo and John Hardie carried the peaches to Mrs. Elliott, she sent back a packet of coffee. It seems now that several of the Union officers manage to keep Littleton's place pretty well supplied."

"That's good news!" Emily said. "And it reminds me to ask what we're going to do for Mrs. Lamperson Smith, in return for all her generosity?"

"Well, we could divide the coffee," suggested Elizabeth with a mischievous smile.

"Not until we've exhausted every other possibility," protested Emily. "We don't even know if they're coffee-lovers. But I wonder if Albert could find out what size of a woman Mrs. Smith is. For, seems to me, it would be nice to make her a dress."

"That's a good idea," agreed Elizabeth. "I'll speak to Albert about it this very night."

"Then there's another thing," murmured Emily, trying to gather her forces to even mention it. Finally, taking a deep breath, she said in a shaky voice, "Dear William's clothes...his good suit and some shirts...up there in the closet doing nothing..."

But Elizabeth protested, "Don't worry about it right now! Just don't torture yourself! There'll be time for deciding what..."

"I know. But I still can't help but think of men such as poor, crippled Lamperson Smith, who may be down to their last rag..."

...don't you believe it!" interrupted Elizabeth. "I'm pretty sure that Mrs. Smith has a spinning wheel and a loom--to keep her menfolk decent. Shoes, now! That's another matter. What is to be done about our own children's footwear is beyond me! When winter comes, they can't go barefoot like they can now. And their feet are not going to stop growing!"

216

"Are there no shoes in the stores?"

"Oh, a few," Elizabeth assured her. "But even if you could get a fit, Albert told me the other night that prices are away out of reason, anywhere from five to twelve dollars a pair!"

"My!" gasped Emily. "Not many can afford that!" Pausing in her work, she sought a quick solution. "Perhaps we can get Mr. Gill, the shoemaker near Beeman's Blacksmith Shop, to make some."

Elizabeth looked at her in surprise. "What from, may I ask?"

Emily did not answer for a while. A frown creased her forehead as she finally said, "You don't suppose that our brother, Edward, could send us some leather from Mr. Stewart's tannery?"

But Elizabeth only shook her head. "Albert says all Alabama tanneries are forced by law to make every scrap of leather they can get into shoes for the Confederate Army. It seems a tannery is so necessary that men who work there are even exempted from service in the army!"

Emily's face lit up. "That's wonderful! Maybe Edward and Alvah won't be in danger of conscription."

"Alvah doesn't work in the tannery! He's a tinner."

Emily sighed. "At least Edward has an important job there. And as for shoes, I am going to talk to Mr. Gill the very next time I pass his shop. Maybe he'll tell us what people are using in place of leather."

But even lack of shoeleather took a back seat that night, when the cry of FIRE! was raised. Their knowledge of it came from Jim Pollard's warning at the side door, "Rouse up, Albert! There's a big fire downtown! Looks to be toward your shop!"

Dressing hurriedly, Albert woke Romeo to alert the men back in their quarters. Soon everyone, except the small children, had put on some kind of garments and run outside to peer toward town. As Albert and the men, carrying lanterns and buckets, left at a run, a red glow could be seen above town to the east.

"It looks a little to the north of Albert's shop," Emily said, "and farther away, too. I suppose the Blue Coats have taken over the fire department?"

"I suppose," agreed Elizabeth, shivering nervously, "but will they care? After all, it's not their property!"

"Still, I think they'd try to put it out! I do trust it's not near Uncle David and Aunt Susan!"

"It's not growing any larger," called Romeo from the middle of the road. "In fact, I believe it's dying down."

Edward, ever the excitable, ran up to his mother. "But, Ma, I still think I should go closer. Then I'd run back and tell you!"

"No!" his mother said firmly. "You're as close as you're going to get. We'll know soon enough."

But it was nearly an hour before the men returned. Long before that, the red glow had completely faded from the sky.

"We would've been back sooner, but we were helping Knox to put back in his house all the things that had been set in the street during the excitement," Albert explained to everyone waiting in the sitting room.

"Oh, surely it wasn't Aunt Susan's house!" gasped Emily.

But her brother-in-law shook his head to reassure her. "No! It was the jail. Still, that was close enough to just about frighten the wits out of David."

"But how could the jail have caught fire?" asked Elizabeth, in bewilderment.

Albert paused a few moments before replying. "Well, from what I heard--and don't take this for the truth, for I don't know that it is--the fire was set by some of the Union soldiers confined in the building. Luckily, the Federals got the flames out in pretty good time. It's thought the damage can be repaired."

"Yes, but at whose cost?" Emily asked the unanswerable. "I'll go to Aunt Susan's tomorrow to see if we can help in any way."

Edward, eager to see the damaged jail, spoke up. "And I'll go with you, Aunt Emily--just in case you have anything to carry."

And the word "peaches!" came from the throats of all those who were not trying to smother a yawn.

Chapter Seventeen

July 4, 1862

"I often think of how we used to celebrate the Fourth of July when I was a boy up in New York state," mused Albert, as he took one end of a split log from the pile in the wagon drawn up along the garden fence.

Since all the shop crew were from New York, they knew what was meant: "Picnics!...Good old lemonade!...But the parade came along first, and, of course, the band!...Then those speeches!"

"Do you remember that old lawyer in Owego who used to stand up on the platform every Fourth and read the Constitution?" one of the men asked. "What was his name?"

"It's a-laying here on the tip of me tongue," spoke up Conway, "but, for the life of me, I can't get it loose."

"Ho! Conway! I thought everything rolled off your tongue like molasses."

"You wrong me, lad! Indeed you do."

"Don't forget the horse racing!" urged one of the men. "It was the top of the day for me when I was a boy."

Albert nodded. "I believe it was for me, too. It's been a long time now since I've seen even two horses race, let alone a whole line of them on the go."

"It's been many a day since we've seen much of anything around here!" growled someone. "Does look like the Blue Coats could get up a race or do something to celebrate The Fourth. It's as quiet this morning as if midnight was on us."

"Maybe the Federals have had some news to dampen their mood for celebrating."

"More'n likely it's just rumors they're hearing! That's all my ears are collecting."

Thinking to change the subject, Albert said, "I'll bet none of you has ever before spent The Fourth building a corncrib?"

Agreement came quickly. "No, this is my first! But I might've, if my pa could've caught me!"

"Just where are we putting this structure?" someone asked.

Albert pointed to the southeast corner of the garden. "Right along here...in the corner nearest the house."

"Lot of thieves about, Albert!"

"It's going to be locked and guaranteed thief-proof!" He spoke earnestly. "And if our logs hold out, I'm hoping to set up more'n one crib." He paused to gesture toward the west end of the garden where Romeo and Edward were busy gathering ears of corn under the explicit guidance of Uncle Pompous. "Looks like our gardeners are doing us proud. Of course, we finally got rain, and that made all the difference! And then, Lamperson Smith thinks he might come up with a wagonload of ears beyond what they'll be needing. We want to be ready to take all we can get."

"Wonder when Tyler's Mill, across Pinhook Creek, will start up again?" someone asked.

"It's operating now," replied Albert. "Bolton's girl reported to me last week that she'd seen the mill wheel turning."

"So many uses for corn!" spoke up someone. "Hominy, for one. I had a ma that could make some of the best."

Albert agreed. "Mrs. Elliott is another who's an expert at it. I've agreed to furnish all the corn...for half the hominy she can make. Her garden's lacking enough space for corn. But they've got the field peas, also black-eyes. She hopes to spare us maybe two or three bushels for drying. Littleton's boy, Robert E., can't do any painting now--no demand!--so he's gardening instead. And it's a good thing, too!"

"What I'm yearning to know is when a man can expect a wee bite of this corn," spoke up Conway. "It's not in your plan to be saving every single ear, is it, Albert?"

Albert laughed. "I can answer that! We're dining on it today! I see Aunt Sophia busy right now scrubbing out the black-iron pot ready for boiling whatever it'll hold. We're eating picnic style, right out in the open, with the flies and all!"

Heads turned to take in the backyard area near the well house, where noon shade would lie. Makeshift tables of boards laid over sawhorses had been set up there for the feast.

"Mrs. Elliott, Mary Ann, and Caroline will be with us," Albert told them. "Seems Robert E. persuaded his pa to let him help them at the Coffee House today."

"I'll wager it'll be wild up on the courthouse square!"

Albert nodded. "Littleton serves no liquor to soldiers, but it would be hard to keep out the ones who've already partaken. But he knows a few Union officers now that he can call on for help."

Work on the corncrib picked up mightily after the promise of a picnic. Floor foundations were down, and the straightest split logs they had were being laid across.

"Do as you will, you'll have rats creeping in," prophesied Conway. "My own belief is, you'll be needing a good mouser!"

"That's what Uncle Pompous warned, too," Albert admitted, "and I should have started looking for one. I wonder...."

Stooping to raise one end of a split log, Lucius called, "Just ask Addie Virginia. She'll know if there's an extra cat anywhere in this part of town. That little gal...OWWW!"

They all turned to see Lucius on the ground, a log beside him.

He was rocking back and forth, clutching his right foot in both hands, and moaning. All work came to a stop!

Albert was the first to reach him. He knelt. "Did that log hit your foot?"

Nodding, Lucius gasped, "After I tripped on something!"

"Bear up!" Albert advised and turned to the nearest man. "Give me a hand, and we'll move him over near the well house. Someone please fetch a chair from the kitchen. And ask Emily to come!"

Even before they could get him seated, Emily was there issuing directions. "I'll need a bucket of cold water from the well. He can put his foot in it to help keep down the swelling." Studying his pale face, she asked. "You don't feel sick, do you?" When he shook his head, she turned to Magdalena, who was waiting in case she was needed.

"Dip a cloth in cold water...and place it across his forehead to help take his mind off the pain. And please fetch me a towel."

James Conway came up to say, "If there's anything I can do for you, lad, just name it!"

But Lucius shook his head, trying to smile. "No thanks! I have the best nurse there is. So don't stop work!"

After examining the foot, Emily wrapped it in the towel. Then, she drew Albert off to one side. "I'm sure his big toe, also that next one, are broken. You could get Dr. Sheffey over, but I doubt he can do much." She hesitated, and then added, "Well, he might splint the second toe, but I can do that. In the meantime, we'll keep putting his foot in cold water every little while. But I do suggest that we send for Mother Elliott. For she may know of a poultice that can be applied to help keep down inflammation."

"I'll go myself," said Albert, turning away.

But she held him back. "Also, if there's anyone in your bunch who's a good whittler, he could start making a crutch."

The combined skills of Mrs. Elliott and Emily were needed to get Lucius settled as comfortably as possible. Dazed, he watched picnic preparations going on nearby. Occasionally, he could catch the voices of the crib-builders warning, "Take care now!" All too late for me! he thought, forcing back tears.

Seeing his struggle, Emily tried to console him. "You feel bad from the shock right now, Lucius. But just imagine if that log had been a heavy stone! Your foot might have been crushed! But this injury should mend without any lasting effect."

He nodded dumbly, as he watched the corn gatherers being put to other tasks. Romeo, seated on a kitchen chair nearby, was busy shucking corn for boiling. He held up one of the fullest ears for Lucius to admire. "Uncle Pompous sure knows what he's doing when it comes to gardening!" he declared with a grin. "Nearly killed Edward and me, but I expect it was worth it!"

When Edward was sent across to ask if Addie Virginia knew of a cat they might get, he returned with surprising news. Margaret O'Casey was the cat-fancier in the neighborhood, and had several.

Since Bridgett was not working that day, Elizabeth had planned to send the O'Casey family a dozen ears of corn, with a bucket of milk, and a bowl of potato salad for their dinner. "Choose twelve nice ears," Romeo was told. "The milk and salad are ready. So you and Edward load up. And don't forget to ask about a cat!"

As soon as they returned, Edward hurried into excited speech, "Bridgett will bring the cat in the morning. Romeo and I saw her! She's gray, and her name is Lady Mist."

"And, Ma," added Romeo, "Mrs. O'Casey said you shouldn't feed her, so she'll hunt up her own food. She said that's the way they raised her. And I believe it! For they've no food to give a cat. Why, there wasn't a thing on their dinner table but corn bread!"

Shaking her head, Elizabeth pondered that. "Edward, I want you to go back and take some of our fried peach pies. Just say that I made you come back because you forgot the pies the first time."

"Take my pie," spoke up Emily, her voice catching slightly.

"And mine!" came a chorus.

"They'll be 'nuff fer all to have one," Aunt Sophia spoke up.

Mrs. Elliott, who had been listening, drew Mary Ann off to one side and asked, "I wonder what we can do for that poor widow an' her children?"

"We still have hominy, Grandma," spoke up Caroline.

"We can spare a cabbage or two," added Mary Ann. "Nothin' more nourishin'! An', of course, we've got potatoes."

When they had gathered around the tables, Elizabeth mentioned the lack of lemonade. "Seems to go with a Fourth-of-July picnic!"

"No picnic here!" protested James Conway. "To me own thinking, this is a FEAST!"

"And Lord make us thankful for it!" breathed Albert.

After tasting Elizabeth's potato salad, Mrs. Elliott remarked, "I want your receipt for this dish! I've tasted none like it!"

"It's a German dish," said Elizabeth. "Kind of a hot salad and bits of meat, with a tangy dressing."

"Mother Elliott," put in Emily, "we had a nice German family living near us in New York state. You know they are so thrifty; this salad is only one example. I'll write out the receipt for you. I think this raw-cabbage slaw probably originated with...."

Just then, a loud boom rent the air. Eating stopped! But when another boom sounded, Albert withdrew his watch from his pocket and said, "It's exactly noon! I reckon we're hearing the Federal salute to The Fourth!"

The booms continued for what seemed like an hour.

"I counted thirty-four!"

"By the powers!" cried Conway. "I hope that doesn't mean they have more news to crow over!"

"More'n likely they're just taking pleasure in taunting us!"

The picnic was over. Every scrap of food had vanished and been appreciated to the full.

"Time for resting awhile," suggested Albert. "Lay about for a bit, you men, and take a snooze--if you've a mind to."

While the women were clearing the tables, Emily saw Lucius being helped to the outhouse. The poor boy! she mused. This will be a mighty hard trial for him!

Albert was examining the crutch, already under way. He showed it to Mrs. Elliott, who was nearby. "It's a makeshift only, until we can do better."

"Don't shame your work," she advised. "It'll do well enough as soon as the splinters are smoothed off. Emily might sew padding over the part that his arm rests on." She paused. "As for his foot, that's goin' to be painful an' tiresome for a while. It'll make him feel so helpless. He's not used to that, Albert! So you had best think up some kind of work to occupy his mind. For it's dwellin' too much on hurts an' miseries that causes trouble!"

Touched, Albert said, "Thank you for that wise advice! I will heed it, for I love my nephews as if they were my own. It was an awful sadness to me that my brother, Hiram, did not live to watch his children grow up!"

"Let's see," Mrs. Elliott mused. "It's about three years since he died?"

Albert nodded. "Mary Ann, Hiram's widow, has her girls to care for; and, of course, her other boys, John Gideon and Asa Charles, are her mainstays on their farm up in New York state. And John is a great help with my own place, though I've a good hired hand who lives there...one of the Germans that Emily mentioned."

"Did you ever think that you might be better off up North now, Albert, instead of down here in the midst of this turmoil?" asked Mrs. Elliott. She laughed. "'Tis only my advanced years that give me courage to put that question to you. Forgive an old woman, if it's too personal."

He studied her upturned face briefly. "There's nought to be forgiven," he assured her. "The problem goes so deep! It's my own love of this Southland coupled with the years of work I've got invested--all that!--against a safe and comfortable life back in the North, which my sense of fairness tells me my wife and children deserve. The struggle's heavy on me these days."

Mrs. Elliott placed her hand on his arm in sympathy. "I felt it might be. And, Albert, remember that Emily can always stay with us...."

He held up his hand to stop her from saying more. "Elizabeth," he said emphatically, "could never flourish unless her sister was nearby. That I am sure of!"

"I know," Mrs. Elliott said softly, "for not long ago I had my two dear boys who felt the same...."

"Albert!" the call came from the garden. "We're ready to go to work! You got any idea where you want the door to this edifice?"

Laughing, Albert said in low voice to Mrs. Elliott, "Those men have no idea I've never built a corncrib in all my days!"

That night after the children had gone to sleep, Emily sat by the open window in their bedroom. The night was dark, hardly a candle-twinkle shown. Silence was almost complete.

But in her mind, a new disturbance was brewing. She had heard some of what Albert and Mrs. Elliott were saying; now another avenue for conflict and possibilities reared its head. For the first time, she grasped the awful strain that Albert was under and the effect that his decision would have upon them all. And though she tried to heed Mrs. Elliott's advice to "let things go", sleep eluded her until long after midnight.

Next morning she was awakened by Mattie. "Mama, everybody is up but you, and Enoch won't stay in his crib any longer!"

Emily sat up, reached for a wrapper, and was soon on her feet. Hastily dressing Enoch and helping Mattie, she tried to throw off her lethargy. It was Saturday--no school, but plenty of sewing to do. Her thoughts immediately flew to the shortage of buttons and the problem of shoes. "Shoes!"

The last word, spoken aloud, was taken up by Mattie. "Mama, do I have to wear shoes today? I like to go barefoot!"

"Bare feet are nice in summer," her mother agreed, "but you'll have to have shoes this winter!"

It was Monday, after school, before Emily could make a trip to see Mr. Chamberlain Gill, the shoemaker. She took Archie to carry a sack of corn.

Since nothing could persuade Archie to pass Mr. Beeman's while the blacksmith was working, Emily left him there. "You stand back out of the way, Archie!" she warned, "or I won't bring you again. And I'm leaving my sack of corn, so watch it!"

Mr. Beeman looked up, caught her eye, and grinned. "Never fear 'bout Archie!" he called. "He's a smart lad, and will take care!"

The cobbler's shop next door had no customers, but Mr. Gill greeted her from his bench. "An' what may you be needin', young lady? If it's a new pair of leather soles, I may as well say now I can't help you--that is, unless you've got your own leather."

"I'm afraid there's no chance of that, Mr. Gill. Can you mend leather uppers that have split or have a hole worn through?"

The old man paused with his hammer raised. "I might, if I've a scrap of leather that would fit the hole. But it would be a patch that would show. An' I've only a few bits of leather left. It all goes to the soldiers now! Be it a boy's shoe?"

Emily nodded. "Children's feet grow so fast," she said. "What are we going to do for their shoes this winter?"

He rested his hammer on the counter and looked at her. "That's hard to answer. Most are going to wooden soles...an' some kind of canvas tops. Of course, if you've got an old leather buggy top or a saddle skirt, they will serve; or carriage curtains, if they're leather, can be made into uppers. One curtain will be enough for several pairs."

Emily pondered this. "But what about soles?"

"Wood, as I said, unless you have good cow or horsehide." He showed her a thin, half-moon-shaped metal plate set with sharp prongs. "These are good to pound into heavy leather, or wooden soles for keepin' down wear!"

Emily sighed. "I wonder what women and children will do during the cold winter. Wear heavy knit stockings without shoes?"

"Well, calf and goat skins, or even tanned squirrel skins make good uppers," he advised. "Heavy canvas works, or close-knit tops hold up pretty good--an' don't look bad on the ladies."

Emily hesitated. It all sounded so difficult!

"If you decide to go to wooden soles," Mr. Gill said, taking a pair from below his counter, "I've got some on hand."

As soon as she handled the stiff wooden shapes, Emily saw that they would be a last resort. "They seem so clumsy!" she remarked. "But, thank you, Mr. Gill, for all the ideas you have shared. As a seamstress, I should be able to make use of some of them."

A sad expression crossed the old man's wrinkled face. "I have dealt in shoes all my life," he murmured, "an' it pains me that I can't be of much use any more."

Smiling, Emily said, "But you've been of great help to me, Mr. Gill! And I thank you, sir!"

Collecting Archie and the sack of corn, she led the way toward the Knox home on Green Street. There, on the corner of Clinton, stood the fire-damaged jail.

Aunt Susan welcomed them warmly, and everyone except the baby, who was sleeping, rejoiced over the fresh corn.

"I intended to walk down that way, unless you came by today," Sue Harrison declared. "There are two bundles of sewing here."

"I've kept the orders separate," explained Aunt Susan. "One is wrapped in a piece of old sheet; the other's tied with a strip of cloth." She told Emily who had left each lot. "An' since you have their children's measurements, all you'll need to know is that it is up to you to get as many tiny dresses as you can from each one of the garments."

Smiling, she added. "That must be like a puzzle to figure out."

"It is like a puzzle," admitted Emily. "But, somehow, making a garment from scraps seems to give more satisfaction than working with an untouched piece of fabric! Susan, who is so good with children's clothes, likes to make over, too!"

"What are you doin' for buttons?" asked Aunt Susan's daughter, Mary Ann Patterson, who had been listening with interest.

"Saving every one possible. Each garment seems to need so many of them. Children's drawers even have to have buttons!"

Aunt Susan laughed. "They do indeed! Lest they drop off at the worst time! Much to my shame, I had that happen to me once when I was a child!"

Curious, Emily asked, "What did you do?"

"I wanted to walk right off an' leave 'em, only Elizabeth was with me, an' she made me pick 'em up. Then, I just wadded them up into a ball which she stuffed inside the bag she was carryin' an' we walked on as though nothin' had happened. It was in Knoxville, but not on the street where most of the shops were."

"Thank you for telling me that, Aunt Susan," laughed Emily, for she knew she would treasure that picture of the little girls in their predicament.

"As for buttons," Mary Ann switched back to their original subject, "I like the crocheted ones that have loops to hook over to fasten them!"

Much struck by that idea, Emily said, "Thank you, Mary Ann. No doubt my sister can make some of those. She's so good at knitting and crocheting. I'll ask her to experiment." Then, gathering the bundles, she rose to go. "I wish I could stay longer, but my work has piled up something frightful!"

Archie was collected from the porch, where he was favoring Mr. Knox with a discourse on blacksmithing, and handed a bundle. "We must hurry!" Emily said. "I want to stop by Mary Elizabeth's."

They found Mr. Tinable seated on the front steps, whittling.

Archie's curiousity, never containable, burst forth in several questions, all overlapping.

The whittler, taking them one at a time, said, "I am whittlin' a paddle for stirrin'. The preservin' season is here...although I don't know where we are goin' to get any fruit--or sweetener, for that matter. But the Lord may provide!"

"He may indeed!" agreed Emily. "And if He provides anything to us, you can be sure we'll be sending you a share!"

"What kind of wood is that, Mr. Tinable? I wish you would show me how to whittle!"

The old man laughed. "It's pinewood, Archie. Have you a knife? For I make it a practice never to lend mine."

Amused at Archie's questions, Emily suddenly remembered one to ask, "Have you any ideas as to what we can make shoes from? Seems our children's feet just refuse to stop growing!"

Mr. Tinable nodded. "It's a puzzler! I've been thinkin' on it, an' I've talked to our cobbler friend around the corner. He's got some good ideas. But what I need to do first is unlock the house on the back of the lot an' see what I can find. I know the boys had an awl for punching holes. An'--who knows?--there may be some bits of leather or canvas. I'll bring you word, my dear."

"Are you goin' in the shoemakin' business, Emily?" Mary called from the doorway. "I see you're takin' in washin'!"

Emily laughed. "It does look that way--and I may come to that! But these are things to be ripped up and made over for children's clothes. It's a business that's multiplying now almost beyond my managing. How are you feeling, Mary?"

"Well enough, most days. Can't you come in?"

But Emily explained her rush.

"At least, let me tell you how Kate is enjoyin' attendin' your school! She is already teachin' little Laura Ann to make marks on the slate. And she has Josephine and me both singin' with her. I fail to see how you do it all--especially right now!"

"But, Mary, I love every minute I spend with the children! They are my salvation!"

Mary nodded, for she could understand. "Come back whenever you can! We are really feastin' on the corn the boys brought over!"

Walking north toward the turn to Arms Street, Emily lugged the largest of the bundles, while Archie followed with the other. All of his thoughts were now on his immediate need for a knife.

"If I had one, I could whittle all sorts of things. Why, Aunt Emily, I could even make buttons for you!"

"That would be the hardest thing of all!" she said. "Anyway, I can't settle your knife problem. You'll have to ask your pa."

They found Margaret O'Casey seated on her front porch, ripping seams. She rose smiling. "Do be coming in, Mrs. Elliott, and take this other chair. I'm out here with my work, for there's no light as sweet as the sun gives when you've dainty work in hand!"

"I agree!" Emily said, putting her sheet-wrapped bundle beside her on the floor. "Give me your bundle, Archie, and then run over to speak to Jason and the boys under the mulberry tree."

Margaret laughed. "It sounds like an old game, but it's where I'm hoping they'll play, a-soaking sunlight into their wee bones. But, here! I'm a laggard in thanking you for that noble treat you gave us on The Fourth. It was a real celebration we had that day! Bridgett will be bringing my sentiments to Mrs. Baker."

"It was all Elizabeth's doing," Emily assured her. "Though, we mustn't forget Uncle Pompous and his--rather unwilling!--helpers, Romeo and Edward."

"Blessings on the boys, for they're fine lads!" Margaret said, her tone dipping on a note of sorrow. "Makes me remember my lads, gone who knows where these many days now. It's wondering I am, if I'll ever hear of the bairns again."

"You've had no word?" Emily felt sympathy rise in her throat.

Margaret shook her head. "I've no way to make inquiries. Fact is, Mr. Conway thinks it might make the matter worse, should they be picked up by the soldiers of the Union, that is." She paused, obviously gathering strength, then continued in a confiding tone, "You see Sean, that's my oldest--though he's only fifteen--may be into some deviltry. Oh, how almighty cruel that sounds coming out of a mother's lips! But poor Sean was so mortal wounded over his pa's death--for he near idolized that man, rascal that he was!"

Emily, finding herself caught up in this sad tale, whispered, "And what of your younger boy?"

"Dear Patrick," Margaret whispered in turn. "The sweetest lad, but too quick to follow Sean's lead in everything. 'Tis often I've wondered if Patrick was just after protecting his older brother. But I don't know, and doubtless never will."

"I'm so sorry," Emily said. "If there's a thing we can do...."

All at once Margaret looked shocked. "I can't believe I've set my own burden on your shoulders, with all your sadness! 'Tis a sin I'll have to confess, and soon!"

"Oh, no!" protested Emily. "That's what friends are for...all of us need God and each other in times like these."

As their eyes met in complete understanding, Margaret returned the conversation to dressmaking. "I've finished the lot I had. Is it possible you've more for me there?"

Together they examined the contents of each of the bundles, as Emily consulted her book of measurements and made notes.

"It's hoping, I am, that my way of winding the old thread I've saved--for I know the value of every inch!--is to your liking? My little lads find and smooth the sticks I'm winding it on. 'Tis joy they get from helping. I'm threading all the buttons to the stick for I'm knowing how precious they are!"

"You're doing everything perfectly, Margaret," Emily said, and reached in her cloth bag to pay what she owed.

"'Tis the way I want it, for without this money, we'd be right at starving's door!" Margaret said. "I don't know if Bridgett has told you, but since you're not needing her on Saturdays, she's giving a little aid to Mrs. Hardie."

"I'm so glad!" said Emily. "Elizabeth and I have been anxious about Mrs. Hardie having no help." She had taken up the bundle of finished work and started toward the mulberry tree, when she suddenly remembered, "Oh, my goodness! I've failed to thank you for Lady Mist! We all like her, though she seems to have adopted Aunt Sophia as mistress and has already deposited two offerings of dead mice at her feet, as evidence of her hunting skill."

"She's a sweet craycher!" said Margaret.

"And a valued new member of our family!"

Chapter Eighteen

July 11, 1862

"Seldom do we hear a thing about the progress of the war!" was Elizabeth Baker's puzzled comment to Mrs. Elliott. They had just made a new examination of the injuries Lucius had suffered to two of his toes and had walked with Emily into the sitting room.

"That is so true!" agreed Emily. "Why, all of North Alabama could burn down around us without our even knowing!"

"Word does get here," her mother-in-law observed. "I expect the menfolk are wantin' to keep you from worryin'. Anyway, much is only rumor. Why, Littleton will hear somethin' for a fact one day...and the very next day, it'll be denied!" she shook her head so fiercely that the lace cap pinned to her gray locks quivered. "I don't hold with protectin' women! We're as sturdy as men when it comes to bearin' trouble. Maybe even more so!"

The other two nodded their heads in complete agreement.

"I do know one thing that's happenin' this week," Mrs. Elliott continued, lowering her voice and leaning forward. "Col. Turchin, who let his men go rampagin' around the country, burnin' farm houses an' buildings to the ground an' near destroyin' the town of Athens, has been sent up for court martial."

Elizabeth and Emily regarded the old lady in astonishment.

"Athens burned?" gasped Elizabeth.

"Yes, and thievery! His soldiers were let loose to steal what they could!"

"Athens? That pretty place?" Elizabeth was still trying to take that in. "Why, it could've been our own town!"

"Littleton says what's saved Huntsville is the fact that Union

232

officers found enough fine houses to take over here for their own use. You know, some of them have even brought their families into our midst!"

"I've not heard of that on this side of town," Emily said.

"It's a wonder we haven't been forced, at least to 'board' an officer!" Mrs. Elliott observed. "May come yet!"

"Here I thought doing without food, making over clothes, going barefoot, and staying in, were bad enough!" commented Elizabeth.

"Going barefoot?"

"Well, just the children right now," Emily added, "but the few shoes in stores are out of sight in price, and as for shoemakers, they can't get an inch of leather. All going to the army! Our own soldiers have to have shoes! I don't begrudge them a single pair, but it does leave us to make do with whatever we can find. I have talked to Mr. Gill and to Mr. Tinable. Both have some ideas, such as cutting up buggy curtains, or using heavy canvas."

"Heavy canvas?" Mrs. Elliott asked. "Why, I wouldn't be at all surprised if there's not some of that in my own attic. Enoch was a wagonmaker, an' often was called on to make canvas covers. My! My! I'll have to get up the attic stairs an' see what I can find. I'll go this minute, for Robert E. is at home an' can help me."

Emily got hastily to her feet, urging, "Why not wait until Littleton comes and let him go?"

"It'll be dark then. Don't worry! I'm up there fairly often to look for somethin' I've lost."

"Well, let me go with you then," insisted Emily.

However, the old lady was adamant. "The mess in my attic's not for anyone else's eyes!"

But they were not to learn of the contents of the famous attic that day, for word arrived that Jesse Jordan had been killed in the fighting for Richmond. His mother was next-door neighbor and friend to Mrs. Elliott.

Mary Ann brought the word across. "An' Mrs. Jordan is goin' to travel to Richmond to bring back Jesse's body. She's been granted a pass through the Union lines. So Ma's over there now, helpin'."

Lucius was suffering, not only from the pain and discomfort of broken bones, but also from his difficulties in getting about. His crutch was unwieldy and hard to manage. Most of his time was spent in the kitchen, where he took on the churning as his chore. "It's a good sitting-down job!" he pointed out.

"Now, if that be all yer problem," Aunt Sophia said, "I'se got plenty more sittin'-down jobs jes awaitin' yer pleasure. First, you can start in stringin' these beans for supper."

Lucius groaned. "I see I spoke too soon! But didn't I hear the word 'blackberries' mentioned?"

"They is waitin' over there in the briar patch for Pompous an' them boys to come pick," replied Aunt Sophia. "But the flour bin was bare, so that chile, Addie Virginia, is takin' Edward to get us a bucketful or two at the mill."

"My! what would we do without Addie V.?" asked Lucius.

Aunt Sophia shook her head. "I don' wanna think on that!"

A knock on the door proved to be the two children, each with a covered bucket of flour. They came on inside--and before the door could be closed, Lady Mist also entered, moved soft-footed across the room, and gently deposited a mouse at Aunt Sophia's feet.

"Oh, Lord!" moaned Lucius. "Fried mouse for dinner!"

The mouse--not too dead to learn of its fate--flopped over and made for the open door. Lady Mist pounced too late.

"I has told you...CAT!...not to dirty up my kitchen with those critters, dead or 'live!" Aunt Sophia placed her hands on her ample hips and lectured Lady Mist from the back door.

Alvah--now nearly two and getting about everywhere--ran in the room calling, "Laaay Deee!" To catch the gray cat was his heart's desire, yet unsatisfied.

Still muttering, Aunt Sophia slammed the back door.

Addie Virginia said, "The cat's gone, Alvah. Let's you and me go to find Enoch. We can tell him about the mouse."

Always happy to see her kitchen vacated, Aunt Sophia addressed Edward and Romeo, "Well, they ain't nothin' stoppin' you boys goin' on with Pompous to the briar patch now, far as I can see! Get you some buckets offen the well house. I'm jes emptyin' this flour into my bin, an' thankin' the Lawd fer it!"

It was near noon when the berry-pickers returned, scratched by briars and complaining of chiggers.

"We'd have been back sooner," Romeo reported, "but Edward imagined he saw a snake--and got so upset he tripped over his own feet and spilled a full bucket of berries..."

"...well, you would've, too...if you'd nearly stepped right on the thing! I think it was a copperhead..."

"...copper nothing!" protested Romeo. "You never clamped your eyes on it longer than one second!"

Uncle Pompous spoke up. "No need for all that fright! You boys knew I had ma stick!"

Laughing, Aunt Sophia lifted a full bucket up to the tabletop and said, "Why, you...Pompous--of all folks I knows!--is the mos' scared of snakes. An' don't tell me you ain't! These am real nice berries. Get me one them little pails, Edward, so's I can put out some for that chile, Addie Virginia. Then, you boys!--you, too, Pompous!--go wash yer hands an' arms, 'cause Miss Em'ly is gonna want to spread some salve on yer scratches. We jes' don't want no scratches festerin' in this hot weather!"

Besides blackberries, peaches, and corn, July produced a great richness of vegetables from the garden. Nearly everyone was kept peeling, slicing, shelling, or, in various ways, helping to store this bounty for the winter to come. Everything that could be saved by drying was carefully sliced and spread on rags or pieces of sheets in all manners of places. Several crocks held food that had been salted down, though salt was growing very scarce.

"Since Lamperson Smith is raising two pigs to slaughter for us when hog-killing weather gets here, we should be trying to save as much salt as we can for him," Elizabeth reasoned. "For you can't keep meat without salt. We all know it!"

"Far as meat go, these squirrels Mr. Smith's boy done kill fer us is somethin' special!" said Aunt Sophia. "When I gets 'em all season'd, flour'd, an' popp'd in the fryin' pan, they's gonna be top eatin'!"

"And from what Albert said, the boy got them with a slingshot, while he was cutting wood near the mine," marveled Elizabeth. "I don't see how he could do that!...But, of course, they can't risk the sound of a rifle shot attracting attention."

Emily, who had come into the kitchen to press a garment, said, "If we had known how, we could have saved the squirrel skins, and tanned them for making shoe leather!"

Elizabeth looked at her in amazement. "Surely we're not going to have to tan leather!"

"Well, no. But then, if we did, Edward could tell us how!"

"Law! Miss Em'ly, I knows you thinkin' of shoemakin', but that tannin' is man-work!" Aunt Sophia was outraged. "'Sides, them ol' vats smell terr'ble bad. When I wuz a chile, there wuz an ol' vat in that field below the Big Spring. It stunk somethin' awful!"

Suddenly, the back door opened to admit Romeo, followed slowly by Lucius on his crutch. Both spoke at once; Lucius, however, got the floor. "Mr. Pollard stepped across to tell us that today some Union soldiers burnt down every building there was in the town of Whitesburg, down on the river!"

Romeo added, "It must have been awful! Those Blue Coats are about the lowest scum there is anywhere! If I was old enough..."

"...well, I just thank the good Lord you are not!" interrupted his mother. "Though I do agree about the 'scum' part. I think the North must be short of men to have enlisted some of the ones sent here!"

Lucius spoke up, "Well, I doubt if many want to come! They may think it's a war not worth risking their necks over!"

As Emily went back to the sitting room, she could not help but consider what Lucius had said. She knew so many Southern men who would have become leaders, or at least hard-working citizens like William, had they not been killed. And now Jesse Jordan was gone! That boy had been studying the law!

"Mama! Bessie has got blood on her sampler!" Mattie announced.

Bessie held up the evidence.

"Did you stick your finger, honey?" asked Emily, going over to where the little girls were seated at work on their first efforts at sewing. "Which finger is it?"

236

The finger still bore evidence of the prick, but was soon doctored. "Cold water--never hot!--will take out blood," Emily said, "so take your sampler into the kitchen, and your mother will show you what to do."

"Then can I quit, too?" begged Mattie. "I may stick my finger just any time."

"No," Emily replied. "You may not quit. We all must learn how to avoid pricks and to carry on after we've had one."

Pricks were certainly to be avoided; Lucius was absorbing that lesson! Since he was available--and, if not ready and willing, at least unable to escape--Elizabeth and Emily hoped to persuade him to become shoemaker for the family. It would keep him occupied...and might even produce a pair of shoes!

"Shoemaker!" he protested when the plan was put forward. "Make a pair of shoes? Why, that's like asking me to start a hat-making factory, right here in the kitchen!"

"Oh, no!" Elizabeth denied. "We can do without hats, or we can get Uncle Pompous to make some from straw. He's an expert when it comes to weaving straw. Someone taught him when he was a boy."

"Well, if he's such an expert at that, he can probably come up with a pair of shoes, too!"

"Hmmmp!" commented Aunt Sophia. "Pompous a good hat-maker, but he couldn't never make a shoe. He ain't got that kind a' brains! But Mr. Lucius here kin do anything he want to! I'm a-tellin' you one thing, iffen somebody don't make me a pair a' sandals, shoes, or somethin', I'm gonna be cookin' in ma bare feets!" She pulled aside her vast skirt, revealing the tattered remnant of her right shoe.

Either that exhibition, or Sophia's practiced use of flattery, persuaded Lucius. "Well, if it's a choice of barefoot cooking, that's different!" He thought for a minute before asking the two important questions: "What can I use? And who's to teach me?" He waited with an impish grin, obviously not expecting any answers.

But there he was very wrong!

"Mrs. Elliott has found in her attic a lot of heavy canvas and some leather buggy curtains," Elizabeth replied. "She's given it to us. Of course, we haven't found a bit of heavy leather to make into soles. Maybe you can come up with a source for that!"

"As for someone teaching you," Emily added, "Mr. Gill, the old cobbler, has promised to draw you some patterns--and also sell us some shoemaker's thread. Then, when he heard about your accident, he even said he would come down here and get you started."

"That was good of the old gentleman," Lucius said. "I used to stop there to talk to him, so I guess he remembers me."

"He does indeed!" Emily assured him. "Also, Mr. Tinable has found some tools in the boys' paint shop behind their house: one is a shoe last made of iron like that used by cobblers for making or fixing shoes, also a hammer, and an awl for punching holes. Since he knows a little about the craft, he has offered to help."

Listening to this recital in astonishment, Lucius was moved to say, "Looks like you've got me cornered. Have you considered the possibility that I may not be able to do the job?"

"No!" replied Elizabeth and Emily in one breath.

"Now, Mister Lucius," Aunt Sophia stated firmly, "I knows, an' you knows!, that you kin do anythin' you wants to!"

Lucius grinned at her. "For that, you'll get the first pair I turn out...and they may cripple you for life, Aunt Sophia!"

Of course, shoemaking didn't work out quite as expected! Like many things, it was easier to talk about than to do. In spite of Mr. Gill's instructions and patterns, his gift of some glue, with the loan of one of his wooden shoe lasts to fit a man's foot, the need for leather heavy enough to make soles and heels had them at a standstill.

While Lucius waited for the leather to appear--which he seemed to think would drop from the sky!--he grew expert at whittling shoe pegs. These had to be less than one-half inch long, counting the pointed end. Another thing he learned to do was run a length of shoe thread through a lump of beeswax, all the time twisting and twisting until it became slightly stiff and extra strong. To make sharp points at the ends, Mr. Gill taught him how to twist in and wax a hog bristle.

It was this waxed shoe thread that gave Emily an idea. Why not make moccasins? "All the small children can wear them inside the house, at least!, this winter." she pointed out.

"Why, I'd be glad to have a pair myself!" Elizabeth said. "Why couldn't all of us, men included, wear them whenever possible and save our good shoes? Do you think Lucius could make them?"

"I think that he and I together can!"

"But what would you use?"

Emily considered. "We could make soles from the buggy leather, even if we have to double it, and uppers from the canvas. I think Mr. Gill would help us get started. Why don't we try to make Aunt Sophia a pair as an experiment?"

"Law, Miss 'Lizbeth!" Sophronia grinned broadly. "Why, I be a-hoppin' like a flea in a pair them mocc'sins. Keep ma feets warm as toast!"

When the matter was put to Mr. Gill, he furnished patterns for three sizes: a man, woman, and child. "Have them stand on a piece of paper and then draw 'round both feet--leave plenty of room, at least a half-inch. Then you'll have to alter the pattern for the top of the moccasin so as that part fits the sole." He looked at Emily, as he mentioned changing the pattern.

Turning to Lucius he continued, "You'll need an innersole, and a smooth lining for the canvas top would be nice, 'specially for the children an' ladies."

"How would the tops fasten together?" asked Emily.

"You can always put on some ties, or some kind of buttons."

After they had thanked Mr. Gill, and Aunt Sophia had served him blackberry cobbler and a glass of milk, the old gentleman left.

"He was glad to help us," Emily told Lucius, "for he regrets not being able to do his usual work for people!"

"Next time I bakes a pie, I'se gonna 'member that gentlemum, I sure is!" declared Aunt Sophia. "An' he'll get a piece, even if I has to take it up there my ownself!"

"We'll get it to him!" promised Emily. "Now you take off those worn-out shoes, Aunt Sophia, and stand flat on this paper."

"You sure that piece big 'nuff, Miss Em'ly? My feets jes goes on an' on!" Her rich laugh burst all around them.

With this actual foot-pattern (surely about as large as they'd ever be called on to make!) Emily and Lucius moved their work out to the east porch, where the light was good. At first, they had a curious audience of children, who soon tired of watching. Archie, though, gave them his steady regard along with endless questions and seemed determined to stay with the project to the end.

And it took the best part of two days of experimenting to make a credible pair of moccasins to fit Aunt Sophia.

"Law, Mr. Lucius!" she said in an awed voice as she pranced around the kitchen in the finished product. "I done say you can do anythin' a-tall. An' it true! 'Course we all knows what Miss Em'ly can do!...Miracles!...I thanks you!"

"You're welcome, Aunt Sophia," replied Lucius. "I'm glad they fit you!"

"And the best thing is that we've got a good pattern, and can make you another pair in half the time," added Emily.

"The children's small moccasins won't take near so long," said Lucius. "Why don't we try a pair of those next?"

Hearing that, Archie stepped eagerly forward. And their most faithful observer could not be denied!

"Stand on this paper," Emily instructed.

"Make them plenty big," the little boy urged, "'cause you know I have to do a lot of walking with you, Aunt Emily!"

In less than a day, Archie was strutting around in his pair. A line of children soon formed on the east porch, but Emily decided they should make some for little Alvah next. "He's running around everywhere now...I'm so afraid he going to get a splinter!"

While the shoemaking went on, everyone helped Emily as much as they could with her other tasks. Still, the days were so full and busy that she almost collapsed into bed at night. Even grief and worry were overshadowed by the simple necessity of keeping up with orders for garments and moccasins. Finally, she decided to call a vacation for the school.

"A vacation? What's that?" asked Jason.

She smiled to calm the anxious look on his face. "It will only last for about three weeks, until around the middle of September. Then school will start again!"

Seeing the looks of disappointment and uncertainty mirrored on their faces, she hastened to explain. "All schools have vacations so the pupils and teacher can have a rest. But we are all here so close together, we'll see each other often."

Addie Virginia's hand shot up. "I'm not needin' a rest myself, but I know you are, Miss Emily. An' if I can do anything to help you, I want to know it." She paused, thoughtfully. "I think I'll spend my school hour tryin' to teach Charlie some more letters. Pa would like that!"

"Do you think you could teach my sister, Florence, anything, Addie?" Alice Hardie asked hopefully. "She needs teachin' bad, only she won't listen to me a minute!"

There were other similar requests, and before Emily could take in what was happening, they were busy making arrangements to pass on the things they had learned. Amazed and thankful, she felt her heart swell with love for these little children, who had meant so much in her life...who had, in fact, rescued her from despair.

It was inevitable that the moccasin-making supplies should begin to give out--not canvas, of which they had a great supply. It was the leather buggy curtains that were nearly gone. Only enough remained for one pair. Who should get them?

The question was answered when Albert mentioned that the Smith boy, Jackson, needed shoes. "It's hard walking up there on those mountain paths without something on your feet!" he said.

"And he's done so much for us!" cried Elizabeth. "Picked fruit and shared the bee tree! And all those squirrels! It's high time we did something for him."

So as soon as Albert brought them a drawing of Jackson's feet, they could start. While they were working one day, Lt. Fraser came along Mill Street. Seeing them on the porch, he stopped and called, "I see you are busy!"

Emily rose. She hadn't seen him since William's death. Now, an irresistible impulse drove her down the porch steps and over to the

241

fence. "Good afternoon, Lieutenant," she said. "I have not had a chance to thank you for your kindness when William...my husband....Won't you come in a few minutes?"

He looked at her first in sympathy...then in surprise at being invited. "I'll be delighted to, Mrs. Elliott."

Once on the porch, the Lieutenant took great interest in their shoe-making project. Lucius explained about their need for cowhide to help them make real shoes for winter.

Lt. Fraser nodded his understanding, then inquired, "Have you injured your foot, young man?"

When he heard the sad tale, he immediately asked permission to examine the toes. "I'm a qualified physician," he assured them in an earnest tone, "and do have considerable experience with broken bones."

Emily fetched a pan of water and towel, and watched closely as Dr. Fraser removed the bandages, examined the splinted toe, and also the big toe that was still dark and swollen. "Both toes seem to be doing well. Did a local doctor do the splinting?"

Emily shook her head. "My mother-in-law and I did it. We have both had some experience."

"You did well. It's going to take some time yet. That big toe may remain stiff! Try to make him a protective moccasin, hardened around the big toe, so he won't hit it on something. And, young man, you should get up and move around as often as possible." Dr. Fraser had replaced the bandage and now turned to wash his hands.

"Thank you so much, Dr. Fraser," Emily said. "It's a relief to have that diagnosis."

"I'se hopin', Doctor," Aunt Sophia said from the kitchen door, "that you'll take a bite of ma blackberry cobbler." Squeezing her bulk through the door, she set a tray on the table and served all of them with cobbler and cold milk.

The doctor's immediate comment was, "This is a rare treat! Good enough to cure anything!"

When he rose to go, Emily walked with him to the side gate. He paused to inquire, "I wonder if I could ask a great favor of you? I'm hoping you will write to my parents and my little twins, Margaret and

242

Victoria, and let them know you've seen me. They would welcome your letter!"

As he scribbled names and an address on the back of one of his cards, Emily hastened to assure him, "I'll be glad to write, for I shall never forget your kindness to our family during this terrible time."

When she reached to take the card, he grasped her hand in his, and spoke in a low voice, "Tell Mr. Baker, we will be pulling out soon."

She should have experienced a great and unspeakable joy at the news; instead, she felt herself go rigid with some nameless, personal grief. Finally, she heard herself whisper, "May the Lord go with you and keep you safe."

"And be with you always," he said.

It was then that they exchanged the long, wordless look that—try as she might—she would never forget! It completely disarmed her and filled her with such unaccountable sadness that, after he turned on Arms Street, she could only seek refuge in the outhouse to try to gather her strength to go on.

That night, without saying anything to anyone else, Emily gave Albert the message Lt. Fraser had left.

There was no doubt of the relief and joy reflected in Albert's face. "I've been hoping and praying for this," he said. "Now, I can see a little way ahead. At least we can close the deal on the coal mine. We didn't want any hitch to interfere when we went to take up our option on the forty acres. This will be between us, for the time being."

Two mornings later, a large bundle was discovered lying inside the side gate. It contained two tanned cowhides, along with five loaves of white sugar and ten pounds of coffee.

"I knew that leather would come to us from somewhere!" Lucius exulted. "Do you suppose it was Dr. Fraser who left it?"

Emily only nodded. Somehow, she couldn't speak. But before the day was out she had borrowed a piece of Elizabeth's notepaper and written a letter to the Fraser family. It was a satisfying letter to write, and she hoped that there would be a chance to mail it in the days to come.

The moccasins for Jackson Smith were soon finished, and Albert reported that they were a good fit and much appreciated.

A week later, he brought home three cured deerskins. "They are from Jackson," he told Emily and Lucius. "He wants you to make a pair of moccasins for his ma. She's barefoot," he said, as he unfolded a piece of old newspaper on which her footprints were outlined.

It was Lucius who gave their promise...for the mere thought of the plight of Mrs. Smith--that good and generous soul--had so touched Emily that she could not speak.

"About the cowhide," Albert said, "likely Gill will make shoes from that with no questions asked. The deerskin, now...that is so soft, it'll do well for moccasins. Do you want him to make those, too?"

"Oh, I think we ought to go ahead, now that we know how," said Lucius. "What do you think, Aunt Emily? After all, there isn't much else I can do for a while!"

"Oh, I agree! And they'll be easier to make from these soft skins." She laughed. "You may be able to do it alone!"

"I might at that!"

It was that night, the twenty-eighth of August, that Albert reported to Emily that the deal on the coal-mine property had been closed. "We got the forty acres from Frank Brannan...for two hundred and seventy-five dollars (mostly Conway's money), and Judge Scruggs recorded the deed today. So that's a great relief!"

It was three nights later that the Union Army began its exodus from Huntsville. Movement on the railroad, and the racket from passing wagons and horses went on all night.

The event was a great surprise to most of the family...a time of relief, thankfulness and rejoicing for them all.

Aunt Sophia expressed it well, "I'se so thankful to ma Lawd as He has taken away them Blue Bellies." She did not learn until the next day that several hundred Negroes had gone with the invaders. Her comment was, "Them was taken at gun pointin'...or else they'd never of gone!"

But the thought foremost in most people's minds was: What's to come next for Huntsville?

Chapter Nineteen

August 31, 1862

"What day is this?" Emily asked sleepily. The previous night's disturbance coupled with her past weeks of overwork had left days confused in her mind.

"Law, Miss Em'ly," Aunt Sophia turned from the stove where she was cooking batter cakes on the griddle. "It do be Sunday mornin' an' them Blue Bellies am all gone from this town! Hallelujah!"

Elizabeth came across to hug Emily. "It is the last day of August, if you want the date. We are all so happy we are having a feast, at least as near as we can get to one. You look tired!"

Emily had to admit it. "I didn't sleep much." She stifled another yawn.

"Albert and some of the men plan to go to church," Elizabeth said, "but he thinks the rest of us shouldn't venture out yet. He intends to find out how conditions are downtown."

Reports filtered in all during the morning. Addie Virginia ran across to tell them that smoke visible above town was from fires set by the Yankees before they left. "Mr. Pollard told my pa how they burnt up everything they couldn't take along! Corn, and even meat...MEAT! Pa said that was a terrible sin, for some people are almost starvin' to death!"

Both Elizabeth and Emily were too shocked to speak.

Not Aunt Sophia. She raised her clasped hands and came near to shouting. "O Lawd, we do thank you for deliverin' us from thieves an' murd'rers, for it's YOU have done it! Amen."

Addie Virginia, though surprised at this reaction to her news, bowed her head and added, "Amen!"

Archie, Mattie, and Bessie, who were in the midst of their big feast at the kitchen table, paid little attention. They were used to Aunt Sophia's fervent outbursts.

"Did you come to play?" asked Bessie.

Her mother intervened. "This is Sunday, Bessie. Addie Virginia came to give us news." She placed her arm around the child's thin shoulders and urged, "Sit down right here, while Aunt Sophia puts a batter cake on the griddle for you. Do you like honey?"

"Yes, ma'am!" was the reply. "That'll be good."

It was later that evening that they learned some more.

"Capt. Frank Gurley's been in town twice," Albert reported. "I heard that his Confederate Calvary captured all the Yankees still here, including the ones that were sick in the hospital."

Emily was shocked. "You mean to say those Blue Coats went away and left their own men in the hospital? Oh, how inhuman!"

"I don't know," put in one of the men. "They may be better off with the doctors and women here to look after them."

"That may be," agreed another. "But they'll still be bound to end up in a Confederate prison camp."

Albert nodded. "As for Capt. Gurley...I heard he got a hero's welcome--even to being crowned with wreaths of flowers!"

"I'm not surprised!" said Elizabeth. "He is brave and daring; besides, he's from this county, and people admire and love him."

A different atmosphere now pervaded the town. Emily, who went out on Wednesday morning to deliver sewing, noticed the change. People on the streets were chatting to each other freely and cheerfully, as they had not done for a long time.

She noticed the pasture on the east side of Jefferson Street, where people had feared to take their cows while the Yankees held the town, was today the scene of feasting on the high grass. Most of the cows were being herded by young boys, apparent substitutes in the absence of Negro help.

At Richard and Mary's house, the door was unguarded. Somewhat surprised, she hallooed and walked in. An answer drew her to the

246

kitchen, where Alonzo, Mary Josephine, and Kate were working. It seemed that there were apples everywhere in the room.

"Hello, Aunt Emily," Mary Josephine greeted her with her sweet smile. "We're tryin' to save these apples 'fore they spoil!"

Alonzo spoke up, "None of us knows a lot about how to do it!"

"If you're drying them," Emily said, "you're doing right. When you've sliced them, then spread them out on some clean rags until they get good and dry. Where's your mother?"

"She's feeling so poorly today, we made her lie down," replied Mary Josephine.

"And that girl of ours just up and went off with the Yankees!" Kate revealed in disgust. "After we'd all tried so hard to treat her nice!"

Emily hung her bonnet on a hook on the wall. "I'll go see how Mary feels," she said. On a table near the door, she found water in a pitcher, with a washpan and towel. After she had washed her hands, she added, keeping her voice calm, "Alonzo, I expected you to let us know if you needed help."

"Grandpa said we would, unless he can find somebody to help us this morning. He's gone to see."

Mary's bedroom was dim, but Emily could see tiny Laura Ann lying asleep on the bed beside her mother. Mary stirred as the door opened, looked up, and said apologetically, "I seem to have given out all at once."

Emily drew up a chair. "I expect you're worn out. Too bad your help left you! Have you been doing something special?"

"Only tryin' to save some fruit that someone gave Grandpa. How are we ever goin' to get through the winter, if we don't save all the edibles we can find?"

Emily nodded in sympathy. "I know! We feel the same, but since you're expecting, Mary, you just can't afford to overdo! Have you any unusual pain?"

The head on the pillow shook back and forth. "I'm just tired." Then, suddenly, her smile broke through. "Isn't it wonderful that those Yanks have all gone! I could dance a jig...if I were able. Alonzo even took our cow to that pasture across the street. Poor animal! I can just

247

imagine how happy she must be."

"I saw all the cows and their young herdsmen. Such a pleasant sight!" Emily said as she rose. "You stay and rest; try to sleep! I'll be here for a while, longer if Mr. Tinable doesn't find you some help."

Mary's eyes closed as she whispered, "Thank you."

In the kitchen, Emily found an apron and began to get the work organized. She advised Alonzo to watch their cow. "It would be so awful if someone walked off with her! Who milks?"

"I try to," replied Mary Josephine. "I'm not afraid as long as Alonzo stands there with me. I've been wonderin' what I could fix for dinner, Aunt Emily. There's a little ham and some potatoes."

Emily turned to Alonzo. "Will you run over and let Elizabeth know where I am? And please tell Aunt Sophia to send some of the late beans from our garden. She may have some already strung." As he turned to go, she added, "And ask her to send a pot of her blackberry jam." She turned to ask Mary Josephine, "Have you some cornmeal? What about butter?" When both answers were affirmative, she said, "Then I'll make corn bread."

"Oh, Aunt Emily!" cried the little girl. "I'm so glad, because my bread just falls down flat in the middle!"

Later that day, when Emily arrived home and told Elizabeth of the situation at Richard's, Aunt Sophia asked, "What 'bout if I wring the neck of tha' ol' rooster--the one that's so mean? He'd make plenty broth. Then tomorrow I could drap in some dumplin's an' jes a mite of meat to go to Miss Mary's fam'bly. And us could have the rest fer our own supper."

It was a plan that met with agreement all around.

Bridgett had already gone home. Magdalena had the children and babies on the east lawn, while Lucius and the boys were on the side porch shelling field peas.

"Everyone's working but me!" Emily said to Elizabeth. "Forgive me, but I'll have to lie down for a bit."

"To my mind you both oughta lie down!" pronounced Aunt Sophia firmly. "If anything happen, somebody'll come up an' nudge you."

It seemed to Emily that she had rested hardly a minute before the

248

nudge came. Mattie brought it. "I hate to wake you, Mama, but Addie Virginia's here, and she's got to tell you something!"

Alarmed, Emily sat up. "Well, tell her to come on up then."

"She's out there in the hall," Mattie divulged. "I'll get her. And Mama, Addie don't want me to hear what it is--but you'll tell me, won't you?"

Emily looked into the troubled face of her sensitive daughter. "I will, as long as it's something you need to know."

Addie Virginia closed the door purposefully and said, "I hated to bother you, Miss Emily, but I promised to let you know if them mean boys of Mrs. O'Casey's ever came back." She paused to draw a breath. "Well, they're back--at least Patrick is! But, Sean,...he won't ever be back. He's been shot dead!"

With those words, the face of Margaret O'Casey rose in Emily's mind. That poor woman! "Who's with Mrs. O'Casey?" she asked.

"Well, Ma is, right now, but she can't stay long. Magdalena is watchin' Charlie for me. Oh, Miss Emily, Mrs. O'Casey's cryin' so bad--an' so is Bridgett! What can we do?"

"I don't know," Emily said truthfully. "But I'll get up and go to see. Thank you for telling me. Why don't you and Charlie stay here until your mother gets back? There's nothing cooking on your stove at home, is there?"

Addie Virginia shook her head. "No, ma'am. We haven't got much to cook, but Ma said she'd mix somethin' up when she gets home."

Downstairs, Emily told Aunt Sophia the problem.

"Those poor folk!" lamented the kind old woman. "It never rain but it pour! I know Miss 'Lizbeth'll want to send over somethin'. I'll be thinkin' on it, an' ask her soon as she rouses."

In the yard, Emily explained the matter to Magdalena. "I don't know what I'll find, or how long I'll have to stay." Noting with satisfaction that Addie Virginia and Charlie were among the other children, she hurried toward Arms Street.

The three little boys were under the mulberry tree in the side yard. They appeared sad and mopey. Seeing her, Jason came running to say, "Sean is deaded now!" He whispered. "So do you think he's gone up there in the sky with Jesus...like Mattie's brothers?"

249

Emily nodded. "I do, Jason, for Jesus loves all children!"

Jason looked alarmed. "But Sean was a man!"

Emily smiled, but shook her head. "No, Jason. You're not a man until you're eighteen. So Sean was still a boy...one who did not understand how risky it was to run away." She hesitated, knowing it must be his mother's business to explain. Anyway, Jason looked relieved as he went back to his little brothers.

Later that afternoon, Emily tried to describe the scene in the O'Casey home to Elizabeth. "It was all so much worse than I could cope with, Sister. So much worse!"

"How is Mrs. O'Casey bearing up?"

Emily shook her head. "I just don't know! I deemed her to be a strong woman, but I fear this has been an awful blow. And poor Bridgett, who always seemed to have so much spirit, only looked dazed--even unbelieving that it had happened."

"Now THAT I do not understand!" remarked Elizabeth. "They knew the boys had put themselves in awful danger, and surely must have been expecting...."

Emily nodded. "I know, but you can be expecting disaster...and still not believe it when it comes. For I know!"

"Did you find out how the shooting happened?"

"Seems they were trying to steal some food from a Yankee squad camped near a river--what river I don't think the younger boy has the least idea! A scout shot Sean, and he tumbled into the water and was carried off by the current."

"Maybe he wasn't dead?" murmured Elizabeth hopefully.

Emily shook her head. "No, he was dead all right, for Patrick had been hiding nearby, and saw it. Afterwards, he watched--even followed the river a long ways; but Sean's body never came up."

"Did you see the younger boy?"

"No, for he is in bed...sick and near starved, so they said."

Elizabeth rose from her chair in a hurry. "Then, it's food the boy-- that whole family!--needs. I think Sophia already has some things started."

By the time the men arrived from the shop, food was ready.

"Och! That poor widow woman!" exclaimed James Conway. "If they ain't having more'n their fair share of bad luck!...and all of it come at once. Well, it'll be me taking the food over and having a kind word with the family." He strode across the kitchen to look at what was ready. "By the powers! But it will take more than one to carry all this."

"I'll go along, too," declared Albert. "Offer our sympathy, at least! Aunt Sophia, let everyone else eat, and keep ours back."

Elizabeth came in to hand a folded note to her husband. "I've written to Mrs. O'Casey," she said. "Here's another from Lucius to Bridgett. And, Albert, tell Bridgett we won't expect her until her brother is better, and her mother can spare her."

James Conway started toward the door, then turned back. "I'll be expecting the Catholics here to help, for 'tis a Christian act to do so-- the poor, suffering woman being one of our own!"

It was the following Monday before Bridgett returned to help. "You may be sure I'd not miss a wash day!" she said, with a shy smile. "For I am mindful of your courtesy in letting us have our grieving time together."

"How is your mother?" was Elizabeth's immediate question.

"Some better, I'm thinking," Bridgett replied. From her apron pocket, she drew a folded slip of paper and presented it. "Ma has sent you a few words of thanks, Mrs. Baker and all--though, not a word could she find that was ample to record her true feelings of thankfulness."

"Your mother is a dear person, Bridgett," Emily said, stepping forward to greet the girl. "I admire her greatly. She is a strong person and will rally in time. But how is Patrick?"

A look of dejection seemed to overcome the young girl. Her red head drooped slightly. Finally, she said, "I'm hardly knowing how to answer. The poor lad's so starved in his body--and in his mind he blames himself for Sean's death."

"Why is that, Bridgett?" asked Lucius, who had just limped in in time to hear the last statement.

She hesitated before she answered in a low voice, "It appears the

251

little lad was put on the lookout for danger--so 'tis natural he feels a failure." She raised her head and spoke to Lucius. "I thank you for the kind words in your note, for I'm knowing you meant them every one."

"I'll be coming over to see Patrick, now that I can walk some. Meanwhile, if you'll make a tracing of his feet for me, I'll sew him a pair of moccasins for the cold weather to come."

Bridgett stood speechless while tears wet her cheeks. At last, she managed to say, "Oh, what a blessing that will be! For cut up and blistered is what his poor feet are."

"I'll send him some ointment that will help," offered Emily.

"Here you some mush, chile," Aunt Sophia said, kindly. "So you set right down here an' eat it!"

But at that moment, Mattie, Bessie, and Archie ran in, crying, "Bridgett's here!"

"What else have you to say to Bridgett?" Emily asked Mattie.

Confused for a minute, her face suddenly cleared. Quickly, she curtsied and came over to Bridgett. "I'm so sorry about your brother dying," she said. "I only saw him once. That was out here at the fence--and it's been a long time ago now."

"I never saw him even once," said Bessie, quickly performing a curtsy, "but I'm sorry anyway."

Archie--not to be outdone--produced his best bow and spoke his own thoughts, "Lucius told me about it--and I thought it was mean of that old Yankee. If I'd been there, and had a pocket knife, which Pa won't let me have yet, I'd have cut off..."

"...no, Archie!" his mother protested quickly. "That's enough! Let Bridgett sit down and eat her mush. And all you children take your seats at the table."

"...yes'um, thank you!" Aunt Sophia spoke up. "Fer we needs to get this breakfas' over. Other things waitin' to be done."

It was four days later, on a Friday, that Lulu Belle again got out. She wasn't missed until about four o'clock in the afternoon. Magdalena had milked her in the morning. Later, Edward had herded both cows to the pasture south of the railroad tracks.

"I led them both back, just like I always do when it's my turn to do it!" he declared stoutly. "Then I left them cropping grass out here in the back, like we been doing since the Yankees left."

"Was the gate to Mill Street wired shut?" his mother asked.

"I guess so. It always is. That's not my job anyway!..."

"...Edward!" interrupted his mother sternly. "I will not stand for impertinence--and you know it! Go to your room and stay there until I send for you!"

"Which direction do you want me to look?" inquired Romeo. "She may have gone to that pasture on Jefferson Street. I could run up there right quick and see if she's there."

"I can inquire along Mill and Arms to see if anyone saw her go by," offered Emily. "Mattie, you can come along with me."

"Likely she am gone to dem train tracks," said Aunt Sophia.

Elizabeth nodded. "I'll send Uncle Pompous that way." Then, at a loss for another searcher, she was forced to summon Edward. "It will be your job to search for Lulu Belle along the Spring Branch for she may be cropping grass over there. Go down Limberg and ask people you pass."

Magdalena, anxious witness to all the search plans, suggested, "I could take Archie and walk down toward Pinhook."

"Me, too!" begged Bessie. "Mama, I want to go. You know I love Lulu Belle!"

Hastily, Elizabeth sent Bessie running after Magdalena. "Stop to see if Mrs. Elliott has seen her!"

But no one had seen Lulu Belle. By five o'clock, all searchers had returned to report failure.

"It so near milkin' time, I 'spects that lady be moseyin' back any minute," was Aunt Sophia's assessment.

Magdalena was almost in tears by then. "I'm so feared somebody have stole her. She such a gentle, purty thing."

No one could deny that!

When Magdalena came back from milking Fire Fly, she reported, "Fire Fly didn't give much milk. I 'spect she missin' her buddy!"

By the time the men came, it was already dark. "I doubt if we can do anything this late," Albert said. "Best wait till morning, and if she's not back, we'll make another search."

But neither the second search, nor any that followed, produced evidence. Lulu Belle had vanished.

"We're going to be short of milk," Elizabeth calculated. "I'll have to reduce Mrs. Bolton's and Mrs. O'Casey's shares...or we won't have enough for ourselves."

While the loss of Lulu Belle was a sad blow, there was good news in another quarter. They could now advertise the coal mine. Even without a newspaper, word got around fast; orders poured in.

"We're taking on more hands," Albert reported one night. "Also looking for another wagon driver, one with his own wagon and team and who doesn't mind driving over that rough mountain road."

"Lamperson Smith and his lad, Jackson, are passing word around the country as they come in town," added Conway. "And hard up as people are, we're hoping somebody will be craving the job!"

Lucius spoke up. "I'm missing out on helping in any way. And I have to admit it's a disappointment!"

"Maybe not," his uncle said. "We've been thinking you might be some help with the records. There's a lot to it, and takes a good bit of time that Conway and I could put to better use."

"That's the truth of it!" agreed Conway. "With your schooling, not to mention your care with details--for it is plain to see you have a mind to finish any job and do it neat--you're bound to be the very lad we're needing."

Nearly bursting with pride, Lucius could only stutter thanks.

"After supper," Albert told him, "Conway and I'll show you the book we found for noting down our income and expenses. Right now, of course, you'll have to work on it here at the house."

So Lucius took a hand in the mine operation. Each night Albert brought home some slips of paper with notations, and, on the next day, Lucius made the entries in the book.

It wasn't long until he confessed to Emily, "My bookkeeping is cutting into my moccasin-making time. I'm five pairs behind!"

"That doesn't surprise me!" was Emily's comment. "Your work is so neat! I'd think you could sell them outside the family, if you wanted to. I'd offer to help, but my own sewing orders are piling up so that I wish I had another assistant. In fact, Susan will be starting to school soon, and I don't know what I'll do then!"

Lucius nodded, then said, "I've got my eye on Patrick O'Casey. That boy got a rough deal from his wild, older brother, but he is seeing things straight again. He's a neat-handed boy--can whittle things from wood in no time at all. He's already learned to make shoe pegs and to wax thread. That's where I started, you know."

Delighted at this news, Emily said, "You have my encouragement if you're thinking of sharing the work with Patrick. It's a good idea, besides being a generous one."

After that, Patrick sat on the porch with Lucius, and at noon, was invited to the dinner table. Aunt Sophia took great interest in the undernourished boy, while all of them were glad to see his handsome face fill out and lose its pallor.

Romeo, feeling left out of all of the activities, complained a little to Emily. "I think I'm old enough to go up and help at the coal mine...or do something!"

"Why don't you speak to your pa?" suggested Emily, who had an idea what Albert would say, but didn't want to discourage Romeo.

Albert thanked Romeo sincerely, saying, "You have a ways to go yet with your education, Son. As my eldest, I'll be expecting you to do bigger things than mine coal! You've got to get prepared." From his wallet, he drew two dollars. "This is a small reward for your hard work in the garden. That work will be more valuable than most anything else you could do for our family."

Romeo took the money and thanked his father.

"I hear McCay's school will be starting--no exact date yet, by October maybe--and before that, I expect you boys and Pompous can dig the potatoes and store all the root vegetables in that cellar back under Aunt Sophia's room. They'll all keep a long time under there. And don't forget the winter squash for making pies!"

When Edward heard about the prospects of school to come, along with the certainty of more garden work in the near future, he nearly exploded. "We've not had one minute of vacation this whole summer, Romeo! Work in the garden!...Scythe the grass!...Herd the cows!

255

Why, it's worse than slavery!"

Romeo tried to calm his brother without much success. Even the receipt of his own two-dollar reward did not make up for all that Edward felt he had been forced to endure.

A few days before her school was set to begin, Emily walked up West Holmes Street to deliver some sewing to the Beeman girls. As was her custom, she had Archie with her to help carry bundles. While she was in the Beeman's home, he was permitted to watch the blacksmith at work.

Today there were no horses to shoe, and Mr. Beeman had time to chat with Archie, in whom he recognized a kindred soul. After the making of moccasins had been discussed in detail by Archie, the story of Lulu Belle, "the runaway", was told.

"How long ago has that been?" Mr. Beeman wanted to know.

"Nearly a week, I reckon."

"The reason I asked," said the blacksmith, "I was over at that Jefferson Street pasture to bring my own cow home, one afternoon, when two boys were arguing over a cow. One said it was one of Mr. Steele's cows that they'd been looking for. The other boy did not agree, but they took the cow along with 'em, anyhow! She was real pretty...and gentle."

"That's sounds like Lulu Belle. She'll go with anybody!"

"Well, you might try Matt Steele's pasture by his Planing Mill and Door and Blind Factory over on East Clinton Street."

Archie thanked Mr. Beeman. In his excitement, he forgot all about his Aunt Emily and set out for home on a run.

When Emily came out of the Beeman's, she was surprised to meet Magdalena and Edward hurrying toward town, with Archie trailing.

"Miss Em'ly!" declared Magdalena, almost stuttering in her excitement, "Mr. Beeman do tell Archie that he think Lulu Belle am over at Mr. Matt Steele's place. So we's goin' to see!"

In her delight, Emily gripped Archie's shoulder. "This boy is the best I know at finding lost animals! Do you need help?"

"No'm, for Mr. Edward's with me."

Emily, taking Archie with her, went around to Jefferson Street to check on Mary Elizabeth. She found her sister-in-law feeling better and happy with new help. Kate was there, eager to start to school and ready to show off what little Laura Ann had learned!

"I'm going to be a schoolteacher!" piped the tiny girl. "See! I can already make four letters, Aunt Emily!"

It was not long before Magdalena and Edward arrived with their lost Lulu Belle. All three got a rousing reception. Edward sought the limelight by starting the tale.

"When we got in sight of the pasture, we could pick out Lulu Belle easy. I went right up to the boy that was herding and told him that was Mr. Albert Baker's cow, but he didn't believe it for one minute. He went inside that planing mill and called a man to come outside. The man didn't believe it either."

"What did you do?" asked his mother.

"Why, Magdalena said she could prove it was Mr. Baker's cow!"

"How could you do that?" Emily asked.

"It were easy 'nuff," replied Magdalena, "I jes say: Come now, Lulu Belle! What you mean runnin' off like that. It yer milkin' time! An' that sweet, gen'le lady, jes give one 'Mooooo' an' come right 'long with us."

"Amazing!" said Elizabeth. "How glad we are to see her home!"

"I told that man," Edward said, to assure himself full credit, "that if there was any question, he could see Mr. Baker up at his Marble Yard on Washington Street."

"You did well, Edward!" congratulated his mother. "Magdalena, we all thank you for being so clever!"

Emily added, "Don't forget that Archie was the one who learned where the cow was!"

"That a mighty queer story!" Aunt Sophia marveled, "But I'se sure glad to see The Lady home!"

"Soon as I get my bucket," Magdalena declared, "I'se goin' to milk you, Lulu Belle...an' you gonna get a good talkin' to!"

Chapter Twenty

September 15, 1862

On the day Emily had appointed for school to start again after vacation, the children were all there. Faces, cleaner and more polished than usual, also shown with eagerness. And nearly all of them had the name of a new pupil to suggest.

Emily had to shake her head over all their suggestions. "I do wish we could take some more," she said, "but you can see that the room is crowded now."

Seeing the disappointed faces, she added, "And think about it: any child just now starting will be far behind and will hold back the class. You are ready to make words with your letters and will soon be reading from a book." And that thought so captivated each child that the idea of adding to the class was soon forgotten.

Instead, they became so fascinated with the study of the lower case letters that Emily increased their class period by thirty minutes each day. We need to make progress while the weather is pretty, she told herself, for the season of bad colds will soon be here to slow us down.

Yet it wasn't colds that struck first. It was measles! How the disease started was unknown, but it closed the school in a hurry.

Emily (always fearful that Mattie and Enoch Carlton might take an infection) had a difficult choice. Should she help to nurse the first two patients, Bessie and Little Alvah?

Still, there were other hands to nurse. "You must keep your children and yourself away from the sick ones, Emily dear," urged Elizabeth. "Magdalena and I can manage the nursing. If things get really bad, Aunt Sophia can help. In the meantime, you can lend a hand in the kitchen."

"It is so hard for me, Sister!" Emily confessed. "For I have such a strong desire to care for the sick, especially when it's our own family!"

"I know that," Elizabeth said. "But you've often expressed a fear that your children, especially Enoch Carlton, will get some infectious disease, and I think you should be cautious!"

So Emily agreed. She helped to prepare breakfast each morning, did the milking, and handled the milk. Most of the vegetables were now going into the root cellar and did not require kitchen preparation.

During her morning hours in the kitchen, Mattie and Enoch were in the playroom nearby. The baby could crawl about safely on the matting-covered floor. When Emily went to check on them, she often found Mattie talking to her little brother, trying to teach him new words. What a fine opportunity for them to be together! she thought. It may help to forge a lifetime friendship.

Special food must be prepared for the three sick children, for Archie soon contracted the disease and had to be put to bed. Food for the patients, as well as meals for the nurses, was placed on trays on the dining room table to be picked up by Magdalena. They were all trying to be so careful not to spread the disease.

Lucius, Romeo, and Edward, all of whom had had measles, helped in many ways, as did Bridgett, who was kept away from the sick at all times. It was a great relief to Emily to learn that Jason had not come down with the infection, for she feared that he and his tiny brothers were too undernourished to fight such a disease.

Emily and the boys helped Bridgett with the washing, which was much heavier because of illness in the household. More sheets and pillow slips, towels, and aprons needed boiling.

Every afternoon, rain or shine, Emily took Mattie and Enoch outdoors for several hours. When the sun shone, she let them play on the east lawn; on wet days, they were kept on the side porch.

One night, Albert reported, "I saw Mr. Tinable today. He said neither Kate nor the other children have taken measles, and Mary Elizabeth seems to be well."

"Oh, I am so thankful for both of those pieces of news!" cried

Emily. "This is not the time for measles to get into that house!"

But Addie Virginia, little Charlie, Mattie P., and the Hardies were not so lucky! Emily worried about Mrs. Hardie, who had three sick at once. But all they could do was send a little food.

As the days passed, Bessie and Archie got much better and were able to come to the window in the upstairs bedroom. Hearing this, Emily took Mattie and Enoch Carlton around on the west lawn where they could wave to each other.

"Oh, Mattie," moaned Bessie in a thin, little wail, "I've been so sick...and I missed you!"

Mattie looked up, her tears overflowing. "I'm sorry, Bessie. I missed you awful bad! Are you nearly well?"

"I don't know," wailed Bessie.

Archie stuck his head from the window to call, "I am well, but Mama won't let me out!...I have to talk to Pa again about getting me a pocket knife...."

At that point both children were ushered back from the window, and Magdalena appeared, waving. "I missed y'all, ev'ry one!"

"Mag!" shrieked Enoch Carlton.

"You still 'member Mag? You big boy!" called Magdalena. "I'se sure gonna give you a hug when I gets a-holt of you agin!"

However, it was a while before that happened, for Alvah was not improving. A doctor had to be called in.

When Emily heard that, she was nearly crazy with anxiety. "Do you know what the trouble is, Aunt Sophia?" she pleaded. "I feel so awful not being up there to help!"

"Law, Miss Em'ly," the old woman said. "So do I! But I reckons we's doin' best like we is. We jes gotta keep prayin'!"

Several days went by. The doctor came each day, and after his last visit, released Bessie and Archie as cured.

Although they had lost weight and were pale and wan, their joy at being up and about was wonderful to see. They both ran around the house looking at everything as if it were brand new. Bessie's companionship with Mattie blossomed afresh; Archie's questions on every subject spouted forth continually.

Still the nurses did not appear. Alvah was too sick!

Emily thought perhaps Bessie knew what the trouble was, though she refrained from asking the child. Finally, Albert told her. He came into the sitting room, where she was looking over her sewing orders, wondering how she could ever catch up.

"Elizabeth," he said, with a solemn and sad note in his voice, "wants me to tell you, Emily, that the doctor thinks little Alvah will lose his sight."

"What!" cried Emily in horror. "Surely not!"

"He says the measles have settled in the boy's eyes! There is nothing to be done, I'm afraid. It's a bad blow!"

Emily could not speak; neither could she stop the bitter tears that began to flow. Her mind was in a turmoil. Sweet, patient baby--to be so afflicted before his life had hardly begun! "Oh, Albert," she whispered, looking up at him. "I might have done something, if I hadn't been so selfish!"

"That's exactly what Elizabeth said you would say," he stated, as he shook his head. "Well, it's not true! The doctor said there was nothing that could have been done! The infection has all gone now! What you can do, is lend some of your strength to Elizabeth, for she's had a long, tiresome struggle--and it's only the beginning."

"Oh, Albert! You know I'll support Elizabeth and little Alvah in every way possible! You do know that, don't you?" Try as she might, she could not keep anxiety out of her voice.

He smiled. "Don't be a goose!" he chided her. "'We know that! Elizabeth's resting now. She'll probably be downstairs in the morning. In the meantime, I'm going to prepare Aunt Sophia."

"It will be a terrible blow to her!" Emily predicted. "She has been praying so hard."

"Well, the Lord doesn't promise to answer prayers like we want Him to," Albert said sadly.

"I know!" whispered Emily. Her glance sought the window, where the darkness began. And she realized with a sinking heart that for little Alvah it will always be dark. Always dark!

This new disaster made it hard--almost impossible!--to take up their lives at the place where illness had entered. Nothing was the same. Little Alvah's plight had changed their priorities; the adults in the family were forced to look more deeply into their situation.

Elizabeth, both worn out physically and disheartened, needed a rest and change. Realizing this, Emily tried to bring it about in every way she could. It wasn't easy! Alvah's blindness was always on his mother's mind.

The autumn weather was ideal. All along West Holmes Street the big trees were in glorious color. A pleasant walk could be taken down to Pinhook Creek, across the bridge, and out Pulaski Pike as far as Tyler's Mill, now in full operation.

Once Elizabeth was persuaded to walk in that direction, with the little girls and Archie as company, and sometimes Edward, she enjoyed it so much that the stroll became a daily event. Just the change of scene and the sweet air, with its lingering odor of smoke and dusty foliage, seemed to restore her spirits.

Emily often spread a quilt on the west lawn--no longer grazing territory--and entertained Enoch Carlton and little Alvah. Rocks, leaves, and sticks were given them to examine. Pressing Alvah's fingers around each item and encouraging him to learn its name, became a game that Enoch could enjoy, too.

When Alvah cried for his mother, Emily took him on her lap and sang to him. When Magdalena was with them, they got him onto his feet and encouraged him to walk.

One day, while walking Alvah, they were surprised to see Addie Virginia standing outside the east fence.

"Addie Virginia!" their greeting came in one voice. "How are you? And little Charlie?"

Wordless and with a sad expression on her face, the child went on watching Alvah. Finally, she said, "We're all right, I guess. Ma says we are. But Charlie's still mighty cross."

"I'm so glad to see you!" Emily said sincerely. "Will you come inside the fence?"

Addie Virginia shook her head. "I better not today, Miss Emily, for I'm helpin' with Charlie." With tears in her eyes, she continued to study Alvah. At last she called to him, "It's just me, Alvah! It's Addie Virginia! I'll be comin' over to play with you soon." She waved. "Bye,

Enoch Carlton! I'll see y'all later!"

Emily and Magdalena looked at each other, shaking their heads. So it was in this way that a blind child would be viewed...with a mixture of sadness, pity, and curiosity, and, in Addie Virginia's case, a heart full of love.

Mrs. Elliott came over nearly every time she saw them outside. On each visit she brought something for Alvah--a soft little pillow for him to cuddle, or a sweet-smelling flower. He appeared to know her and would offer his smile.

The old lady, in turn, seemed to sense what would appeal most. "Want to stand up and come to see my ring?" she would ask. "Here I am!" He would get to his feet and toddle over--steered straight when necessary--and stand by her knee to feel her fingers for the ring. Sometimes she would have something hidden in her hand.

"I am so exercised by this," she told Emily, "that my thoughts continually return to this child." Pausing, she added softly, "My prayers, though, are goin' up!"

All their prayers were "going up"!

While they had been fighting their long war against measles, momentous events had come to pass. Among these was President Lincoln's issuance of his Emancipation Proclamation.

Albert told Elizabeth and Emily about it one night while they were resting in the sitting room after supper. "On the first day of next January," he said, "all the slaves will be free."

"I'm glad!" they cried, almost in one breath.

"Of course, I am going to tell Uncle Pompous, Aunt Sophia, and Magdalena," he continued. "I think they'll be more confused than anything. Anyway, they'll always have a home with us, only now I'll pay them something each month, as much as I can. The mine is flourishing these days. We got another driver, so more deliveries can be made. It's such a difference with the Blue Coats gone!"

"How much are you getting for a ton of coal?" asked Emily.

"Ten dollars, but we could--and may have to!--go some higher. Conway and I don't want people to think we are profiteering off this! There are a lot of expenses connected with running a mine."

263

"Why, Albert!" protested Elizabeth. "Nobody is going to accuse you of profiteering!"

"I don't know," he said, shaking his head. "You can be accused of most anything these days...and I am a Northerner!"

Albert was right when he said freedom would only confuse, even frighten!, the Negro members of their household.

"It don't mean nothin'!" was Aunt Sophia's assessment. "Why, I wouldn't no more leave y'all than fly to the moon! As fer money, be nice to have a little. Our church am needin' some work mighty bad, an' my pennies would help."

Uncle Pompous said the whole thing was brought on by: 'a mess a' rabble-rousin' no-accounts widout enuff to do'. "Now, me," he declared, "I'se got plenty to do, an' iffen I don't feel like doin' it, nobody give me the strap. Mr. Albert all time handin' me cash money, anyhow. He know I'm wantin' tobacco, iffen I can get a-holt of any! The Lord know I gotta good home, an' ain't fixin' to leave it no-how...not fer Mr. Lincoln, or nobody!"

It was Magdalena who was most disturbed. "Miss Em'ly, do that new law mean I got to leave here, where is ever'body I loves? An' go off somewheres else? Oh! Miss Em'ly." A loud hiccup of terror escaped the frightened young woman.

"Why, no indeed, Magdalena! You can live with us just as long as you want to. All that law means is that, if you want to leave, we have to let you go..."

"...my land! I'd never wanta do that. NEVER!"

Emily gave her a hug. "Then don't worry about it. From now on, Albert's going to pay you a little money. That'll be nice, won't it?"

Magdalena shook her head. "I don't know what I needs it fer, lessen it slate pencils. Though I might get a little somethin' fer Alvah, iffen I knew a thing would pleasure him."

They all wanted to pleasure little blind Alvah...but there were so few ways to accomplish that!

Besides the brightly colored leaves and Indian Summer weather, October brought school for Romeo and Edward. After being out for

264

five months, the return to studying and the quiet of a schoolroom was hard for them to take.

At home, Uncle Pompous, who had often--and loudly!--complained about their work, now moped around like someone lost. In spite of all, he had become so attached to the boys that by mid-afternoon, he would be waiting at the east gate to release the wire and welcome them in.

The person he let in one afternoon early in October was none other than Elizabeth and Emily's brother, Alvah Babcock...who was trying to slip in the back and surprise everyone.

He did that! And the news he brought to his sisters was both a surprise and a shock.

"Enter the army?" gasped Elizabeth, when she heard it.

"Oh, Alvah! Why?" cried Emily.

He looked a little embarrassed. "Well, the truth of it is: I'm going to get conscripted. But, that isn't the full reason either! For I've got so disgusted with the cruel way the Union Army acted round here, that I'm plenty mad enough to fight 'em! They've just torn up the property of poor, defenseless people, and robbed, and persecuted them for no reason that I can see!..."

When he paused, no one said a word. For who could deny it? It even came into Emily's mind that, were she a man, she might share Alvah's feeling. And with that thought, she knew that she had at least glimpsed William's motivation. For such a long time she had sought such a glimpse. But what good was it now?

"Which unit are you joining?" Albert asked that night.

"Capt. J. J. Ward's Alabama Light Artillery," Alvah said. "The muster's tomorrow. That's the tenth, isn't it?"

"Have you got your kit together?" Elizabeth asked, endeavoring to keep her voice steady. "Can Emily and I help you in any way?"

He grinned. "No, for I've got a lot more stuff than I'll ever need. Mrs. Stewart made me take about twenty different medicines, and enough socks for the whole regiment."

"I hope Edward's not thinking of joining!" Emily said.

Alvah shook his head. "No, I doubt it. He won't be in any risk of getting conscripted, on account of the tannery. I don't think he wants to join, anyway."

"Well, do you want to?" asked Emily curiously.

He thought about that awhile before he replied, "Yes, I do! I do, Sis!"

"You're a brave fellow!" Albert said. "And I wish you all the luck in the world, and a safe pass through it!"

That wish was fervently echoed by his sisters, though both of them realized that a fresh worry and uncertainty had been added to those they already bore.

The measles epidemic and its resultant troubles had caused the postponement of Emily's school. These troubles not only included Alvah's affliction, but the Hardie children had had problems from the infection. Mattie Pollard, too, had only slowly regained her strength.

"I think now that I'll wait until the third of November before starting the school," Emily said one evening to Elizabeth. "Is it important for the children to feel good before they come back? I am trying to convince myself that it is. Yet I wonder if just the joy of being together might hasten their recovery."

Elizabeth did not know. "It seems to me that even Addie V. has not entirely recovered."

"I noticed that, too. She lacks her old energy--her spirit! I do hope it soon returns. I miss her dashing across with all kinds of things to report." As she said those words, Emily suddenly was aware that there might be another reason why she had decided that school should be delayed. Was it really the children's health, or was it something else? Was it, perhaps, because she had fallen so far behind with her sewing orders?

For since Susan Pollard had returned to her own school, it was true that Emily could not keep up with orders. In fact, she had ceased to accept new ones. She mentioned this to Elizabeth now.

"I wish I had time to help you out," her sister said. "Haven't you thought of anyone? What about Margaret O'Casey? Could she do handwork like buttonholes and hems? Seems it's that sort of thing that takes so much time."

Emily paused in the act of joining two seams. "Why, of course!

Margaret could do those things!" she cried. "Why hadn't I thought of it? It will be the very thing! And now that Patrick's better--and I understand helps her with the younger boys--she will surely have the time for earning a little more money. Oh, thank you, my dear! What a problem-solver you are!"

And it did prove to be the solution! Margaret showed ability as a seamstress. She had had enough experience even to undertake some things on her own. Both practical and willing, she soon became invaluable as an assistant, and, gradually, Emily began to feel a lightening of her load.

One afternoon while Emily and Magdalena had the children out on the west lawn, they noticed Mrs. Elliott coming across the street faster than she normally moved. She was waving a sheet of paper in each hand.

Sensing news, Emily rose and went to meet her. "I hope you are the bearer of good tidings!"

Her mother-in-law beamed. "I count it so, for this day's given me a letter from each of my younger girls!"

Emily could not contain her surprise. "You mean letters have come through from Mississippi and Texas! Why, I am amazed!" She recalled her own efforts to mail her letter to the family of Lt. Fraser. Albert had finally found a man traveling north under a pass, who had promised to mail it.

"I'm amazed, too," the old lady agreed. "But here they are!"

After Magdalena had placed a chair for her, she continued, "It is so good to hear from Sue. She writes that things are quiet all around Aberdeen--though I doubt she'd tell me there was fightin'! Anyway, I already know there's plenty of that in Mississippi!"

"Where is Aberdeen, exactly?" asked Emily.

"It's on the Big Black River in Holmes County, near the center of the state. Seems a lot of people have gone there from Madison County. Must be some big attraction!" She paused to look at Emily sadly. "It was beyond me why William Kirk ever took my Susan an' six little children there, anyhow! Surely he could have found work around here. They were livin' out near Hayes Store."

267

"What about Bettie and her family?" Emily asked, knowing of Mrs. Elliott's anxiety over this daughter so far away in Texas.

"Bettie writes that Collins County is far from the war; but no matter how she glosses it over, I have the impression that life's on the rough side there. No doubt it's like pioneer days back in Tuscaloosa...not always to a woman's taste! But James Carty was just determined to take Bettie an' the baby away out there!"

Smiling at the sweet, old lady, who bore things so well, Emily hastily changed the subject. "I'm glad Mary Elizabeth is hearing from Richard more often now! It's near her time, you know! This next week, I believe!"

"I hope an' pray all's well," Mrs. Elliott said. "With Richard so far off--an' in what danger none of us knows--Mary must feel extra bad an' frightened, too, I don't doubt!"

"I'm sure she does," Emily agreed. "I'll be there to do all I can for her."

Two days later, the summons came. Emily and Elizabeth went immediately to see what they could do. The doctor was already there and asked Emily to stay.

Elizabeth took Kate and little Laura Ann to visit with her own children, until Mary Elizabeth could take them back.

Before the day of the twenty-second of October was over little John Dugger Elliott entered the world, a treasured blessing for his mother, who had longed for another son, and for his brave father, many miles away in the midst of the awful uncertainties of war.

Chapter Twenty-One

November 17, 1862

After two busy and very trying months, November arrived to add its short days and chill winds to the problems that the citizens of Huntsville were trying to meet with such courage as they still were able to muster.

All outdoor chores that were movable were brought inside. Of these, washing was the most invasive; it seemed to creep into every corner of the kitchen.

"Law, but I hates winter!" moaned Aunt Sophia. "Can't step my foot down fer people wringin' out a wet towel. Y'all needn't be su'prised iffen them men gets a stewed towel fer they supper!"

With an amused glance toward Elizabeth, Bridgett said, "My own thinking says you've put things handy, Aunt Sophia. But then, I'm already knowing how you and Mrs. Baker can see ahead when it comes to making arrangements of such importance as washing. Might be now, I could move this tub a bit further from the stove..."

But Aunt Sophia would have none of that. "No, chile, jes so as you don't drip on ma floor no more'n you has to!"

"Then I'll just fling my shawl about me and check on the white things in the boiling pot outside. They'll be needing a stir!"

Elizabeth sighed. They missed Lucius, now at the Marble Yard, as well as Romeo and Edward, who were in school.

"By rights, Pompous oughta be tendin' that boilin' pot!" Aunt Sophia declared, "but I reckons his old rheumatis' has got to get used to these cold days."

"He's suffering more than usual," Elizabeth said. "And we want him to stay by the fire in his cabin as much as he can. He's not idle,

269

for he's getting a lot of the dried corn shelled for taking to the mill. We are so fortunate to have that corn!"

"We's lucky them Blue Bellies is not 'round the corner keepin' that mill wheel from a-turnin'!"

Sounds from the front hall indicated that the children had begun to don their wraps. The school session was over.

In a few minutes, Emily entered the room. "It's my day to hang things on the line," she said cheerfully. "Mattie and Bessie will help by turns. That's one way for them to get some fresh air!"

"What's Archie doing?" inquired his mother.

"He's playing a little game with Alvah. Do you want him?"

Elizabeth, though obviously reluctant to deprive her sightless Alvah of even a minute's entertainment, chose quickly. "Yes. We need him to draw water for us. He's big enough to do that!"

Sophronia regarded her mistress in shock. "Miss 'Lizbeth, that boy have water slop ever'where on ma floor!"

"Then he can learn to mop it up," was the determined reply.

With everyone possible pressed into service, washing continued all day. By dark, about half the things had dried; the remainder had to be removed from the lines and held until the next day.

Besides the noise made by railway engines and deafening blasts from steam whistles, those living close to the tracks experienced another problem. When the wind veered to the north, any clothes left hanging on the line would probably be dotted with black soot from the smokestacks of passing trains.

After many long, hard washdays, Bridgett often left carrying a basket of food for the O'Caseys' supper. Tonight, the basket held one of Aunt Sophia's famous squash pies, made--not from squash at Windham's Grocery--but from that grown in their own garden.

The sight of two pies on the Baker's supper table, raised a chorus of "oohs" and "aahs" that would flatter any cook!

"May blessings attend you, Auntie dear!" James Conway's mellow voice expressed all their sentiments. "'Tis perfection with which you've crowned this meal!"

Aunt Sophia's widest grin encompassed her face as sounds of agreement came from everyone.

Albert added his congratulations. "Don't forget our gardeners, Romeo and Edward, who grew this tasty vegetable."

Edward, caught with a mouthful of pie and unable to reply, sat chewing with a flaming face.

But Romeo said in his honest voice, "Oh, all of you know 'twas Uncle Pompous that raised this squash. 'Course, we did help. Old Edward gave it about a hundred buckets of water from the well."

Swallowing, Edward found his voice, "Squash needs plenty of water, so Uncle Pompous says. I didn't believe it, but...."

Albert looked at Sophronia questioningly.

"Yessir, Mr. Albert," she answered. "Pompous be sittin' front that coal fire in he cabin, eatin' a big slice this very minute!"

Emily, a witness to this scene, unaccountably felt a moment of complete happiness. In spite of all their losses, heartaches and struggles and deprivations, they were still a family of souls who cared for each other and generously let it be known!

Apparently, Elizabeth was thinking along those same lines, for she said, "We are so fortunate. There are people in this town tonight who are near starving--in fact, Mrs. Pryor came over in the interest of a family down near Pinhook Creek who have six children and hardly a morsel in the house to eat!"

"Did you find a way to help?" Albert asked.

"I didn't have any cash," Elizabeth admitted. "Instead, we gave potatoes, a bag of meal, and one of dried peas." She paused, as if to give emphasis to the rest of her report. "But Emily gave a dollar--and Bridgett gave a quarter."

"Bridgett gave a quarter!" Albert repeated in surprise.

Elizabeth nodded solemnly. "Oh, yes! You know, I realize more every day what a fine girl she is. She uses her strength for our benefit, is generous with her tiny bit of money, and she's a deep thinker--and one who has a light touch in a difficult situation."

"'Tis my own true belief that Margaret O'Casey is a woman to be praised!" James Conway added. "Through all their troubles and bad luck--and it's been plenty!--she has held those children together and is trying to teach them right from wrong. A good Catholic she is. If only we had a priest in our midst!"

271

"Are you still raising funds to build a church?" asked Emily.

"Och! Lass. And we set off at a right brisk pace, owing to the generosity of people in this town. Not all Catholics either! But due to the recent troubles, giving has slackened to a trickle."

"Don't lose heart!" urged Albert. "More donations will come, and mine will be among them."

"Have you picked a spot for your church?" asked Elizabeth.

"That we have! Right where the cow pasture is, almost in front of Richard and Mary Elizabeth's house on Jefferson."

"What a splendid location!" Emily said. "Just perfect!"

"A town can never get too many churches!" one of the men said. "Though I'm Baptist myself, I like to visit others."

All week, Emily continued to recall that conversation. She had recently allowed problems and circumstances to interfere with her church-going. And I'm the worse for having missed! she realized. Finally, on Friday morning, she confessed that to Mrs. Elliott.

The reply was sympathetic. "I've been missin' services, too. I knew all the time that I should be makin' the effort to go!"

"Well then, this Sunday let's make the effort together!" Emily suggested. "I would love to go to the Methodist Church with you, and to take Mattie."

As far as dress was concerned, Emily could only wear her heavy black dress with a black shawl. She dressed Mattie in a brown and green plaid, made from one of the dresses Aunt Susan had given.

"It's so sweet, and becomes her greatly!" Elizabeth commented. "From what did you make the green bonnet, Emily?"

"I thought you'd guess immediately! It's the bodice of my old, green dress, now too tight. The rest of that dress is available. Do you fancy it for Bessie? Or should I make it for Bridgett?"

"Why, Bridgett, of course! Green for Ireland!"

When Mrs. Elliott joined them in her dark gray dress and black shawl and bonnet, Emily thought they made a presentable group. At least they were a happy one. For to be walking toward church with their neighbors that Sunday morning seemed a special blessing.

The day was cloudy--and cold enough to make them step along at a brisk pace, which Emily noticed did not tire her mother-in-law. But, not long after they turned right on Jefferson Street, Mrs. Elliott came almost to a standstill.

"Is anything wrong?" Emily asked. "Are you getting tired?"

"Oh, no!" denied the old lady. "Only, I was suddenly struck by such a vivid memory! I don't know whether I ever told you that it was right along here to our right that Susan an' I first lived in Huntsville. It was when we came from Knoxville back in 1818."

"Right here?" asked Emily, pausing in surprise.

"I believe so. We were dwellin' with our uncle, Thomas Cain, an' he owned about a fourth of this block, the part that corners on Jefferson an' Clinton. I think he said it was Lot Ten. But his house stood partly on the next lot to the north. I can recall how he complained at havin' to buy twenty feet off that lot, so as he would own all of his house." She laughed. "I reckon the house had been built before the lots were marked off!"

"What did the house look like?" asked Emily.

Mrs. Elliott stood thinking before she replied, "Best I recall it was wooden an' one-story with a real long wing behind--full of bedrooms, I guess. Seems like they had some boarders. I wonder if that old, dilapidated buildin' on the back of the lot isn't a bit of the original house? But I can't be sure. I only lived there a little while, for Thomas Carlton an' I married, an' then went off with my uncle, James Cain, to try our luck on the Black Warrior River, where the new town of Tuscaloosa was bein' built."

They had walked on to the north side of the Public Square. Now she continued, "Uncle Thomas had his silversmith and watchmaker's shop here about the center of this block." She paused to point to some stones along the front of a vacant lot a little to the east of the alley. "These very stones are probably part of the old foundation that was left after everything on this block burned down back 1850. Oh, but that was an awful fire! I remember it well. We thought the whole town would go. An' three blocks did!"

Emily had heard that story before and could imagine the terror the fire must have aroused. Yet hearing it today on the very spot where the flames had swept away the buildings belonging to Thomas Cain,

273

her husband's great-uncle, gave the event a new reality.

As they started walking on, Mrs. Elliott continued, "Uncle's shop was downstairs in a two-story frame building; lawyers rented the upstairs. Then, on the back of the lot was another two-story house, where Uncle Thomas an' his family lived for a time."

Emily was busy trying to take all of that in as she helped her mother-in-law and Mattie to cross Washington Street in safety.

Then as the tall, brick sanctuary of the Methodist Church came in sight, Mrs. Elliott was reminded of more to tell. "I've surely told you that another uncle, William Cain, a tailor, was a member of the Board of Trustees when this church was built in 1833, just two years before Enoch an' I moved here from Tuscaloosa."

"I want to hear more about that," said Emily. "But we'd better hurry on in, if we want to be seated before the service begins!"

As it was, they had to sit near the back in the left-hand section. But they could see very well. Mattie, in an aisle seat, had a good view of the minister and choir seated on a platform behind the alter railing. Seats for the congregation were in two sections. Also, above these were narrow balconies, where benches ran counter to those on the main floor.

Mrs. Elliott whispered in Emily's ear, "The balconies were for the slaves, who were always welcome in this church. Now they have their own African Church, where they can be more comfortable with the kind of service they like best."

As soon as the service was over, the last song sung, and the benediction pronounced, Mrs. Elliott rose to speak to a number of acquaintances and to introduce Emily and Mattie. Though to greet people properly was difficult in the church aisles, made narrower by the population of hoop skirts.

Outside, they had a better opportunity to speak to friends, but Mrs. Elliott quickly pointed to the sky. "Emily, will you just look at all those dark clouds--and the wind has risen, too!"

Viewing the change with concern, Emily suggested, "I wonder if it would be wise to stop at Aunt Susan's?"

But, snuggling her shawl more closely around her face, the old lady shook her head. "Let's hurry along. I think we can make it!"

Near the intersection of West Holmes and Jefferson, they were surprised to find Edward and Romeo waiting with umbrellas.

"Edward wanted to come all the way," Romeo said, "but I feared we'd miss you. Ma sent us."

"What I wanted to do," Edward stated, "was to hitch up Wego to the carriage and come to get you! But Ma wouldn't hear of that!"

"I think not!" was Mrs. Elliott's reply. "Walk along with me, Romeo, an' we'll share an umbrella if the rain starts."

"Rain!" cried Edward. "I doubt that is all it'll be, for Uncle Pompous told Pa that he can smell snow coming!"

"Oh, mercy!" Emily moaned. "I hope not...but Pompous is famous as a weather prophet. Have you enough coal, Mother Elliott?"

"More than ample!" the old lady replied. "Albert has been real generous. Otherwise, we'd have been desperate for fuel!"

They were near the corner of Mill Street when the first drops fell, but before the boys could raise their umbrellas, Emily knew that the drops were not rain, but sleet! "Can't you go in and eat dinner with us, Mother Elliott?" she asked hopefully.

But it was not to be...for the old lady knew the pitter-patter of sleet when she heard it! "Thank you, my dear, but I best get inside before the way grows slick! Bless you, boys, for comin'."

"Oh, we're going right to your door!" they insisted.

"Bye, Grandmother!" called Mattie. "Won't snow be fun?"

"Not much!" called Mrs. Elliott.

Emily shuddered. During her early years in New York state, she had had to endure enough misery caused by heavy snows. Of course, big snows seldom came to North Alabama, so she could understand the children's excitement over the possibility.

Inside the kitchen, Sophronia was bewailing the weather, "Law, it gonna come a snow, Miss 'Lizbeth! Mag'lena an' me wuz goin' to our church! We's havin' a big service this afternoon! An' all us 'Mother's of the Church' is s'posed to be there! An' I wuz gonna wear my white robe Miss Em'ly done made me."

Peering from the window, Elizabeth could only confirm the fact that sleet or snow--or both--were falling. She hastened down the hall just as Emily and Mattie reached the stoop. "I sent the boys with umbrellas!" she said, throwing open the door.

"They're helping Mother Elliott up her front steps. Thank you for sending them!"

Mattie was so excited she could hardly wait to get her clothes changed so she could go in search of Bessie and Archie. She found them peering from the window of the playroom. The babies were on the floor, where a wool rug had now replaced the summer matting.

Cries of, "It's snowing!" echoed happily around the walls.

In her glee, Mattie soon got Enoch Carlton to his feet and led him to the window. "Look out there, Buddy, where that white stuff is falling from the sky! That's snow!"

"...'no!" intoned the baby, doing his best with the word.

Emily, coming in in time to witness the scene, felt it imprint forever on the mirror of her mind. Her darling baby, marveling at his first sight of snow--and there on the floor poor little Alvah turning anxiously toward a scene he could only imagine. She and Magdalena exchanged agonized glances and moved in concert across the room to help Alvah to his feet and over to the window.

"Let's put your hand on the windowpane, Alvah," Emily coaxed. "Feel how cold it is! That's because it's cold outside. It is so cold that snow is falling from the sky. Snow is fluffy and white and floats down in little bunches called flakes."

"It's light as a feather!" Bessie said.

Archie added, "And it's covering up everything. It is sticking to the windowsill, and the grass is all turning white!"

That gave Magdalena an idea. "Wonder if I raise the window jes a bit an' hold it up, Miss Em'ly, you could pass his hand through so he could feel the snow. For nothin' else feel like snow do!"

So Alvah had his first feel of snow, and surprised them by saying the word, then shivering dramatically.

Late that afternoon, the children had snow cream, made by stirring huge pans of clean snow into a kettle of Aunt Sophia's rich custard that had been thoroughly chilled.

Addie Virginia, her feet and legs bound and wrapped with rags, arrived at the back door with her milk pail just in time to enjoy a dish of the cream. "I never in my whole life ate anything that good!" she

276

cried, shivering between cold and ecstasy. "I have got to know how to make it, Aunt Sophia, so's I can tell Ma. Charlie will like it! Even Pa will like this! I don't remember if we ever had much snow in Georgia. It's such fun! So pretty a-fallin'!"

Albert, scooping up his last bite of the delicious cream, rose to his feet. He suddenly felt moved to give these Southern little ones some more delight. Outside, snow was covering everything. "I believe more than three inches have fallen," he said to Elizabeth with a grin. "Guess it's time I went to the barn to see what kind of a sled I can knock together. Goodness knows, I have had enough experience in building and using sleds!"

All the boys rose as one to help. Hearing of the project, the shop men took an immediate interest. Together, they found enough lumber to build two sleds. But, by the time the equipment was ready, the sun had set, so the sport had to wait until next day.

"It's still snowing," observed Albert, "and cold enough for it to keep on sticking. Should make pretty good sledding tomorrow."

And so they found it! Good sledding many places! A new fall of snow during the night added to the durability of the surface.

As Albert told Elizabeth and Emily later, "Word got around to your pupils, Emily. They came with brothers and sisters, young and old, and most were bundled up clear to their teeth."

"How did you handle all those children?" she asked, amazed.

"Why, the shop men all pitched in, and we divided them amongst us. That way we could watch our bunch and not have to worry about the others. We'd send a sledful downhill while the empty sled was being towed up. Of course, we had to carry the smallest children up, too...and even some of the older ones needed help, on account of being so wrapped up by their mothers!"

"My!" Elizabeth said. "You and the men are due to be thanked!"

"We got it! Just seeing the young ones enjoying themselves in a way they'll never forget was thanks enough." He paused. "Though Romeo and Edward didn't get much chance to slide. But I promised them their turn tomorrow. They'll ask Alonzo, Patrick O'Casey, and the oldest Hardie boys to join them. The men and I are going down to

the Marble Yard to shovel out snow, and also see if we can help anybody downtown."

"Mr. Albert," Aunt Sophia said next morning, as she placed his
bowl of hot mush before him, "Uncle Pompous say tell you Southern
folks calls this 'hog-killin' weather'. So he think Mr. Smith jes might
be slaughterin' today. Iffen he is, he might be sendin' you a passel of
fresh liver an' spareribs. 'Course he'll be needin' a lot of salt fer saving
the rest!"

Albert paused with the spoon halfway to his mouth. "I must ask
Windham to see if he's got any salt! He was hoping to get some from
Atlanta."

"How could that be?" asked Elizabeth.

"By wagon, probably. After all, the Union forces don't control Atlanta, nor most of Georgia, nor Alabama right now."

"In that case, I hope you can get some candles, too," his wife continued. "During these dark days and early nights we've nearly used up
our supply!"

"And, speaking of hog-killing," Emily added, "I wonder if Mrs.
Smith is planning to make sausage--and, if so, whether she has
enough pepper. I know she grows her own sage."

"That is a good question, Emily," her brother-in-law remarked.
"I'll ask Windham about pepper. Anything else we need?"

Six months before, many items would have come to mind, but now
with their garden produce so carefully saved, they could think of
nothing they needed that there was any possibility of obtaining.

When on the next night, Albert arrived with the fresh liver and
spare ribs predicted by Uncle Pompous, he also told about his trip to
Windham's Grocery. "The shipment got in just before the snow and
Windham saved us salt and a little pepper. I sent most of it to Mrs.
Smith." He placed a bundle on the table. "If these candles don't last
the winter, we may have to make our own!"

Emily could feel tears stinging her eyes. Being able to make a
light on dark winter evenings was so valuable to her. "I do thank you,
Albert!" she whispered. "We'll treasure them mightily."

And there were plenty of opportunities to treasure them as the last

278

cold weeks of November and early December moved along.

About the second week in December, the weather grew warmer.
"Alabama weather always a-foolin' us!" Aunt Sophia complained.
"Tho' I don' know no other! Maybe all weathers do that."

The boys had just come in from school, and were waiting to get an
assignment from their mother. They knew it would be either for chopping wood, getting something from the root cellar, or drawing water,
none of which they cared for in the least! But neither of them were
prepared for what they were to be called on to do...for not only was it
unexpected, it foretold an outcome so happy as to be unimaginable.

A knock came on the back door.

Edward, who was nearest and also self-proclaimed guard, opened
the door expecting a neighbor, or someone he could recognize.

But the man who stood several steps beyond the door, seemed to
be a complete stranger. A Confederate uniform hung in tatters on his
thin frame. His hair and beard, long and unkempt, marked him as old;
yet, something about him proclaimed youth!

That something was his smile and the light of joy in his eyes. "I'm
Joshua!" he said. "I reckon you don't recollect me, Edward! I look so
terrible. Been a long time gettin' here."

"Joshua!" shouted Edward, throwing the door wider. "Is it you? I
can't believe it! Romeo, here's Joshua! Come inside, sir!"

Aunt Sophia--startled by all the carrying-on, and never having
heard of Joshua--grabbed a knife from the rack and held it behind her
back. She very nearly brought it to light when she got a full view of
the apparition that stepped into her kitchen.

But Emily had heard the name called and rushed back. She shook
her head at Sophronia and smiled at the apparition. "Why, Joshua!
How wonderful!" Then turning to the old woman, she explained,
"Aunt Sophia, this is Joshua, who was a patient in the hospital. You
may remember Addie Virginia speaking of him?"

Sophronia was immediately all smiles. The mention of Addie was
all that was necessary. "Yes'um!" she grinned. "How is you, sir?"

"Tolerable, thank you." Joshua beamed at them all.

"Have you seen Addie Virginia yet?" asked Edward.

Joshua looked shocked. "Oh, no! I'm hopin' to clean up--before I present myself to her."

"We'll see if we can't help you with that," offered Emily. "In the meantime, why don't you take a seat at the table and let Aunt Sophia give you a cup of hot soup. She always has some waiting on the stove."

"I'd be pleasured to, ma'am. Indeed I would be! For the cold's been a-pressin' on me."

Turning away with tears in her eyes, Emily hurried toward the sitting room to explain the situation to Elizabeth. "He's such a deserving fellow, Sister, and so kind! What I'm thinking is, I'll give Romeo and Edward two dollars, and, if you don't object, they can take him up to Richmond Terrell's Barbershop, so he can get a good hot bath and have his hair and beard trimmed. You might wait until after that to greet him, for he's very embarrassed over his present appearance."

"Yes, indeed! I agree! We must do whatever we can to help that poor fellow. I remember how Addie Virginia and Edward worried so over him, and how Addie cried--and Edward, too, I expect--when he was taken away a prisoner."

"Another thing," continued Emily, "when I first saw him just now, I thought he was William. My heart nearly stopped!"

"Oh, my dear!"

"He's about William's size and height. Oh, Sister, I must have been saving William's clothes for Joshua! I'm sure they will fit! And his own are the most pitiful rags you can imagine. I'm going up to get some of William's, so that Romeo and Edward can take them along. Joshua's old things can be burnt after he's bathed!"

While the boys and Joshua were gone, Emily stepped across Mill Street to tell Mrs. Bolton, who was pleased over the news, and readily agreed to let Addie Virginia eat supper with them.

So Joshua, washed and barbered, sat proudly in his new clothes at the supper table. A radiant Addie Virginia was on one side; on the other, Edward hovered proudly.

In his humble and uncomplaining voice, Joshua told them, "I do expect you're wantin' to know how come I'm not in the prison they was sendin' us to when we left here. Well, t'were a strange thing that happened! We must've been all the way up in Kentucky when I woke one dark night to find the rail car in front of ours had run clean off the track an' ours had followed after!"

"Did it turn over?" gasped Edward.

"Not exactly, but it got banged up so as we could pry the door open an' get out. An' get out we did! All of us ran as fast as we could in different directions."

"You didn't get hurt, did you?" asked Addie Virginia.

"No, little lady. For I was lucky! But I couldn't remember the name of no place ceptin' Huntsville (I know more now though!) an' so I headed back here. It's taken near six months, for I've had to stop a lot to work for somethin' to eat, or to help people." Pausing, he looked around at them. "All 'long the way, folks has been so nice to me--but none ever as nice as y'all!"

"You're more than welcome for what we've done," said Albert.

"Have you remembered any more about yourself?" asked Emily. He shook his head a bit sadly. Then he seemed to perk up, as he said, "But I'm still hopin'! I listen to every word I hear, in case it'll bring back some memory." Then, he took from his pocket a dirty, creased piece of paper and held it up for all to see. "This here is the thing that's kept me goin', for on it is the name an' address of this little lady here, who's my true friend!"

"Addie Virginia is a wonder!" spoke up Emily. "We all love her dearly. But all about you here are more friends."

"That they are, lad!" agreed James Conway. "For you've landed in the midst of a fine family. There's room for you back there in the house where all us lads sleep--when we are not out working or stuffing ourselves with Aunt Sophia's good cooking!"

"Thank you kindly," said Joshua with his warm smile, "An' I'll take pleasure in doin' whatever I can to help out."

"Sounds a good enough bargain to me!" Albert declared.

Addie Virginia's face glowed with joy, while Edward directed a look of pride and thanksgiving toward his pa.

Emily sighed happily. Sometimes, she thought, there are things that work out so wonderfully well!

Chapter Twenty-Two

December 12, 1862

"Mary Elizabeth received another letter from Richard today," Emily told Albert and Elizabeth one night. "She was so happy!"

"I hope Richard is well," said Elizabeth.

"Apparently he is, though worn out. Their living conditions at best are so awful. Most of the time they have to sleep out in the open. There's no food some days, and not much anytime."

"Are they still in Mississippi?" asked Albert.

"Yes, but they move about all the time. Mary says he's keeping a diary through it all. And writes in it every day!"

Albert seemed impressed. "It takes a very determined person to keep a diary in the best of times. Don't believe I could do it if I were living under such conditions!"

"Nor could I!" Elizabeth was emphatic. "One week's my limit."

Albert folded the newspaper he'd been reading. "I've memorized this edition of The Atlanta Journal that Littleton passed on. Now Pollard can have a go at it." He paused. "What strikes me is that Atlanta seems so little affected by the war. This paper has a lot of advertisements for things we can't get around here."

"Is there one for knitting thread?" asked his wife. "I'm low!"

He shook his head. "I expect thread has nearly vanished."

"Let me ask downtown," suggested Emily. "Have you enough to finish the socks you planned to knit for Christmas?"

Elizabeth put down her work and began to count up. "Let's see, I've finished the ones for: Lucius, Romeo, Edward, Uncle Pompous, Archie, James Conway, three pairs for the shop men, and one small pair for Jason. That's ten pairs finished. Now, who is it I lack?

Hmmmm. Oh, yes, Alvah, Enoch, and you, Albert. And, if the thread lasts, I'll make a pair for Joshua."

"Well, you can skip me," said Albert. "I've got two good pair. What I'd rather have for Christmas is the collar and cuffs turned on my good shirt. They're starting to fray."

"Why, of course, Albert!" Elizabeth assured him quickly. "Why, I should have noticed that your shirt needs attention!"

Emily winked surreptitiously at her sister, who knew she had a new white shirt made to give Albert for Christmas. She had cut up a linen tablecloth--a wedding gift seldom used, because she and William had always boarded. From the remainder of this cloth she had made small mats edged in some of the crocheted lace included in Aunt Susan's gift. Each of her school pupils would receive one of the mats. There were three larger sizes, also, one each for Mary Elizabeth Elliott, Mary Ann Figg, and Susan Pollard.

"Conway and I are making the smaller children some animals out of bits of marble," Albert announced. "They'll be polished smooth with no sharp edges. I can find nothing to buy for them."

"Oh, Albert!" cried Elizabeth, her voice breaking in gratitude toward her husband, whose kindness seemed to know no bounds. "The animals that you and James make yourselves will be more prized by the children than anything you could buy!"

"I'm taking special pains with Alvah's," he assured her. "It's a turtle and will just about fit in his hand. Marble is always so cool and pleasant to the touch!"

"That is the sweetest idea," Emily whispered. "And I know just how pleased the children will be!" She paused. "My gifts are only new clothes for the little girls' dolls. I know it's shabby to give money, but I'm giving Archie a dollar toward those firedogs he covets. Romeo and Edward may get money, too, unless I can get their vests made in time!"

"Have you finished the green dress for Bridgett?" Elizabeth asked. "She'll be stunning in that!"

"I hope she likes it," Emily said. "What do you think about my making the rest of that brown and green plaid for Magdalena? I've a piece of solid brown, also from Aunt Susan's gifts, that should combine with the plaid and make a bonnet to match."

"That's a lovely idea! And what about Aunt Sophia?"

Emily smiled. "Well--don't laugh now!--but you know that gaudy taffeta dress that Aunt Susan gave, I'm thinking of ripping it apart-- for none of us will ever wear it!--and using it for other things. The color is so bright! Do you think Aunt Sophia would like a bonnet from it? And maybe a shawl of some kind?"

Elizabeth nodded. "The very thing! The brighter the better for her to wear when she goes to the African Church!"

"I'm hoping the bonnet and shawl will go with the blue dress I made her last Christmas--the one she saves for dress-up."

"What are you giving Mrs. Elliott?" asked Elizabeth.

Emily sighed. "That's my big problem, for I don't know. Nor do I know what to make for Margaret O'Casey. She's helped me so much that I'd like to give her something special."

"A warm garment might be the answer," suggested Elizabeth.

"I know!" cried Emily. "For I am beginning to believe that she and Bridgett only have the one warm shawl between them!"

"What about Mrs. Lamperson Smith?" asked Albert. "She has been mighty kind to us, besides all the help Lamperson--and Jackson, too!--have given us up at the mine, and in other ways."

Elizabeth and Emily looked at each other in embarrassment at having forgotten someone who had befriended their family.

"Oh, we must give something to Mrs. Smith!" Emily declared. She hesitated. "Though I can't imagine what! And in these times, a gift should fill a real need!"

Elizabeth's knitting needles had ceased to click. Finally, she asked, looking at Albert, "Could we invite the Smith family to eat Christmas dinner with us? Both Emily and I are anxious to know them. Do you think we'd be presuming, Albert?"

He observed his wife with a smile. "Certainly not! That family is down-to-earth and would not know how to take offense. Write a note, and I'll give it to Smith. Maybe you should mention there will only be our family and the shop men."

"Will Mrs. Elliott eat Christmas dinner with us, Emily?" asked her sister.

Emily shook her head. "No, because they're having Mr. Tinable and Richard's family at their house. It's little John Dugger's first Christmas."

The note was sent to the Smith family, and accepted by word of mouth with the gift of a huge, fat turkey gobbler and two dozen quail. The quail breasts were breaded and fried for supper, while the turkey became the sole occupant of a pen hastily built by Albert and the boys.

"I don't believe it's possible for the children to get as much joy from eating turkey meat as they have from admiring that beautiful live bird!" Emily remarked to Aunt Sophia one morning.

"Law, I hopes they ain't give a name to that critter!" the old woman replied. "It bad luck to eat anythin' as has been named!"

"'Turkey' is all I've ever heard them say," Emily assured her. "I took Alvah out there, and he was so intrigued by the gobbler's call. Apparently, he couldn't imagine what kind of bird made that cry! I tried to describe it best I could."

Aunt Sophia paused to consider. "That bird do have a loud word to say, don't it! Wonder what it mean?"

"Probably nothing we'd want to hear!" Emily laughed.

Archie was the one most generous with attentions to the doomed bird. He liked to drop corn kernels into the coop and watch them gobbled up. "It's saying 'thank you'!" he informed Emily. "So I'm trying to learn to say 'you're welcome'." He gave a demonstration that was surely far from recognizable to any turkey.

Uncle Pompous, witness to this scene, said, "Boy! If you ain't done warn that ol' turk he headed fer the oven! Shame on you!" He cackled loudly at his own wit. "Now when Sophia get him into the pan, he gonna jump right on back out...."

Archie looked so alarmed, that Emily hastened to reassure him. "Uncle Pompous is only teasing you. Just admire the turkey while it is here in the pen, and we'll all enjoy it at the dinner table on Christmas."

"Not me!" insisted Archie stoutly. "I'll not eat a bite!"

But when Pompous promised to save Archie some of the feathers to keep, he changed his tune. "Iffen your pa want to, he can trim you a writin' quill from one of them bigges' feathers!"

That was the wrong tack to take, for Archie reasoned, "I could trim my own quill, if Pa would just let me have a pocketknife!"

After school one morning, Emily came in the sitting room with the hope of making some headway on her Christmas sewing. Just as she began to sort her work, a light knock sounded on the front door. It was Susan Pollard! "I'm out of school for Christmas and wondered if you needed some help," she said with a smile.

Emily gave her a warm hug. "My, you are an answer to prayer! I have so many gifts under way that I doubt if I'll be able to finish any of them!"

"I'll work on the ones nearest to being done!" the young girl laughed, teasingly.

Thinking how nice it was to be working once again with Susan, Emily handed over the vests she was making for Romeo and Edward.

The sitting room was comfortable to work in, for it was warmed by a coal-burning stove. The dining room had a similar stove, but the other rooms had grate fires that burned either coal, wood, or a combination of both. In the mornings, only the small children's bedroom was warmed by fires; the grownups dressed in the cold.

Each day, it was necessary to carry in enough fuel to keep the fires going. Uncle Pompous, Romeo and Edward had that job, along with chopping kindling, taking out ashes, pasturing or feeding the cows and Wego, and any other outside tasks that came up.

Susan, busy making buttonholes and sewing on buttons, suddenly asked, "Are you making one of these vests for Lucius, too?"

Opening her mouth to answer, Emily sat stunned. "No! For I've simply forgotten Lucius! How could I?"

"You probably just counted wrong," Susan consoled her. "There are so many! Do you want me to cut one from something?"

"Yes, I do! But from what I can't imagine. It should be wool, or something heavy. I also need warm material to make a shawl for Margaret O'Casey. Then, I don't know what to make for Mrs. Smith, who has been so kind to us this year."

"Mrs. Smith might like a nightdress," suggested Susan. "You've white material, haven't you, and some of that crocheted lace from Mrs. Knox? It could be made with long sleeves and a double yoke, so she could enjoy it this cold weather."

"That is a good idea, Susan," Emily agreed, thankful she had not used all of the lace in making the Christmas mats.

"Since we have the measurements for that dress you made Mrs. Smith, I could cut the nightdress," offered Susan.

"Thank you," Emily said. "You'll find white buttons in the box on the table." She rose. "And while I'm upstairs looking for more material, do go out and let everyone know you're here, Susan. They will be so glad to see you!"

In her bedroom, Emily had a big bag of scraps left from sewing projects for people who had not wanted leftovers. There were two odd-shaped pieces of a red-and-brown plaid that were large enough to make the front of a vest, and some black sateen for a back and interlining. But there was nothing for a warm shawl!

"Oh, I like that red plaid for Lucius!" Susan said. "But do we have his size?"

"I'll get it somehow tonight," promised Emily. "But I can find nothing for the shawl. Still, I'm not giving up until I've looked through the remainder of the things Aunt Susan gave."

There was no heavy shawl material, but she found a warm dress, scarcely worn, that she thought would fit Margaret O'Casey. "This gray color will blend so nicely with Bridgett's green dress!" she told Susan. "Of course, I'll have to cut a lot out of the skirt! Margaret doesn't wear hers very full."

"The leftover gray pieces might make something pretty for Mrs. Elliott," suggested the young girl. "Maybe an apron?"

Emily looked at Susan in appreciation. "I am so glad I always encouraged you to be creative! That's a wonderful idea! I've been thinking of designing some sewing aprons with separate pockets to keep your scissors, thread, and all handy while you're working."

The sewing apron turned out to be easy to make and so pretty and useful that Emily made several from scraps. They'd make nice surprise gifts for Elizabeth, Susan Pollard, and Aunt Susan.

On the Saturday before Christmas, the shop men cut a beautiful cedar tree on the mountain and brought it down in the wagon. They attached it to a stand so it could be set up in the parlor.

"Put it right there inside the front window!" Elizabeth guided its positioning. "Oh, it's so beautiful! Just look, children, at what our friends have given us for Christmas!"

The fellows, standing proudly by, were every bit as delighted and proud as the children.

"I'm more than willing to string popcorn for it!" said one.

"Popcorn it is!" James Conway echoed. "'Tis a sure thing we'll see no cranberries to string--like we did up New York way!"

An evening of popping and stringing corn, interspersed with songs and several recitations, proved a delight for children and adults as well. Even Uncle Pompous played several tunes on his old mouth organ. He rarely played any more, excusing himself with, "Too sad times! I don't feel no music in ma ol' head!"

At school on Monday morning, Emily led the children in to view the tree decorated with popcorn.

"It's so pretty!" cried Addie Virginia. "What do you call it?"

"A Christmas tree. You may not have seen one before, but where we grew up in Tioga County, New York, we had German neighbors who introduced us to the custom--and we've always had one since. Now instead of lessons this morning, I thought we'd each make a small decoration to hang on the branches. Whatever you want to make."

"If I had a knife," put in Archie immediately, "I'd whittle me a Baby Jesus in a manger."

"That would be lovely, Archie!" said Emily, determined to encourage this creative child, while she longed for the time when he'd be allowed his own pocketknife. "Instead, why don't you draw Baby Jesus in his manager on a piece of cardboard? I'll help you color your picture."

Mattie P. held up her hand. "Miss Emily, I have a little piece of blue ribbon. Could I ask Susan to help me make a doll from an old handkerchief. The ribbon could be its sash."

This idea appealed to everyone, and other ideas followed.

Jason promised that Patrick, who was a good carver, would make something from wood. Others wanted to use their own ideas. Emily tried to furnish what was needed, where possible. "The things you make will be yours when we take down the tree after Christmas!"

Several of the men contributed items, and Elizabeth found some decorations from past years. Finally, Emily and Susan made pretty gathered circles of bright taffeta and shiny satin materials from the scrapbag. These were dangled from the limbs by a thread.

The tree looked so pretty that Elizabeth suggested they invite the children to bring their parents over to see it at six o'clock on Christmas Eve night. "We can serve something hot to drink, and I'm sure Aunt Sophia can make a few tea cakes. You might give the pretty little mats to the children at that time. It may be about all the Christmas many of them will have!"

Emily gazed in gratitude at her thoughtful sister. "That'll be lovely!" she exclaimed, with a catch in her voice. "The children can sing the carols they've been practicing. You have made me the richest gift of all, dear Sister!"

It was then that Emily realized how she had been dreading this first Christmas without William. Trying to put her feelings into words, she murmured, "I've dreaded this Christmas so much that it has made me keep extra busy so I would have no time...to remember past years. Now, because of everyone's efforts to make this a special time for the children, it's no longer sad. In fact, it is joyous! Just as Christ's birthday should be!"

Mattie wanted to make an Indian for the tree. "Like the one in Papa's painting," she specified to Edward, whom she chose to help with the project.

Ever confident, Edward replied, "Sure, Mattie! You want him to have clothes on, or be naked like the one in the picture?"

"That Indian man's not naked!" protested Mattie. "He's just taken off his shirt in case he falls in the water!"

Romeo regarded his brother with some doubt. "You'd better find out what clothes Indians wear before you start!"

289

After that remark from Romeo, Edward became determined to make an Indian so perfect in every way that it would be bigger and far better than anything else on the tree. Closing his eyes, he tried to picture how this could be done.

Mattie watched him for a while before she said, "Please don't go to sleep, Edward, 'cause we haven't got long. Everybody but me has already hung their decoration..."

"...I'm thinking--not sleeping!" protested her helper.

Emily, so amused she could hardly keep from laughing, decided to come to the rescue. "Mattie, since we have a Baby Jesus on the tree, wouldn't it be nice to have a baby Indian? He might have a pretty blanket wrapped around him, so only his head would show."

Regarding his aunt in admiration and wanting no objection, Edward stated, "I'll have the head made in a minute, Mattie, so you can find the blanket!"

Mattie asked permission to look in the scrapbag upstairs. She found an old, ragged piece of blanket, which her mother trimmed neatly with the scissors.

After seeking in vain for a quick head-making idea, Edward had to look imploringly at his aunt. "Guess I'll have to carve a head from a piece of wood...."

Emily was ready. "Of course, you could do that," she agreed, "but it would take a long time. Why not use this empty spool that thread came on. Look for a short stick to fit in the hole for the baby's neck. Mattie will make the hair."

Mattie, delighted to have such an important part in the baby's creation, took the scrap of coarse black linen handed her and, at her mother's direction, unraveled a mass of black threads. She held these up proudly. "Oh, Mama! Isn't this hair beautiful? But how is the baby going to keep it on?"

The problem was solved with the stick, carefully whittled by Edward so that one end formed a wedge to hold the hair in place and the other made a handsome neck.

Yet Mattie was not satisfied. "That Indian in Papa's painting has dark skin," she pointed out the obvious, "but this spool-head is light colored!"

Closing his eyes again, Edward quickly produced his one clever idea. "I'll put some of Papa's brown boot polish on it!"

Once coated brown and dabbed with soot for eyes and red paint for its mouth, the head and neck were snuggled in the blanket and hung on the tree with some ceremony.

Mattie, though regarding their creation proudly, was still not fully satisfied. "I wish that Indian in the picture could look around here and see this beautiful Indian baby."

At these words, Emily had to turn away, but Romeo, who had come in to see their creation, was quick with an answer, "Mattie, Indian men never look around while you're watching!"

As Emily told Elizabeth later, "That one episode just polished my Christmas to a shine!"

Yet another outstanding event was to come that same night. They were clearing the table after supper when Joshua came over. After standing speechless for a few moments, he finally began to address Elizabeth in a kindly voice, "I've seen your pretty baby who is sightless, ma'am, an' I wanted to tell you 'bout my own ma, as she was sightless from the time she was a wee girl. It's a fact that I can't recall my last name, but I can remember Ma, like she's right here with us." His voice shook with emotion.

"I wish she were here now," Elizabeth whispered sincerely.

"So do I," he murmured, "for I need her! But what I wanted to tell you is how Ma seems to get along without lookin' with her eyes. She knows everyone by their voice, their step, even their breathin', an' she 'pears to know what we're thinkin' on, or are plannin' to do. She's so lovin' with us an' helps us see what's best." His voice grew rough. "She says as how she can do that because Jesus is always with her, ma'am."

"What a wonderful mother you have!" Emily whispered.

"I'm not braggin'," the young man added, "only tellin' you, so as you will take courage--for your boy can learn anything, an' do most anything, so long as he believes he can!" His voice faded.

"Thank you, Joshua!" Elizabeth said, gratefully. "You've given me so much hope!"

"And me a valuable lesson," Emily added, as she rose to pour a glass of water for Joshua.

Taking a sip, the young man said, "This is good, sweet water!" and with that remark suddenly became rigid, his glass held ready, as he repeated, "Sweet water!" over and over, as if he savored on his tongue some delectable morsel that he could not bear to lose. "Don't let me forget those words!" he begged. "For Sweetwater is the name of the town near to where we live!"

Joyfully, Elizabeth jumped to her feet to fetch Albert. "Hurry in here!" she pleaded, "for Joshua has remembered the name of the town near where they live. It's Sweetwater!"

"Why, I believe there's a town by that name right up in the Tennessee hills!" Albert told the happy young man.

"That's it!" cried Joshua, joyfully. "Now I can go home, if somebody will show me the way!"

Albert was silent for a long time. He was desperately seeking a way around what he must say next. But there was none! "Joshua, I'll help you when it becomes possible...but, right now, there is terrible fighting up there...from Nashville to Tullahoma...maybe even over to Chattanooga!..."

"...in Sweetwater, too?"

Albert shook his head. "Probably not. But certainly between here and there!"

"Oh, Albert!" wailed Elizabeth. "I didn't know all that was going on so near us!"

"Have courage," he said, patting her shoulder. "At least it's not here! And you have courage, too, Joshua, for I will help you until the times comes when you can go safely up into that region to find your home. I promise!"

Joshua smiled his sweet, trusting smile. "Thank you! And now I've got to go tell Edward and Addie Virginia.... Sweetwater!"

Emily sat thinking of how Joshua had done a difficult thing in talking about his blind mother--and in doing that kind deed, had solved part of his own puzzle.

Later in the sitting room, Albert spoke of how pleased he was. "I'm so glad to see that nice young man coming out of the fog he was in. I think I'll offer him a job at the mine."

"Going down in the mine?" asked Elizabeth. "Oh, Albert, no!"

"Not that!" her husband assured her. "But to meet men who come up there in their own wagons hoping to buy coal. It usually means having to wait their turn, and after they've toiled up that rough road, some of them aren't too happy at being put in line, even though we're keeping a fire going for them to gather around."

"How is it that Joshua can help?" asked Emily anxiously.

"Why, I've found he meets people and talks to them in a kindly way. I believe he could smooth out some ruffled feathers amongst those who have to wait--and sometimes for a long while. Maybe it's because Joshua has forgotten his own name that he tries so hard to remember the names and faces of others and is so kind and patient toward them."

"That boy will help you in any way he can, Albert!" Elizabeth assured him. "I'm so glad the mine's drawing business."

Albert nodded. "Believe me, it's a load off my shoulders!"

"And I know you must be happy to be able to help people who are so desperate for fuel," added Emily.

Though it rained on Christmas Eve, the school children's party was well attended. The only mother who could not attend was Mary Elizabeth, who thought it best not to get out with little John Dugger. Mr. Tinable came in her stead, bringing Kate and tiny Laura Ann, whose big eyes danced at sight of the tree.

Albert was glad that Andrew Bolton accompanied Viora and their children. Emily watched in sympathy as Addie Virginia tried to restrain little Charlie, who wanted to examine every ornament. A brave soul when it came to situations far beyond her years, the plucky child was no match for this lively little brother.

"That's all right, Addie Virginia," Joshua said soothingly. "Charlie and I'll go in the playroom and find something to do."

Calmly, Charlie held out his hand and went with Joshua.

Emily was impressed. It was just as Albert had said! Joshua had a talent and willingness for smoothing out things.

The Pollards all came, Caledonia bringing a plate of tea cakes to add to the refreshments. "They are not much!" she apologized. "I had to use honey instead of sugar, like in Ma's receipt."

"Oh, but you have walnuts in them!" Elizabeth noticed. "Adds a lot to the flavor!"

Bridgett and Margaret O'Casey wore their new dresses, and drew eyes in their direction. Margaret also brought food...some of her famous gingerbread, but this time cut in the shapes of little men to please the children.

While Jason gathered with his classmates, Patrick, patiently leading a wide-eyed Donny and Jim, was cordially welcomed by Lucius and Romeo.

Even John Hardie came, walking down with his wife and Alice. A few minutes later, John Hardie, Jr., also appeared. A neighbor had offered to stay with the younger children, and Mrs. Hardie seemed thankful and happy to be out amongst friends.

Aunt Sophia and Magdalena presided in the dining room--and off to one side sat Uncle Pompous, dressed in his best, performing on his mouth organ for the entertainment of the older boys.

Mattie and Bessie met the visitors with curtsies; the children sang; Emily distributed her mats; and Jason surprised everyone by giving each child a little wooden man carved by Patrick. Only the babies in their cribs upstairs were unaware of the Christmas joys warming the hearts of these neighbors and friends, who sought for one short evening to put aside their anxieties.

Christmas Day was almost an anticlimax, though the turkey upheld its promise, and the sage-seasoned, corn bread dressing was delicious, there was a tiny feeling of 'too much', after the long months of austerity and sacrifice.

Only the presence of their guests, the Lamperson Smith family, helped maintain the happy air the season demanded. For the Smiths were themselves truly happy and thankful. "We're just so glad that Lamperson came through the war with a stiff leg only!" declared Mrs. Smith. She spoke with a sincerity that softened any insensitivity to Emily's loss. "For days there, I feared I'd have to lay him in the graveyard alongside our tiny firstborn and our little girl baby." Her round, cheerful face blossomed with enough happiness to encompass them all. "Ain't it wonderful what the Lord can do!"

"Amen!" echoed Aunt Sophronia, as she served big slices of her squash pie. "It do be marvelous!"

"It's surely true," Mr. Smith acknowledged. "For He came right alongside me as I'se draggin' myself all that long way home from that terr'ble battle up in Nashville!"

"We was sure glad to see Pa come hobblin' in. Just don't know how he done it!" added Jackson, in his slow, kindly drawl.

As Elizabeth said later that evening, "You just can't help but like the Smith family. They're so thankful for all they have--and so willing to share!"

"Salt of the earth!" declared Albert.

"I'm glad she liked the nightdress," Emily said. "It wasn't so much!"

"It was 'much' to her," Elizabeth insisted. "Wouldn't surprise me if she wears it for a 'day dress'!"

All at once, Emily smiled. She was remembering the way dear Archie's face had lit up at sight of the pocketknife his pa had for him. "I was so happy, Albert, when you gave Archie that knife he had been longing for!" she murmured.

He nodded silently. "I was lucky to find one. Actually, it was left in Littleton's place by a Union soldier--but no need for our boy to know that! It'd be about impossible to find a new one!"

Emily mused to herself that Archie probably would not care who had owned the knife. It was his now! She sighed, suddenly aware of how tired she was. "If only we could have heard something from dear Alvah, or even Edward!" she said, as she rose to bid them good night. "Otherwise, it's been a really nice Christmas!"

What more could be said? They all knew it had been a pleasant reprieve, but their situation was still one of uncertainty and danger--for who knew when the Union army would sweep down across the Tennessee line and hold the people of Huntsville captive once again!

Upstairs, Mattie was still awake. "Mama," she said. "I do like Christmas so specially much!"

"I'm glad you do, darling," whispered Emily, as she stooped to kiss her little daughter good night. "I hope you have many, many more! And that some day you'll have little ones of your own to make happy at Christmas! For there's nothing else so nice."

Dropping into her nearby rocker, she watched over the children sleeping peacefully in the candlelight. It was a moment to try to relax, to seek a measure of happiness, and to give thanks. As she did so, a feeling came that perhaps a season of her own life drew near its end. Through it, she had learned to endure sorrow by serving others. "If I am to be given another season," she prayed. "Oh, let me take that one lesson forward with me!"

Across the room, the candle suddenly flickered, while its tiny flame leaned to the window, seemed to search, and grow stronger.

EPILOGUE

So many unfinished stories! So many men's lives disrupted, or ended--by death on the battlefield, or by injuries and illnesses untreated! Mothers, wives, and young women set adrift in the aftermath of a war not of their choosing, nor even of their understanding! Children left with no memory of their father! Homes destroyed; businesses ruined! Chaos...and lingering resentment.

These are but a few of the shattering effects of the monstrous struggle between the States, generally referred to as the Civil War. Why it happened, how it could have been avoided, and what, if anything, it accomplished are questions that will engage historians for years to come.

On these pages I have tried to record some of the suffering and loss the great conflict caused in the life of my own family in Huntsville during about nine months of 1862. In so doing, I came to realize that their experiences, as bad as they were, could not compare to the losses suffered and insurmountable problems faced by numbers of other households in the North Alabama area, as well as all over the South.

I have tried to take the viewpoint of women who, while knowing haunting fear for the safety of distant loved ones, were forced to cope with a daily life in which dangers, trials, and shortages existed. Some were called on to make decisions for which they were ill-prepared--decisions that in normal times would have been made by a father, husband, or brother. Such desperate women could later be haunted by choices they had made that brought suffering, even despair, to their loved ones.

In portraying the Albert Baker household, I emphasized the family's daily life so as to focus on the role of women, their problems, their unique solutions, and their heroism. This focus also served to contrast the lifestyle of 1862 with that of the present day.

297

Each family who lived in Huntsville during these trying times had their own way of coping, their own reactions to trials and hardships. They either were hardened to despair by the awful calamities around them, or were undergirded, as was my own family, by their belief in God and His protecting care.

Of necessity, this must be an unfinished story. Such was the nature of the fractured times in which it happened. However, there are a few additional facts:

On March 20, 1863, three months after the story ends, Emily Elliott made affidavit before Robert D. Wilson, Justice of the Peace, that she was the widow of William C. Elliott, deceased, a private in Capt. John G. Dickson's Company E, (35th) Regiment of Alabama Troops, and that her husband died in the service of the Confederate States, which entitled her to any arrears of pay due him at the time of his death. Robert S. Spragins, their neighbor on West Holmes attested to her identity. James N. Scruggs, Judge of Probate for Madison County, certified to Wilson's office and signature.

Eventual result of this application was a document issued by the Treasury Department of the Confederate States on November 30, 1864, acknowledging a total of $97.36 payable to Emily for all of William's services to the Confederate Army:

Two months and one day at $11.00 per month	$22.36
Bounty (for enlistment before conscription)	50.00
Commutation for clothing (First six months)	25.00

When, or if ever, this amount was forthcoming is not clear.

Probably soon after Emily made her application on March 20, 1863, she and Elizabeth and all of their children returned to Tioga County, New York, to live on their dairy farm for the duration of the War. Apparently Albert was able to procure them a pass, but did not accompany them.

There is little doubt that what prompted this move was the proximity of the Union Army in Southern Tennessee; and, in fact, by July 7, 1863 Huntsville was again in Federal hands and was to remain so off and on until the end of the war.

With Union occupancy, the situation in Huntsville became more desperate: food was scarce and expensive, and other necessities all but disappeared. It was inevitable that the Federal Army would discover the coal mine and take over its operation; after that, everything went into reverse for Baker & Conway.

Indications are that by late 1864, Albert was living in New York state with his family, and James Conway was in charge of the operations in Huntsville.

This, however, is far from the end of the story. Albert was not giving up easily on the Southern home he had come to love. Despite the South's defeat and the conditions that existed during Reconstruction, ads began to appear in Huntsville newspapers of 1866 for both the Marble Yard and the Coal Mine. Two of Albert's nephews, Lucius and Charles Asa, were in Huntsville.

In 1874, John Gideon Baker came down to put his capable shoulders to the revival of the family business. Two years later he returned to New York to marry Mattie Elliott and bring her back to her birthplace. Shortly afterward, they were joined by Emily and Enoch Carlton. Within a few years, Albert and most of his family were living once again in Huntsville, this time on the northeast corner of Lincoln and Eustis Streets in the house that still stands today.

The saga of the Baker family's remaining years in Huntsville must be another story; and one that will be more fulfilling for it must recount their contributions to their adopted city.

As for the present tale, its real heroes were those who gave their lives for the cause in which they believed.

William Elliott lies buried in the Confederate Cemetery in Lauderdale Springs, Mississippi, where he died on Monday, May 19, 1862.

On Sunday, February 7, 1864, Richard Elliott was taken prisoner by the Union Army a short distance below Huntsville on the south side of the Tennessee River, while he was on furlough hoping to see Mary Elizabeth and the children. After peace came, he was able to return to the city and resume his painting business. However, his health had been broken by his dreadful wartime experiences. He died on April 3, 1867 and is buried in Maple Hill Cemetery, in Section 2, Row 9. A Confederate States marker, placed by his great-grandson, William R. Ormond, honors his war service: "Richard I. Elliott, Serg

Co E 35th Ala Inf, Confederate States Army, Nov 28 1822 - Apr 3 1867"

As you enter the present main gate of the cemetery, in Section 7, Row 5, there stands an obelisk inscribed on three sides:

On the side facing the main gate the inscription reads: "Alvah A. Babcock died Sept. 15, 1865 in the 28th year of his age." According to his service record, Alvah was captured by the Union Army at Macon, Georgia, on April 20 or 21, 1865. Whether he died in captivity, or after he returned to Madison County is not known. What is known is that he was a native of New York state who fought for the Southern cause.

On the opposite side of the obelisk (facing approximately north) is the inscription: "Edward Babcock died Sept. 29, 1865 in the 39th year of his age." Whether Edward took an active part in the War is not known. Below his name on the stone is chiseled a rectangle bearing the words "Constitution" with a dagger pointing at its heart. It may be noteworthy that these brothers died within fourteen days of each other.

Between these two inscriptions on the east side of the obelisk the wording is as follows: "Charles A. Baker died Aug. 11, 1866 in the 21st year of his age." Charles Asa, who was a year or more younger than his brother, John Gideon, and two years older than Lucius, did not serve in the war. His death was attributed to a sunstroke suffered while painting the steeple of the Church of the Nativity on Eustis Street.

So were the male ranks of the family decimated during the years 1862 through 1867, mostly because of the war. There were no deaths during that period among the female members of the family. The women were left to shed their tears and shoulder the burdens brought on by a war in which their loved ones made the supreme sacrifice. In so doing, they left an example of strength and determination that will forever remain a blessing to our family.

Sarah Huff Fisk
Huntsville, Alabama

ABOUT THE AUTHOR

Sarah Huff Fisk grew up in Huntsville, Ala., the town she writes about with such warmth. Years of research back to its beginnings have given her mental pictures that are clearly revealed in her numerous writings and drawings.

Among these, "Shadows on the Wall: The Life and Works of Howard Weeden", which she co-authored with Dr. Frances C. Roberts, has gone into its fourth edition.

Her drawings of pioneer life seem perfectly to illustrate the children's book "Long Ago in Madison County" by Allie Norris Kenney.

Another drawing, depicting buildings and activities around the Public Square in 1823, was made for the 150th anniversary of the town's Water System.

She is one of the founders of Alabama's Constitution Village, a living-history museum in Huntsville that attracts thousands of visitors each year.

And now, this book with its intimate story of her ancestors and their experiences during a troubled time brings to life an entirely new view of Huntsville from this versatile author.